BOOKS BY
DONALD CULROSS PEATTIE

CARGOES AND HARVESTS, *Appleton*, 1926.

FLORA OF THE INDIANA DUNES,
Field Museum, Chicago, 1930.

PORT OF CALL, *Century*, 1932.

SONS OF THE MARTIAN, *Longmans, Green*, 1932.

THE BRIGHT LEXICON, *Putnam*, 1934.

AN ALMANAC FOR MODERNS, *Putnam*, 1935.

SINGING IN THE WILDERNESS, *Putnam*, 1935.

Green Laurels

The Lives and Achievements of the Great Naturalists

Donald Culross Peattie

Author of "Singing in the Wilderness"
and "An Almanac for Moderns"

The Literary Guild
New York

To
the friend who in the green dusk
led me from Trinity Pass to Paradise

ACKNOWLEDGMENTS

For permission to quote from the volumes listed below the author and publishers of this book make grateful acknowledgment to

Alfred A. Knopf, New York, THE NATURAL HISTORY OF ANTS, by Réaumur, translated by William Morton Wheeler (1926).

Henry Holt and Co., New York, THE GROWTH OF BIOLOGY, by William Locy (1925).

Appleton-Century Co., New York, THE NEW HARMONY MOVEMENT, by George B. Lockwood (1905).

The Clarendon Press, Oxford, HISTORY OF BOTANY, by Julius von Sachs (1890).

University Press, Cambridge, DIARY OF THE VOYAGE OF THE BEAGLE, by Charles Darwin, edited by Nora Barlow (1933).

H. F. & G. Witherby, Ltd., London, LINNAEUS, by Dr. B. D. Jackson (1923).

Historical Department of Iowa, Des Moines, RAFINESQUE, A SKETCH OF HIS LIFE, by T. J. Fitzpatrick (1911).

The Filson Club, Louisville, LIFE AND WRITINGS OF RAFINESQUE, by Richard Ellsworth Call (1895).

The Indiana Historical Commission, Indianapolis, INDIANA AS SEEN BY EARLY TRAVELERS, edited by Lindley Harlow (1916).

CONTENTS

Contents

Contents

Contents

Contents

LIST OF ILLUSTRATIONS

List of Illustrations

[xvi]

List of Illustrations

List of Illustrations

FOREWORD

O F all things under the sun that a man may love, the
living world he loves most purely. In a lifetime's devotion to it there is no self-interest. Men so devoted tell
us of their well-companioned days, but they are reticent
about their best reward. In Nature nothing is insignifi-
cant, nothing ignoble, nothing sinful, nothing repetitious.
All the music is great music, all the lines have meaning.

So from these men we should receive at least a reflection
of the immense reality they behold. Theirs are the eyes
that understand what we all see. They sketch in the great
systema naturae, and we the gapers peer over their shoulders. And, since we are invisible to them, we take a glance
at the profiles of the men themselves, stand off to see them
in perspective against the background of their times, or
come close to notice wrinkle and peccadillo.

I am writing about the naturalists, distinguished — as
well as they can be — from the biologists. These latter I
think of as the indoor men, the naturalists as the outdoor
men. To put it another way, the naturalists deal with living beings *in situ* — in their active, vital inter-relations;
the biologists are more concerned with isolated organisms,
living under controlled laboratory conditions, or they may
be interested solely in the activity of one organ, or even
with partially inorganic matter, chemicals and the physics
of protoplasm. On page twenty-three there is an indication of how all the natural sciences interlock. In so vast a
subject a writer must choose his province, and mine lies
out of doors, where all is alive and various.

Foreword

Its reigning figures flock to the mind. To give account of them only would be to create the false impression that a few naturalists have stood out in solitary grandeur, owing nothing to others, owed all by humble disciples. To do justice to all would be to write little less or more than a biographical dictionary of the subject. I wish that such a volume existed; to my great inconvenience, I have found none such, or even a good history of natural history in any language that I can read.

So I have chosen rather to write of the mighty names, with abundant reference to many others, both the quasi-great and the big little men. The task of selection and exclusion has been a poignant one. That I have no space to characterize all who come into the story, the reader must forgive, and he will believe, I trust, that I am not unaware how far the lesser men have built up the great ones.

With regret I have omitted the great Nature writers and those men of letters who have appreciated Nature but brought nothing new to science. W. H. Hudson's nostalgic recollections of the wild life of the pampas, his tender feeling for the English countryside, can find no place in a short account of the progress of natural history. Maeterlinck and Richard Jefferies too belong to the literature of Nature. Our own American Thoreau was no scientist; he took many an occasion to deride and deplore science, and so on his own pleading we must applaud him rather in his chosen role of Transcendental moralist and poet of Nature. If Thoreau cannot be admitted to these pages, still less may his follower Burroughs.

Nor do I suppose that all the figures here discussed at

some length are equally important. John Bartram was by no means such a great naturalist as Camerarius, who comes in for little more than honorable mention, and Rafinesque's genius is debatable in the extreme compared with that of Huxley whom I admit only in connection with his fight for evolution. But my endeavor is to represent many branches of natural history, especially those dear to me, and I emphasize typical men of each age. I am human enough, moreover, to dwell upon the more piquant personalities. We love, alas, not so much for virtue as for charm.

Charmed though I am by the men I have chosen to put into this book, I am not misled into supposing that I am writing a series of complete or consistent biographies. I plan no reference book; though I have chronological tables and a jungle of dates before me, I doubt if many will creep into my text. Much that I hope the reader will want to know, I shall fail to tell him.

For there is a story to be told greater than that of any great life. This is the story of man facing his world — man in his nakedness, abstract curiosity glittering in his simian pupils as he stares at the wall of the primeval wood and listens to its sounds, and wonders. The distinguishing characteristic of the human species is our ability to put two and two together and get the abstraction, four. We correlate, we deduce, and thereby we create something. The creation of art is a familiar idea, but science too is a creation. It is not Nature itself, it is what we make of Nature, an arrangement, a pattern, an interpretation. Scientists believe that in the making of this pattern there is a gradual perfection. In art there appears to be no progress; who dares say that sculpture today has advanced beyond Scopas? In art there is only change; science, which traces its beginnings back to that identical moment when art began — the charging bison on the cave walls in Spain — is conscious of growth.

So confident of progress is science that in our triumphs lurks the danger that we will think too poorly of the eras which held views no longer ours. But the history of science will correct such juvenile vanity. The old ideas are the ancestors of our own; we build upon the sunken piers of obsolete wisdom.

I have spoken of my selection of certain individuals to stand forth and tell the greater story of how Nature has unfolded in the mind of man, and I have given, perhaps, the idea that whim has guided me in the choosing. But indeed they come cast for these rôles, and when I omit such a splendid scientist as Louis Agassiz, for whose story I have the greatest personal fondness, it is because most of what he stood for in natural history had already been expressed by Cuvier, the master of the school of nineteenth century anatomy.

So, more than life-stories of men, these are biographies of ideas. And beyond and above that, they are — what I suppose I cannot help writing — incidents from the adventure of Nature itself. I have been trying to see what men so much greater, if more ignorant, than your modern, were looking at. I have been trying to retrace the way into a world marvelously the same as that about us today, and yet new and fresh and strange because man had not yet explained it to himself. That explanation is but partially

Foreword

completed; we do not know what tenets cherished today
must be discarded tomorrow. Forever the challenging
whistle, the bright flash of truth, eludes us in the green
growing forest.

GREEN LAURELS

I

SCHOOLMEN AND HERBALISTS

THEY have given me a desk in a great scientific library, in an intimate spot among the stacks, and I am privileged to wander these catacombs of knowledge, and take down what bones I wish to examine. The first of the books that I shall need lean on each other's shoulders, where I have marshaled them in front of me on the desk. Passed in review, it is a ragged platoon. There are greybeard giants, in their white vellum uniforms of long ago — the herbalists, Clusius of Leyden, Camerarius of Wittenberg, Matthioli of Venice, medieval renderings of Aristotle, Theophrastus and Pliny, and Gesner's *Historia Animalium* illustrated at least in part by Dürer. These old fellows speak to me only in Latin. I have books about these books, histories of their times, bibliographies of works I shall never have done with, and bibliographies of these bibliographies.

The fenestration of the skyscraper that houses this high-perched bookery is Gothic. I look out through small panes, set in long delicate grey mullions, upon the vertical world of the Chicago Loop, where an early March blizzard swirls. It is time for spring; the body aches for it, and the eyes crave its green. Instead, Medicine Hat has produced another white cyclone out of its topper. The flakes

[3]

drive faster and faster. I can barely see across the street, and far down below, the straddling policeman in the blinded traffic wears a fantastic wind-carved pinnacle of snow. The squat cars, abandoned in the drifts, sit about the block like cowled monks at a chapter meeting. Men and women are fleeing their offices early for the suburbs, before the elements shall engulf this human termitarium, paralyzing our arteries, our nerves of communication.

Let it snow. I am going to find out what old Gerarde has to say of the dark red flowers of the male fern, which blossom once a year, and that only at midnight, when the petals immediately fall to earth and are swallowed by it. I open the snuff-brown volume, and a silver-fish, the oldest of living insects, built upon the most modern streamlines, glides smoothly over the rim of the page and disappears into another chapter. A smell, an ancient smell of books and bookishness, fills the room, as it filled the Bodleian, that day I stood there, a young boy out of raw America, and asked to be shown my first incunabulum.

The ink is old, and the pages waver like the floors of an old house. So I switch on the desk lamp and set, for the shivering, storm-swept world outside, a pin prick of violet light in the gathering darkness, high up in the Perpendicular window. A modern Faustus, I ask of God and Devil for a while to be rid of what is left of my youth, and the sweet pervasive calling, like a bird's invitation, of all my happy passions. For, by an effort of my modern mind, I am going back to the Schoolmen and the herbalists, and to Aristotle not as he was but as he was taught. " I must this night away to Padua — " and to Salamanca, Paris, Wittenberg and Oxford.

[4]

Schoolmen and Herbalists

Great and doughty are the arguments resounding in those cold stone lecture rooms, over the cough of the young consumptive students, over the whispering and rioting of the healthy blades on the back benches, and the clangor and tolling of the sacred bells that must have been the glory and the torment of the medieval universities. The old man in the long gown, telling off points on his dirty fingers, is of course talking about something out of Aristotle. Even today we are all Schoolmen of a sort and can no more avoid beginning with Aristotle than the Chinese scholars can dodge starting off with Confucius. It has become a natural habit of thought.

Now, as for the great Aristotle himself, a half-god lost in clouds, often and often shall I speak of him, of his work as an anatomist, as a schematist, as an experimenter and observer. But, historically, we face the fact that we do not have, free of all possibility of corruption, a single word he wrote. We cannot reach him there in the clouds; we have only Aristotle as he has come down to us, corrupted, added to, detracted from, interpreted. Pragmatically, this quasi-Aristotle is more important than Aristotle proper, since the one has swayed men's thoughts, the other perished. The Aristotle of the Schoolmen was the end product of centuries of copying and translating, from Greek into Syriac, from Syriac into Arabic, from Arabic into Latin or back into Greek. The medievals had no more surety of what he meant by the *forma* of their Latin texts than we have when we render it as the word " form." We translate his terminology of the ineffable as " soul," " God," " essence." But these words, even when derived from the Byzantine texts that are the purest but only reached Europe

[5]

when the Greeks fled after the sack of Constantinople, are interpretations of concepts which Aristotle originated. He invented, for instance, the word *entelekeia* — still the favorite noun of philosophers who do not know what they mean — and though it seems to mean " that which carries its purpose within itself," nobody but Aristotle has ever been sure what *that* means.

Nor must I forget to add that many books of great influence were falsely ascribed to Aristotle. It is known that he produced a treatise on botany, but it was lost. So keenly was the lack of it felt that Nicolaus of Damascus coolly forged an Aristotelian botany. The conclusion of all argument was this: " Aristotle hath said it." Three centuries ago Giordano Bruno, driven from college to college for his titanic free-thinking, came billowing down the draughty halls at Oxford and stopped to read a notice posted there, to the effect that " Masters and Bachelors who do not follow Aristotle faithfully are liable to a fine of five shillings for every point of divergence and for every fault committed against the logic of the *Organon*." Matthew Arnold adds to this that in his day under those spires the *Ethics* was considered infallible.

But the Aristotelian logic, which was certainly a splendid discipline for the barbaric mind, is worse than useless to the natural sciences. Take but the classic example from Aristotle's own tongue: *Man is a rational animal: Socrates is a man, therefore Socrates is rational.* You should be on your feet at the end of the first proposition, demanding how Aristotle knows that man is a rational animal, how he intends to prove it, and what it means to be rational. In the natural sciences no unproved assumptions are permissible, no predicates have universal meaning.

Of course, Aristotle, wrapped in the chiton of an immortal's dignity, might reply that he never said all men are rational; he said, man is a rational animal. Here is the nub of it! The difference between the universal ideal concept of man, and the ever-changing, irregular, individual concrete men of this world, is an idea that Aristotle borrowed from Plato. He made great sport of it, but never for a moment was he quit of it. Its light has shone from Plato's day to ours.

Platonic idealism dances as impalpable as an *ignis fatuus* to the literal scientific mentality. Yet it lies at the basis of Linnaeus's life work, the concept of species and genera and other categories of individuals, which led natural history out of the jungle in which the primitive mind entertains the notions of things. It gave birth to the Romantic Natural Philosophy of Goethe's time, to the idea that there are impalpable archetypes of form and design in Nature, of which individual animals and plants are imperfect copies or essays. This philosophy, towering to the skies till it fell of its own weight, nevertheless prepared the world mind for evolution with its concept of real archetypes. There is no telling what will next be born out of the Platonic idea of universals. For it is the very soul of abstraction and generalization. It is the part of natural history that thinks. Without it, the science of Nature would never have progressed beyond collection.

And what is this airy concept of The Philosopher? What is it doing in a book about the outdoor naturalists who see things as they are? It is not idealism in the vulgate sense, some illusory optimism about the goodness of man or God. It is the idea of *Idea*. Plato holds that all things have an eternal universal essence, existing apart from that which is individual and tangible. The modern temper will take his meaning best if it thinks of love, and lovers. Or womanhood, and womenfolk. Lovers come and go, Plato would say; they are a mayfly lot. Love is greater than they, and though it is nowhere, it is eternal.

Let us take this proposition to the skeptical physicist, flashing a light beam back and forth to measure the flight of the ether. How, he asks irritably, can we suppose that our concept of matter can be more real than matter itself? The Platonic rejoinder confesses that the nature of matter may extend infinitely beyond our conceptual ideology, but all we know of it or ever shall is the idea of matter in the human brain. True, says the busy modern curtly, but I shall go on treating matter as if my ideas of it were the thing itself.

Indeed, he can do no other. No scientist can do without Platonic idealism. The travelers of the world supplied Linnaeus with collections, but if they had brought the whole world to Upsala it would have been only a clutter had not the Linnaean concept of categories made order of it. Sachs, the great historian of botany, maintains that Linnaeus was a thorough Schoolman, and it is true in one sense. It is possible to argue that the Linnaean species is not a reality; that Nature knows no species, only individuals, and not even the curious and patient mind of the great old Swede could have entertained the multifariousness of the green and growing world. But looking with a philosopher's view, he saw how to generalize it all. Every epitome is an abstract of reality seen through the diminishing glass of the human intellect.

So in the dusty, droning halls of the medieval universities, the moles were preparing the earth for science. That old Scholasticism has a smell of romance about it, of the world well lost and the time well spent in the pursuit of an airy knowledge for its own sake, that is more than perceptible to my nostrils. It is the very smell of formalized learning, familiar to all of us. I met it first when I was taken from the cool, solemn brook where I played daylong in a grove of tree alders with only a reflective thrush to keep me company, and was brought into a school in a great city. It was an old building, and the smell of chalk dust was a thing of generations; the lighting was poor and must have ruined many young eyes. Lessons were dull and they were long, and I yearned for the brook waters slipping over white quartz stones. But somehow my healthy animality softened, and I developed a morbid pleasure in study.

This appetite fed on itself, and when I was old enough to elect my pursuits, I devoured the great dead subjects, all that was once-removed. My room-mates at college were a Latinist, a physicist, a systematic botanist, and an aristocrat who disdained to do anything too well. We lay on our backs in the deep embrasures of Stoughton, arguing poetry and theology, vitalism and mechanism, good girls and bad girls, the collisions of stars, the feasibility of Plato's Republic and Aristotle's picture of the universe. Each quarter of an hour the bells would clang; some one of us would hear the call to class, gather up his scribbling book and fall down the noisy wooden flights out into the sunny Yard.

Oh, yes, the Schoolmen got their learning out of a fine old cobwebbed bottle, and there is savor even in reading about them. But beyond the narrow, peaked windows glittered the natural world, the transitory, Devil-made world of the theologians. While near-sighted copyists were illuminating manuscripts of Pliny's natural history, which was just a bookish compilation of books, and were steadily corrupting it with each transcription, young men who could not read or write felt the clutch of the falcon's claws on their gauntlets. They knew their hounds and their horses, their hares and stags; they were deeply and unabashedly interested in every detail of these creatures' lives. And there were the poets and the minnesingers, who loved skylarks and nightingales and morning dew on the forest and little flowers by the way. How much they must have noticed, those spring mornings in Provence! But a wayside rose in a troubadour's hand was but an amorous symbol.

Poetry and science often look at the same object, and though their views be ever so divergent, they may both be right about it. Here then are the two visions of Nature which we moderns most commonly associate with the medieval temperament: the Aristotelian abstract, and the troubadour's symbolism. The modern scientific mind respectfully avoids the symbolism, not denying its truth but leaving it to the holy kingdom of poetry. It may embrace the philosophic realities, grateful to Greeks and Schoolmen, but with no intention of allowing these heady speculators to ruin the country. Or it may pour scorn upon the whole Platonic-Aristotelian doctrine.

" Science, according to the scholastic method, is a playing with abstract conceptions; the best player is he who can so combine them together that the real contradictions are skillfully concealed. On the contrary, the object of true investigation, whether in philosophy or in natural science, is to make unsparing discovery of existing contradictions, and to question the facts until our conceptions are cleared up, and if necessary the whole theory and general view is replaced by a better. In the Aristotelian philosophy and in scholasticism facts are merely examples for the illustration of fixed abstract conceptions, but in the real investigation of nature they are the fruitful soil from which new conceptions, new combinations of thought, new theories, and general views spring and grow. The most pernicious feature in scholasticism and the Aristotelian philosophy is the confounding of mere conceptions and words with the objective reality of the thing denoted by them; men took a special pleasure in deducing the nature of things from the original meaning of the words, and even the question of the existence or non-existence of a thing was answered from the idea of it." [1]

This, out of the mouth of Sachs, the historian of botany, is the indictment by empirical, or as we might say, literal-minded science, against the Schoolmen and Aristotle. Any one today may perceive the force of these arguments, so crushing that I have seen no reason to add anything to them. Something more than the noblest of Plato's concepts, Aristotle's grand cosmogony, is needed for scientific realism. This wayside rose, now — if we carry it to Aristotle, he will tell us what its place in the great cosmic plan of creation, how much of God or soul is in it, how it took

[1] Sachs, Julius von, *History of Botany* (Clarendon Press, Oxford, 1890).

on its predestined beauty of form, in what universal mind it blooms, by what laws the very tracks of the stars are linked to its slow, slipping, clinging eclosion into fragrance. This line of inquiry occupied the entire attention of the Schoolmen, and even today many minds are satisfied with it. Though it is now remote from scientific thought, though indeed we must blame it for the paralyzing effect it had for two thousand years upon close observation and experimental learning, the Aristotelian scheme was a magnificent advance upon previous human viewpoints. And just a pinch of it is still a precious ingredient in all thinking.

What we miss in classical and medieval science is flesh and blood. There was no lack of intellect; the mind of Thomas Aquinas impresses me as swift, penetrating and lofty beyond any living intellect with which I am acquainted. But he was a cerebral saint, not the leper-washing kind, and humanity has need of both. Somebody had to bring medieval science down to earth. Aristotle and Aquinas could have talked about the soil and the spirit in it forever, but none of it was ever found under their finger nails. For they were not only highborn gentlemen; they lacked a certain practical inquisitiveness. True, the young falconers, the ladies tending woundwort and heal-all in their garden beds, the peasants who lived intimately with animals and plants, were, as we should say now, close to Nature. But they were not closer to science.

I am going to say here, parenthetically, that the distinctions among pure philosophy, pure science, the art of practically applying science, and a closeness to Nature, are matters which I am obliged to write a book about, in order to establish them for the reader. It is impossible to say in one sentence why Bergson and Burbank and Burroughs are not scientists; each a master in his own field, he could utilize science, not advance it. However far the School-men advanced science, there came a moment when they could do no more for it, because they would not plunge their arms deep into experiment; they would not fill their nostrils with the stench of life, or risk their old carcasses to death, life's shadow.

Ultimate progress sprang from the most unpredictable of all the little buds of the tree of science. Out of super-stition itself grew the science of botany. Though today this somewhat sober subject proceeds on its way respected, undeviating, confident of further triumphs, if it looks back, it must thank the old herb-gatherers, and the herb-alists scratching compendiums of misinformation upon parchment.

The science of zoölogy lagged centuries behind even the herbalistic botany. For the ancient and medieval minds seem to have flattered themselves that they knew almost all there was to know about animals, which were in the Devil's keeping, anyway. And the animal kingdom is not so rich in curative properties. So it chanced that while lords and princes were fond of illustrated works on fal-conry, venery and the care of hounds, a million birds every year flew over the prince's kingdom to the south, swept north in spring in crying, mating legions, and none looked up to wonder why or where they went. Each year hap-pened again the unexplained eel-fare, when the eels leave the sea, and like an army wind up the rivers, swimming by day and resting by night, till they reach the headmost creek and, no man knows how, cross dry land to ponds without issue far in the interior. All the flying, singing, springing, crawling, instinctive, darkly intelligent animal world was about the men of the Middle Ages. Life, like their own, gazed back at them through the eye of the swaying viper, looked down upon them in the vulture's scrutiny, reproached them in the failing gaze of the stag under the hounds. But few looked back at life. The wholly extraverted folk of this earth are never either pure scientists or poets.

I have said that one field of investigation in natural history was, however, in a surreptitious and despised way accomplishing a sort of skulking progress. The trade of the herb-gatherer, the shaman-like profession of the herbalist, were close enough to sorcery to inspire the fear and contempt of semi-enlightened minds. All medicine begins in magic. Its physical materials were perforce collected by those who knew the local minerals and animals and, most important of all, the local flora. The doctor had a menial and even dubious standing; he and the pharmacist were not at first in completely separate professions, and some of the most celebrated physicians might have been seen grubbing about after their own simples. So they called them because the drugs they used were compounds. They regarded the powders and juices of plants, in reality the most complex alkaloids, as simple, aboriginal elements.

There have been herb-gatherers from the time of Theophrastus, and I know not how much further back, for he has sarcastic things to say about their superstitions. But Theophrastus was a startling exception — a botanist in pursuit of plant knowledge for its own sake. He is surrounded by thousands of years, before and after him, of superstitious jungle; he and his century are an intellectual clearing. The Greek, or rather the Hellenized author, in whom the medieval herbalists put their faith was Dioscorides, who was interested in the curative powers of plants. A native of Asia Minor, he traveled widely in Greece and what we should now call Turkey and Syria, and he intended, at least, a very conscientious and thorough manual for the use of doctors and drug men.

Now either the flora of the eastern end of the Mediterranean is actually very rich in useful plants, or the deep stratification of old civilizations there has encrusted almost every herb with some rich human association, for certainly no other flora has so captivated the western mind. Our gardens are full of it; the lily and the rose, the iris and narcissus are our canons of taste; its cereals are preferred upon our tables. Like the Bible, the Koran, Aristotle and Plato, our cultural concepts of Nature are Mediterranean born. For all the wild song in our woods, we shall always be wistful for the skylark and the nightingale. We feel some great lack and loneliness for the classic flora and fauna of Arcady.

The medieval herbalists of Europe's west and north were haunted also by the obsession that the ancients had somehow had the best of it. Even as the Schoolmen revered Aristotle, they took their Theophrastus, Dioscorides and Pliny for final authority; all that grew must be contained therein, and they believed that wondrous secrets, lost to them, had empowered the Attic herborizers. Sometimes the medievals dimly perceived that the

[15]

Greeks had entertained a similar illusion concerning the Egyptians, envying them knowledge and power gone from an age when men had ceased to be giants. The legend of the good old days is perennial.

So the horny forefinger of the learned man traveled reverently down the page of his classic authority. He must often have stopped to scratch his poll, for since the ancient master simply gave his plants the common Greek names of his day, it was not always easy to know what he was talking about. Science without a system of nomenclature is hobbled and can move no step, for common names are untranslatable; Latinity, that strikes the layman as a cant lingo, is really the shortest of cuts. I once tried describing cranberry sauce to a German gourmet; if the Germans have a word for it, I don't know it, but being a botanist also, he understood me. " *Ach, so? Ja!* Vaccinium! "

But the medieval scholar had an infinite latitude for pedantic argument as to what was this growing in the dusty pages of his Dioscorides, for if there was no system of nomenclature, neither was there any method of description in the ancient plant discussions. Armed with such White Knight contrivances, the medieval student might set forth upon the metaphysical sport of trying to find the flora of Thessaly in the Black Forest or the Bois d'Ardennes. To understand his sober faith in such an aim, it must be remembered that to the medieval mind botany was part of God's final handiwork, revealed to men through " philosophic truth." As this principle, rife in the Middle Ages, must like a mathematical proposition hold equally true everywhere, Dioscorides should serve as well at Wittenberg as Euclid.

Schoolmen and Herbalists

The modern mind sees the world's flora as a living thing, and thinks of the distinctive distribution of plants in Japan, in Brazil, in California, as part of the earth's beauty. When I close my eyes and imagine Europe, I see the map of it, the coloring of its mantle of vegetation — the tundras of the north alight with the first frail arctic spring flowers on Midsummer's day; the dark band of spruces and pines stretching from Germany to Russia; the vast brown meadows of the steppes; the great beeches of Burnham and Fontainebleau with their boles deep in moss; the fields of Transylvania trooping shoulder-high with foxglove and Canterbury bell to the foot of the Carpathians; Provence dancing with wild hyacinth and scarlet anemone, with lavender fragrant in wiry clumps on the sheep-cropped bony hillsides; the plain of Marathon blowing with poet's narcissus; and bay and myrtle, ilex and cedar blessing the mighty feet of white Olympus. In truth, the flora of Europe is intensely national, like its peoples and tongues. It is so varied that even today this smallest of the continents has produced no book that covers it all.

But of all this fascinating variation and intense endemicity, the old herbalists had no inkling. When they plodded home bent-shouldered from the fields of Hanover, with a little withering herb, and laid it in page after page of their classic books and found it nowhere there, they were inclined to throw it away. Why, the nasty little thing was heretical, a *lusus naturae*, a freak such as the Devil makes to tempt honest men. But slowly, like the smell of smoke, there curled into the brains of the old wisemen of the woods and libraries the dreadful suspicion that every wort in the world was not in Dioscorides and Theophrastus.

So the day came when men began to make herbals of their own, defiant of classic authority. Of all the curious tomes before me, clasped with hinges and buckles frail as old men's bones, the oldest is *Das Pûch der Natur*. Konrad von Megenberg wrote it; Meister Bämler of Augsburg printed it in 1475. Here at last I recognize, in the woodcut before me, the true flora of northern Europe — the exquisite little twin-flower of the dark coniferous forests, that peeps up through wet moss and little bright toadstools. Here is lily-of-the-valley, that still grows wild around Oberammergau, here Puck's wild pansy or heart's-ease, and ragged-robin that was part of the secret formula, at the great grey monastery of Chartreuse, for the distillation of its precious golden-green liqueur.

We are come now to the only part of my subject that will appeal very highly to those who enjoy books with their noses and fingers and read them not so much for what they mean as with an eye to topography, woodcut and binding. Explored in such ways the herbals are a delicious adventure. Here they stand below my desk-light in their ragged old brown coats where bits of gold design linger like paint on a toy soldier who once stood bright in his uniform. Here are others in white vellum mellowing like old ivory. For the sapient in matters typographical, the interior of these works must be a wonderland, though they are hard upon modern eyesight. The spelling alone lends them a quite spurious charm, and it gathers, as you turn the pages, with the naïveté of the fabulous animals, the plants with human faces or bodies, and the two-dimensional human beings pictured about their medieval businesses.

To the people, then, who like books better than learning, the herbals will provide more fun than anything else I can show them. They will come up against the paradox, however, that the worse the herbals are, the better. The less learned, the more childish, the quainter (opprobrious word!) they are, the more poignant their appeal to our sense of by-gone books.

The same is true when, as antiquarians, we examine the ideas in the texts. For many minds, modern science takes the charm out of the scene. They best enjoy a wood, a field, a garden plot richly misted over with legend; they are, in short, not greatly interested in the clear light of day, in Nature in its grand, indifferent actuality. Their response is quick only to human associations with Nature, associations largely atavistic. This attitude is so medieval that if you share it you will understand the herbalists perfectly, and I need not beg you to be indulgent of them. You will relish — who wouldn't? — the instructions of Apuleius concerning the proper method of gathering ye Mandrake, or Mandragora.

"Thou shalt in this manner take it, when thou comest to it, then thou understandest it by this, that it shineth at night altogether like a lamp. When first thou seest its head, then inscribe thou it instantly with iron, lest it fly from thee; its virtue is so mickle and so famous, that it will immediately flee from an unclean man, when he cometh to it; hence as we before said, do thou inscribe [encircle] it with iron, and so shalt thou delve about it, as that thou touch it not with the iron, but thou shalt earnestly with an ivory staff delve the earth. And when thou seest its hands and its feet, then tie thou it up. Then take the other end and tie it to a dog's neck, so that the hound be hungry; next cast meat before him, so that he may not reach it, except he jerk up the wort with him. Of this wort it is said, that it hath so mickle might, that what thing soever tuggeth it up, that it shall soon in the same manner be deceived. Therefore as soon as thou see that it be jerked up, and have possession of it, take it immediately in hand, and twist it, and wring the ooze out of its leaves into a glass ampulla."

Such a beguiling lunacy needs no excuse save to the humorless modern scientist. We can best deal with that formidable fellow by reminding him that had he lived at the time that this advice was written, he would have taught, with Cesalpino, his students at Pisa (in lieu of Cornell) that the head of a plant was in its roots, that the flower served to cool its vapors, that pollen was its excreta, and its soul was to be found where its stem joined its root. With exactly the same confidence in being up to date that he now wears in the lecture room, he would have gravely expounded the Doctrine of Signatures. According to this singular notion (which attained its theoretical glory under Giambattista della Porta of Naples, but was skilfully advertised and made to pay by the immortal Theophrastus Aureolus Bombastus Paracelsus von Hohenheim), God has left a mark on every plant, to show for what use He created it. If the leaf is spotted like the liver, the plant is good for your hepatic ailments, and so the little spotted leaves that show green as the snow melts in earliest spring still bear the name hepatica. So a heart-shaped leaf is sovereign for an aortal murmur; a foot-shaped leaf will cure the halt. No sort of herb so sought as those, like mandrake, whose roots should suggest the bifurcated trunk of a man; such, surely, must be panacea for all man's bodily miseries. If they did not look sufficiently homunculoid, the root-gatherers supplied the deficiency, as Barnum created a mermaid when the demand of the public to be deceived was too strong to resist. Turner in his *Herball* of 1551 cries out against this practice.

" The rootes which are conterfited and made like litle puppettes and mammettes, which come to be sold in England in boxes, with heir, and such forme as a man hath, are nothyng elles but folishe feined trifles, and not naturall. For they are so trymmed of crafty theves to mocke the poore people with all, and to rob them both of theyr wit and theyr money. I have in my tyme at diverse tymes taken up the rootes of Mandrag out of the grounde, but I never saw any such thyng upon or in them, as are in and upon the pedlers rootes that are comenly to be solde in boxes."

But I am not going to go on a bibliophile's spree, reveling all night with Wynken de Wordes and Aldine editions, recklessly mixing fonts and colophons; there are admirable books about herbals that will cultivate your palate so that you may distinguish the real from the spurious, and every large city boasts a library with the herbals themselves. Nothing that I can tell you about them will equal an hour's experience with them. I have said that the worse the herbals were, the better, and it follows that the better they became, the less they were herbals. As soon as an herbal rises toward excellence, it begins to be a manual of genuine botanical information. The last of the great herbals, Philip Miller's *Gardener's Dictionary*, merges right into the concepts and spirit of Linnaeus, Miller's friend.

But most of us are not so interested in the making of books as in the ideas in them and the men behind them. It is like smelling out subterranean truffles to come at the anonymous author of the *Herbarius zu Teutsch,* a work printed at Mainz in 1485. He intended to tell little about himself, but when from the corners of his book we scrape the facts together, we find that there has passed before us a very fine old gentleman, a patron of science, an observant traveler and an ardent scholar. " *Offt und vil,*" opens the book, " *habe ich by mir selbst betracht die wundersam werck des schepfers der natuer.*" Evidently wealthy, he caused " a learned Master " to compile the wisdom of the classic authorities on plants, but when he set himself to making illustrations, he saw how many recorded plants there were that did not grow in Germany. So he put down his pen and set forth upon a journey, a combined field trip and religious pilgrimage, through Italy and Austria and the Near-Eastern lands. With him he took a painter to make careful drawings of the plants collected, and when, his mind a-flower with all that he had seen, he came home at last to Germany, he sat down and squared his elbows to write his *gart d' gesuntheyt* or *Ortus Sanitatis.* " In this garden are to be found the power and virtues of four hundred and thirty-six plants and other created things, which serve for the health of man." " Now fare forth into all lands, thou noble and beautiful garden," he concludes with affectionate pride, " thou delight of the healthy and comfort and life of the sick."

The text is wholly creditable for its age, and the figures are beautifully drawn. Moreover, here are the curiosity and delight that lie at the root of science; its author was

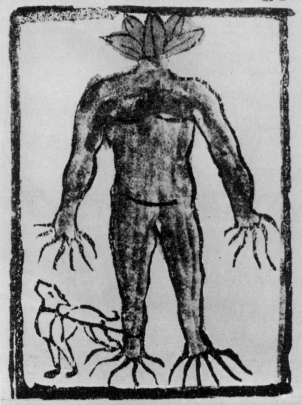

NOMEN HERBAE MANDRAGORA

THE MEDIEVAL CONCEPT OF NATURE

Mandragora, the mandrake, from an old herbal
(*Herbarium Apuleii Platonici,* 1484) represented as
a root having the form of a man, and hence a panacea for the whole body. The dog in the lower left-
hand corner is shown as chained to the root, to pull
it out, since it was bad luck for humans to touch it
while it lay in the earth.

(See page 19)

THE RENAISSANCE CONCEPT OF NATURE
"Acorus" (Iris) from the *Herbarius zu Teutsch*, Mainz, 1485. Though only one year later than the mandrake picture in actual printing, centuries of enlightenment lie between the two pictures, the one superstitious, the other essentially modern and worthy of a monograph upon Iris of today.

(*See page 22*)

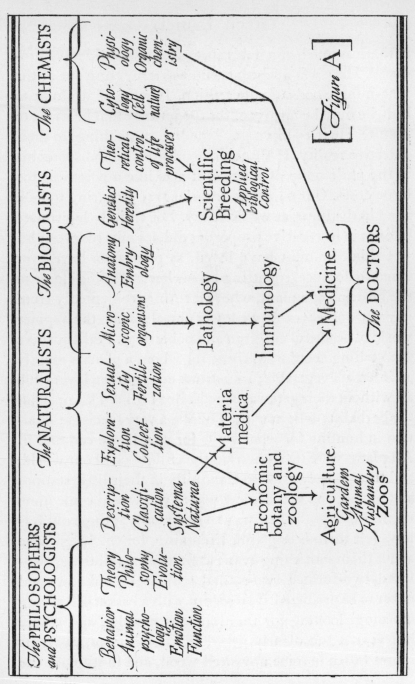

THE INTERLOCKING OF THE NATURAL SCIENCES

perhaps as much of a naturalist as his age could have produced. Here was a scholar who was struggling out of the vine-hung woods of superstition. If some of it clung to him, he must be forgiven, for the journey that he made to Nature. He tried like a good modern to see things in their objective reality. If Platonic idealism is an indispensable to the philosophy of science, it acts like a poison in too large doses. Our nameless traveler was venturing to look at an herb almost as we do today. His entirely legitimate interest in its curative properties did not mist his eyesight.

I think he must have loved, as plantsmen have ever loved to do since, squatting on his heels to come closer to the growing of a plant, where it springs contentedly from its rosette of leaves. So we lower ourselves into the happier world of beautiful children and noble dogs. Perhaps there is no telling about it, to those for whom a plant is merely an insensate vegetable; sometimes even garden lovers dub all without their gateway weeds. But I think I know what the herbalists delighted in. There is a very special fascination in hunting for what waits for you, if you can find it. All plants were mysterious in the childhood of our world, and though they grew so tranquilly in their little stations and niches, you never knew where you would come upon them. Perhaps the best way to feel plants as those old fellows felt them is to go mushrooming, for the fungi have about them something evanescent, deathy, alluring, two-faced, two-formed, two-souled, still largely unknown and never to be predicted. You set out with a basket of a spring morning, looking for the delicious morelle, and where last year it succulently grew, it has withered away, its spores fallen in some unvisited wood, and in its place the slyest of the Amanitas, without the warning red label of its kind, rises pure, cold and translucent as the marble of your tombstone.

To the herbalists, all the world of plants was thus, accursed or blessing. Even when the eyes were clear of superstition, there remained the baffling, exciting fact that most of the plants of Europe were unknown, unnamed, their properties problematic, their ranges unmapped. I like to think about Otto Brunfels, the Carthusian monk, who had sampled the forbidden and quickening elixir of heresy, and leaving his order went wandering up the left bank of the Rhine. He was one of those who trustfully searched for his German plants in his Dioscorides, and he now added a second heresy to his fame. He decided to compile nothing from the old authorities, but to make an herbal of his own. And so he was one of the first to write a book, as many a man has done since — as indeed I am doing now — because it was the book he wanted to read, and nobody else would write it for him.

His name is always linked in my mind with other "German Fathers," Hieronymus Bock, Dr. Fuchs, Valerius Cordus and the truly great Camerarius, and with the Dutchman Clusius or de l'Écluse. Though I have no time to go into their lives, one fact about them all is striking. They were all of them converts to the new Protestantism. I am not one of the people who believe that the Catholic Church has consistently held back science, or one of those who claim that it has consistently helped it. No institution with such a long history could be consistent about anything. And it is now impossible to suggest that the Protestant sects are always friendly toward the freedom of science; the opposition to evolution is most fanatic where Protestantism meets no opposition. But in its infancy the fresh breath of thought inspired by Martin Luther swept the drowsy intellects of men and woke some of them from a vision of the world as it might be to a sight of it as it is.

I suppose I must stop talking about medievals, now that I have reached Caspar Bauhin's epoch-making *Prodromus* of 1623. I am in what is called the Renaissance. To my way of thinking, Renaissance and modernity are the same thing. Indeed, all temporal categories are but contrivances, and if we could make an elaborate survey of the modern mentality, I am convinced that half of it would be found primitive and another quarter of it medieval. Bauhin was a modern. Here is his plate of the potato plant, new come out of the " new founde worlde," bearing underneath no long rambling indefinite Latin description, but instead the name by which scientists still call it — *Solanum tuberosum*. As he himself was a Caspar of the family Bauhin, he perceived the felicity of applying the same system of nomenclature to plants, granting each its genus followed by a specific or " given " name.

This is the stroke of genius for which Linnaeus is renowned. To those who must adore a hero, it is disturbing to find out that their idol did not originate the achievement for which he is famous. But in science discoveries, systems, concepts, bold visions, do not spring full born from the brow of genius. They come slowly up out of the sea of ignorance, with absurdities like seaweed clinging to their limbs, and barnacles of superstition adhering fast to them. By necessity many devoted intellects lift up the great idea into emergence. He who rises with it, standing upon the shoulders of his predecessors, appears the hero. So was it with Aristotle, so with Darwin.

It was certainly not a moment too soon for the evolution of some orderly sort of nomenclature and classification, for discoverers were widening the world, and into the botanical gardens and museums of Europe came pouring strange plants from far places. The padres and the Spanish doctors and planters of the New World were clamoring to have identified and assayed for its properties the marvelous Hesperidean flora. Maize; cocaine of the coca plant; quinine, a sovereign cure for malaria after centuries of helpless suffering; tomatoes so brilliant red they must be deadly poison or the forbidden fruit of paradise; potatoes, a crop that might be so intensively grown that it would at last permit the population of Europe to treble in a few decades; tobacco, that perverse and wondrous weed; rubber, then a curiosity of no great use except for bouncing balls; enchanting new flowers, dahlia and marigold, zinnia, nasturtium and phlox, unseen before by the gardeners of Europe — they came in as seeds, as roots, as powders, as cuttings, as dead herbarium specimens, as living plants carefully balled in earth. What were they? What could be done with them? What price would they fetch?

Oviedo, the Governor General of all the Indies, became the historian and herbalist of the Spanish New World, and India, mother of nations, was found again by her western children. *The Drugs and Simples of India* by the Portuguese Garcia da Orta is the classic herbal of a flora even richer in precious plants than Egypt's land or Solomon's. Poppy and camphor, rubber and tea, coffee and chocolate, indigo and cotton, and the spices from the last, lost isles of Ultima Molucca, these flooded Europe and the imagination of scholars. The world, it seemed, was varied and exciting beyond anything dreamed of. No man could guess how many sorts of plants and animals there might be in the world. Creatures were arriving by incoming vessels, stranger than a madman could have conceived.

And so, belatedly, zoölogy rose out of its slumbers and mentally girded itself for the staggering task that Adam had never completed, of naming the beasts.

Back in the sixteenth century Konrad Gesner, that doughty Swiss, could conscientiously include the basilisk in his *Historia Animalium*, for it was not too hard to believe in, when you were required to accept the report of a rhinoceros. And if Gesner described some of his creatures without having seen them, so did Dürer draw them for him, in the same vivid state of ignorance. But I am giving a bad impression of Gesner's book; it was a veritable dictionary of zoölogy, wherein each animal is set down with its name in various languages, its habits and habitat, anatomy internal and external, its utility and philosophical significance. Gesner was painfully nearsighted, but the habit of bringing objects close to his eyes seems to have made him a better observer than his neighbors with good vision.

And he grasped the idea that science is a great and impersonal fraternity. It ignores nationalities and castes, and offers to share all that it has acquired. Gesner was a tire-less letter-writer, to Belon the ornithologist, Rondelet of Montpellier who specialized in fishes, Aldrovandi, a fellow zoögrapher, and Turner of England. Over the boggy roads, where anything from a highwayman to a wench might delay the post, these learned letters traveled back and forth weaving a correspondence that was a rude brave equivalent of the modern transactions or memoirs of a learned society.

There is sterling merit in Rondelet's work on fishes or in the careful Aldrovandi, but the thing that makes them look medieval to us is their lack of any concept of genera or species. Without this simple language of science, we literally cannot tell what we are talking about. Even Pierre Belon, the first ornithological traveler, has as little idea of species as Gesner or Aristotle, and he cared naught what birds were called in Latin or any other tongue, but he winged, with the instinct of genius, straight at fundamentals. He probed the bird's skeleton and by placing a human skeleton on the same page and assigning the same lettering to corresponding bones, laid the foundations of comparative anatomy. But he lived in an age when it was beneath dignity to accept the idea that anything among the lower animals corresponded to that wingless angel, man, and three hundred years were to elapse before Cuvier should re-discover Belon's greatness. His friends, however, in their fashion appreciated him and showed it. They made up a purse for him that he might journey through Greece, Turkey, Syria and Egypt, and he returned home with a wealth of notes for the *Histoire des*

Oyseaux. There is no telling how far he might have flown above his age, once he had discovered the magic key of comparative anatomy, but the loftiest scientific intellect of today may be snuffed out by a wandering spray of bullets in a gangster fight in the streets. Listening perhaps to the nightingale, Belon in the Bois de Boulogne was set upon one night and stabbed to death for the coins in his purse.

If I were writing a complete history of natural history, I would have to mention and appraise many more of the early books and men that have upbuilded the subject that I love. But I do not promise you to be minutely just or thorough. Let me recommend you to the exhaustive works in my bibliography. I am interested in the great visions and the high deeds and the *Zeitgeist* of each epoch.

I have done now with the medievals, and I feel as though I had in spite of myself dealt them a cut. Science today is so sure of itself that it forgets how for the future the twentieth century will seem to be a darkling, crabbed time, closer to the thirteenth than to ours, my dear Polemarchus. We are, no doubt, still looking at the world through very badly ground lenses; the difference between the spectacles of the astrologer, the alchemist and the herbalist, and our own glasses would seem to me to consist in this: that theirs were tinted by anthropomorphic coloring. They could not look at a goat without seeing the Pan-Devil. They could not look at a leaf without reading in it instructions to them from its Creator. They were bound to this sort of thinking, just as a young man has his views of woman entirely colored by his desire for her.

Schoolmen and Herbalists

But Nature as a mistress is indifferent to her lovers. The whole story of science, the whole burden of this book, is the endeavor of the human intellect to clear its vision, in order to support the white light of day shining on naked reality in all its beauty.

2

THE LENS TURNED ON LIFE

THE storm is gone, upon its groove across the basin of the Great Lakes. The city has struggled damply out of the snow blanket, and here in the country a mild sun has bit by bit argued the cold and snow away, like a pacific man tactfully upbraiding dangerous trespassers, edging them to the gate. Now they have slunk away, and there is the upheaval of a final thaw in the March lawns that are the color of old straw, and in the ponderous black velvet loam, this Illinois sod without a pea-sized pebble in it that goes down, down to Jericho.

It is Sunday, with a Sabbath meekness on the face of things. Across the roll and dip of the great plain I saw, as I went walking with my blackthorn, the distant woods as blue-black, rainy-looking islands upon the immense watery prairie, and near at hand the young yellow of the willow whips, first brilliance of the year. Now this was a scene a midlander could love, but I went thinking, thinking, wagging that human tail my cane, how all that I saw came to me thus only because of a specified convexity in the cornea of my eye.

My sense of proportion, to say nothing of esthetics, is really superbly egotistic. Matter, to regard it more exactly than humanly, is full of holes. The solidest thing is as a net; the space between the electronic particles is like unto the spaces between the sun and the planets. The trouble with our human concepts is that we are so pitifully small when it comes to the great, and so unbearably gross when it comes to the small. We occupy a position in the scale of things that is somewhat on the trivial side of total mediocrity. Little wonder if our ideas are mediocre too.

A bee, the first of the year, went by with that direct flight of hers — the most practical people in the world, bees, having no eye for scenery and hence no temptation either to wander or to wonder. A hawk cut a great circular glide through the pale blue air above me, balanced, it seemed, upon the tip of one wing, the other wing pointing almost to the zenith. He takes the opposite view of things. He sees all, for miles about, is curious about all, and much of the time appears simply to be enjoying his perspective, save when emotions incomprehensible to me suddenly shake him, and set up a windy metallic clamor.

I cannot ever share the bee's-eye view or the hawk's-eye view. Whatever their God-given lenses showed them of reality, I would never know what it was. I saw the scene in my human way — the roll and dip of the great plain, the black-silver lakes of snow water seeking out unsuspected dimples, the cottonwood stands, very white of bark as they always are at winter's end, looking at a distance lofty and thoughtful, but turning out — like literary lions on closer acquaintance — to be talkative and flimsy.

My swinging cane struck something soft, was delayed in some yielding yet persistent medium. And I knew, even through the blackthorn, that it was living tissue. There is something about almost any living thing that is plasmic, resilient, and in a way alarming. We say, " I touched something — and it was *alive!* " There is no such shock in touching that which has never lived. The mineral world is vast, it is mighty, rigid and brittle. But the hand that touches vital matter — though the man were blind — infallibly recognizes the feel of life, and recoils in excitement.

What I had struck was nothing but a big, soggy fungus, a giant puffball persistent from autumn. From the wound I had made in it there was still curling on the airs a smoke of mustard-green powder. I struck it again deliberately, and like a staked snake teased into spewing venom, it coughed forth another belch of spores.

I unscrewed the crystal of my watch, caught a little of the living dust in it, screwed the watch face down upon the upturned glass, and pocketed the whole. At home, at least, I had a pair of eyes that would deprive the infinitely little of half its mystery. Eyes such as neither hawk nor bee possesses, eyes for probing into the nature of Nature, that man has made for himself with monstrous patience, intricate invention piled upon invention.

At my desk, I drew the microscope out of its case, and though it is heavy, it slides out to me, when I grasp it by its middle, with an ease like a greeting. Musicians must feel this response from their instruments. I have neglected this one of mine for months, gone away and left it for years, deserted the very calling of science, at times, for another world. Yet each time out of its wooden case it glides forth this way at a touch of my hand, gleaming, obedient, prophetic.

The Lens Turned on Life

It is a matter of a moment to whisk the fungus spores on a glass slide, a moment more to find them in the lower magnification, and then with a triumphant click to swing the intense myopic gaze of the tinier lens upon them.

From a speck as fine as a particle of wandering cigarette smoke, a spore leaps suddenly up at my eye as a sphere of gold meshed with vitreous green bands that cut up this tiny world, this planetesimal of sealed-up life, into latitude and longitude. Here a living plant has put its substance into minutest compass and launched it upon the air, where only the most wildly improbable chances, really an unbroken series of lucky one-in-a-thousand hazards, would ever see it grow to a puffball. Here was the whole of heredity, here the past and future of a chain of lives. Intricate, formed to a pattern and plan by the stresses within it, organized by the very fact that it had specific form, this frail and tiny speck of life differed, I saw, from the atom of cigarette smoke precisely as the cry of the hawk differed from the squeal of a rusty hinge which it so much resembled.

I would be at a loss to show the difference between the sound made by a living thing and an inorganic noise. But the lens takes soundings for us in the depths of optical dimensions. There is no shock, for the young mind with a bent for science, like the first look through a microscope. I am not likely to forget the moment when I saw the green world of the algae come alive — delicate twisted bands of color in the glassy cell walls, diatoms like bits of carven glass, desmids like a trembling green lace, the hexagonal meshes of the water-net like the work of bobbins, and *Oscillatoria*, that plant that swims with a slow

[35]

eel-like motion. Under the lens I witnessed life's crucial event, when I saw the whip-tailed male cells escape from the sack of a sea kelp and assault the great, inert egg cell, like meteors raining upon a ponderous planet. Under that purposeful attack the planet cell began to roll, with a great, a gentle but irresistible momentum, until one dart, predestined, broke through the surface tensions, dropped to the nuclear core like a solid thing descending through a gas, and then the conquered planet ceased its rolling and the rejected meteors dropped away. Life had begun again.

By a coincidence which has no meaning — or perhaps it has every meaning — human fertilization is startlingly like that in the big red seaweed, and who has seen this latter has in effect looked into the very bottom of the well of self.

Because the lens has left scant privacy to Nature, it is difficult for the modern mind to recall what battles were once waged over the subject of fertilization, the sexuality of plants, the structure of the cell. Men without the weapon of the lens tussled then in bootless speculation as the Trojans and Greeks pulled the body of Patroclus this way and that.

One comes at last to feel that the invention of the microscope by Janssen of Holland in the seventeenth century was the beginning of modern natural history, for the lens added a new dimension to our eyes and enabled us literally to see to the heart of many a problem. The sentence I have just written sounds good enough to pass unchallenged. But it sounds better than it is, for it seems to assert that one man invented the microscope, and it leaves us to infer that, once it was invented, men, peering through it, saw truth at last. In fact, however, having seventeenth-century minds, they did not in the least make of what they saw what we would. Except for a few larger minds, the early microscopists were largely engaged in watching the antics of fleas.

And the revolution in biological thought consequent on the use of the microscope did not take place in the seventeenth century but in the unfinished century, 1850 to our times. It is the modern technical improvements, coupled with the forward march of allied sciences, that have created the merciful triumphs of bacteriology, carried us into a deep perspective of atomic structure and brought light into the dark mystery of protoplasm itself. The seventeenth-century microscopy was necessarily limited by the imperfections of the early instruments, and still more by the state of the allied sciences at the time. But it was, none the less, an era of high adventure in natural history, for the lens, however faulty, gave to all greatly inquisitive minds the first rapturous look at the wonderworld of structure. Without that glimpse, sterility would have fallen upon further inquiry, so that the microscope seems to have come not a moment too soon in the history of natural science.

Viewed in another way, it was an unconscionable time in arriving. Pliny mentions that letters can be enlarged by placing a glass water bowl over them. Roger Bacon and Chaucer talk of spectacles. The English spectacle-maker Digges in 1571 made combinations of simple lenses, and between 1591 and 1609 Zacharias Janssen constructed something like a modern compound microscope. But a simple lens mounted on an armature is after all a microscope too, and had been used in 1590 by Mouffet when studying the anatomy of the bee. In 1592 George Hoefnagel published the results of previous years' work on insect anatomy that show that he had been using strong magnification.

Upon occasion Galileo is spoken of as the inventor of the microscope. In effect he seems to have been the one who thought of turning telescopes on small objects at close range. He therefore invented the type of our modern microscope — that is, two lenses at opposite ends of a tube. But this was by no means the typical microscope of the times, nor the type with which some of the great discoveries were made. Probably it was the kind used by Francesco Stelluti, Galileo's fellow member of the Accademia dei Lincei, which proudly published his anatomy of the bee " made with the microscope."

In the pedantry of the foregoing paragraphs, I invite every one's attention to the difficulty of stating who invented the instrument and who first saw what through it. And beyond that I have nothing further to tell here, for I am interested in quite another sort of seventeenth-century lens — the lens in the human intellect that was at last turned upon life as it is.

The lens is a concentration of light rays. The biological triumphs of the age came as the result of the concentration of many minds upon concrete problems. Whereas in the physical sciences we can thank Galileo or Newton for specific conquests, we have to beware of hero-worshiping individual naturalists. You may have read somewhere that Spallanzani settled the age-old problem of where life originates by proving that you cannot find its beginning,

JAN SWAMMERDAM,
from a painting attributed to Rembrandt.
(See page 47)

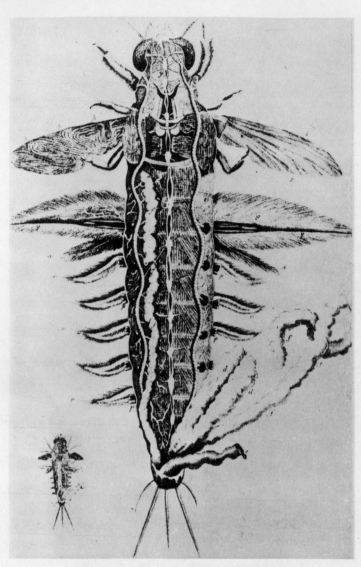

ANATOMY OF AN INSECT LARVA,
by Swammerdam, the master microscopist
and draftsman of the Renaissance.
(*See page 46*)

since all life comes from life, but back of Spallanzani you will find Francesco Redi arguing the same thing in Galileo's time, and in the longer and duller accounts you will come on the name of Jung; I will be much surprised, moreover, if some ancient Hindu or Greek was not there before him. Even today the ghost of the theory of spontaneous generation cannot quite be laid, for a biological problem should never be closed. There is no one right answer. For each age will interpret life in those terms which are most satisfying to it. How God may smile, we can only guess.

But in the seventeenth century, men began to give answers that still content us today. In the past there had been individual naturalists, lone wolf explorers, solitary collectors scattered thinly about the great distances which existed in Europe before there were regular posts. Now men began to form themselves into intelligent societies. I have mentioned the Accademia dei Lincei, the Society of Lynxes — that is to say, the lynx-eyed, detecting the slightest natural significance. Organized at Rome in the opening of the century, it had numbered among its members Galileo himself, della Porta the herbalist, Peiresc the Provençal collector and astronomer, Colonna the botanist, Duke Federigo Cesi, student and philosopher of the life of the hive, Stelluti the microscopist of bee anatomy, and some twenty-five others. Fifteen years after it was founded, symptoms of its death were seen in the resignation of a prominent member, " because the society, and especially Galileo, upheld forbidden views." After the death of its powerful patron, Duke Federigo Cesi, Galileo went to the rack, and the spirit of free inquiry flickered low. Fifty-seven years after its founding, it was abandoned, but not before it had published its transactions, probably the first printed proceedings of a scientific society in Europe.

In the very year that the Lincei perished, however, Italian science threw up a new shoot. In the beautiful library of Grand Duke Ferdinand de' Medici, or among the retorts and ovens of his brother Leopold's laboratory, or in his private botanical gardens, there gathered together illustrious and congenial spirits. Viviani and Torricelli had been Galileo's pupils; Torricelli was the inventor of the barometer. Borelli brought to the study of animal physiology a training in the exact sciences; he was by all odds the most famous and the most unruly member of this Accademia del Cimento, or experimental society, refusing, with a Renaissance Italian swagger, to submerge his individuality and claims to fame by publishing his work anonymously as the results of the academy's findings. The Cimento was even bolder and more important than the Lincei; it did not number many naturalists, except Borelli, Redi, Steno the Dane and Leopold himself, but all of its members were infinitely curious men. They tested what insects would do when put in a vacuum; they removed the air from the bodies of animals by a pneumatic machine, and under Borelli's inspiration investigated their digestive processes. Finally Leopold dissolved the society; some say that the Pope made its dissolution the price of a Cardinal's hat, and others that the quarrels of Borelli and Viviani disgusted the noble patron.

The Accademia contained some university professors, but it was quite outside the jurisdiction of the theological and the even more dangerous medical faculties. While the theologians were inclined to call in the Inquisition to uphold their views, the learned doctors had a way of supposing that no one else had a right to scientific inquiry, and that inquiry must follow conventional lines and submit to a sort of professional ethics. It was a brave band, the Cimento, and it built on the rim of a volcano. The peril in which it stood, the semi-secrecy of its meetings, the sense of embarking upon unknown adventure, must have made it stimulating beyond anything that can be conceived for modern scientific conventions. To the young scientist today, there may come that sense of expansion which is happiness, when he is first admitted to the formal society of his peers, but his attendance grows less regular with the years. It is notorious how seldom one of the grand old titans will consent to leave his private work to listen to tedious papers or tell others what he is doing. Only some active persecution would open his lips.

So in the days of the first microscopists the times themselves were grinding the mental lens. The focus of curiosity sharpened. Men in Florence, in the meetings of the Académie des Sciences in Paris, of the Royal Society in London, savants of Berlin and Amsterdam and Copenhagen, saw that up to the present they had known little of reality. There was more than endless facts to be discovered; there were chains of facts, patterns of them with significance. They saw now that it was not for man to make these patterns, but to find them out.

If I were writing the history of biology, I would tell how the century had been electrified at its opening by Harvey's announcement of the circulation of the blood, and how others applied themselves to the great unfinished business of measuring that mortal tide. When Malpighi turned his lens upon the structure of the lung, he saw for the first time why it is that man draws breath. When Leeuwenhoek peered through his home-contrived microscope, he found the corpuscles of the life stream, that no eye had seen before — and was tickled in his bourgeois soul to set Swammerdam right about them. The heart, the brain, the glands, the nerves, every organ of the human and his fellow vertebrates, became subject to intensive scrutiny. And that scrutiny for the first time revealed the functions of the organs. It is almost impossible for me to believe it, but it is true that not so long ago men did not know that the brain was the seat of thought; some believed that it cooled the blood. No one ever thought more nobly than Plato, but he never guessed what he was thinking with. He had no idea that whatever else thought may be, it is also a physical process, like digestion. So biology was at last founded upon the structure of life itself, and natural history, which is the outdoor view of biology, was tethered at last to physical realities.

As I have said, I have no space for the biological triumphs which lead off in the direction of medicine, biochemistry, and the physics of life, and when I turn now to outstanding microscopists of the seventeenth century, it must be understood that I am consciously omitting more than half their accomplishments. It is my chosen part to tell here not of the ways in which man has made life safer or more comfortable for himself, but of those rarer and more incomprehensible moments when he has lost thought of self and turned his gaze upon the world that does not heed him. In a rapt wonder the astronomer looks up at the island universes that really do not matter to us, and matter more than we. So men have looked downward at the insect peoples, and there have been those who wondered not what humanly comprehensible reason there could be for so much thoughtless wisdom, such seemingly perverted tastes and such immutable ritual, but, forgetting self again, have sought to understand the insect reasons.

Such a man was Marcello Malpighi, born in 1628 near Bologna in the broad basin of the Po. A friend of Borelli, he associated with all the great ones of the Cimento, and Malpighi the microscopist and Borelli the physiologist worked together, a completely complementary pair diametrically opposed in temperament. Malpighi was modest, sensitive, painstaking, frail in health, dignified under criticism. He had spent the latter years of his youth in getting rid of the Aristotelian Scholasticism he had earlier imbibed, and in avoiding the active enmity of some fine Italian neighbors with whom he had had a boundary dispute, and who saw to it that he was kept out of all the lucrative and honorific positions that they in any way controlled. In science many conservatives did not like him.

But professorial troubles, questions of preferment and of priority of discovery are seldom worth recording. The great event in Malpighi's life was the moment when Henry Oldenburg, secretary to the new-born Royal Society in London, wrote and asked him to enter into regular correspondence. Next year Malpighi was made an F.R.S., and Oldenburg suggested that the Italian might study the anatomy of one of the few insects then recognized as of any value, the silkworm. No reply came for two years, when there arrived in the grey northern capital a dissertation upon the structure of the silkworm which for exquisite accuracy and detail opened the eyes of the astonished Englishmen. They voted with a glad voice that " the History of the Silke Worme, by Signor Malpighi, dedicated to the Royal Society, be printed forthwith by the printers of the same."

Presently Signor Malpighi sent them his portrait, by Tabor. It showed them, as it shows us still, where it hangs in their rooms, a pale and studious man, an elegant small line of moustache above the curly mouth, a tiny goatee, and black waving locks to his dark-clad shoulders. A lace-ruffled wrist and a very white hand shine out of the darkness of the picture. It is almost a feminine face, or perhaps more nearly of the sort thought once to belong to the type predisposed to consumption.

Malpighi had labored with such enthusiasm that he had thrown his body into a fever and set up an inflammation of the eyes. " Nevertheless," he told his English friends, " in performing these researches so many marvels of Nature were spread before my eyes that I experienced an internal pleasure that my pen cannot describe."

There speaks the naturalist as we have all learned to love him, a man who does not know where to stop in his great passion for knowing, a man whose curiosity goes beyond what is meant by idle wonderment, beyond any more gaping in the windows at the jumble of life's oddities. Such an investigator's thirst to know is a form of worship, and when he notes down, when he draws what he sees, he believes that he is inscribing tablets with a revealed code.

When he has a fact, and knows it, he will fight for it, not because he was the discoverer of it, but because he deems it a sin not to preach what is so.

When Malpighi with delicate fingers laid open the mechanism of the clever little worm, caterpillar of the moth *Bombyx*, he learned the secret of the spinnerets from which flows the gleaming floss that, hardened, becomes the rippling, shimmering, woman-stuff called silk. But he went on to learn more that no one had asked about but himself. I have no space to tell it, but there was one discovery, which he was so wise as to verify upon many other insects, of capital import. Insects, he found, have no lungs with which to breathe; instead, their blood is aërated by a system of minutest tubes that pierce the armor of the shard and ramify into the depths of the body, so that the life-giving element of oxygen thrills literally through every fibre.

With the death of Malpighi, the glory of his science departed from Italy, but it was shining in Holland. Young Jan Jacobz Swammerdam impresses us now as the greatest biologist of his age, and once more I am going to slight many accomplishments and tell my story in terms of what Swammerdam learned of the cryptic, multiplex and fantastical insect world.

For the insects constitute an exception to almost everything you can say about the rest of the animal kingdom. You no sooner think that you have established a law, discovered a fundamental plan of animal architecture, or learned a secret of function, than you find some long-faced grasshopper sneering denial at you. The very stuff of which the insects are made is not like ours. They are

not built on bones, but encased in chitin. Chitin is the horn
of the rhinoceros beetle, the wing of the dragonfly, the
sting, the eye, the armor, the hairs, the antennae, the very
thread on which the spider escapes you. Nothing will so
permanently revise your biological outlook as to discover
how different an animal may be from yourself and still in
its own environment be a king. The insect, for instance,
has what may be called a brain, but how differently con-
stituted! Its sensory receiving organs are scattered, not
concentrated into a federal government, so that some ants
seem to smell with their feet and even in utter blackness
so find their way upon a beaten track, whether by smell or
touch, that that thought which is memory seems practically to reside in their six wire-like legs. Whereas our
sense of balance is located in the Eustachian tubes near the
ear, it appears in some insects in a particular joint of the
antenna. This sort of topsyturvydom could be developed
at length, but it is obvious that the first man who with a
clean strong lens and a cool head broke into the hitherto
locked world of insect anatomy found himself in an Alad-
din's cave of new truths. Of what he saw, Swammerdam
made drawings that in three centuries have not, I think,
been surpassed.

He was a master of the manual technique of dissection
and the preparation of specimens. He seems to have possessed in those rather square Dutch hands of his the exquisite mechanical accuracy of the modern microtome
which cuts transparent sections with undeviating regular-
ity. He was an adept at the preparation of dissecting instruments, and would have none not of his own making.
He used to sharpen the blades of infinitesimally small and

thin scissors under the microscope, so that he might slit
with them the finest nerves and trachea of an insect. He
was particularly dextrous in the production of glass tubes
no thicker than a hair, which he inserted into the veins of
minute creatures, in order to inject colored wax into them,
the better to trace them. He was adept in the art of mounting specimens in balsam and mastic.

We have a portrait, perhaps by Rembrandt, to show
us what was this fine-fingered Ali Baba of ours. His contemporaries tell us how he was restless, sleepless, suspi-
cious, sharp, fond of finding other men in the wrong —
he liked to correct Malpighi and Leeuwenhoek — and
the portrait shows me a lunging big head, ears set back
rather like those of a cat that has just been smacked, brilliantly intelligent eyes, the wrinkles of a man made dis-
agreeable by ill health in youth. It seems to me that I can
detect the signs of that introspection, a Calvinist disposition to torture the soul, which finally put a stop to the
finest work of his age.

What I would never suspect from the look of the man
is that feather-light touch of his. But such skill is like the
surgeon's; it turns up in men who may even be somewhat
gross and not especially delicate in feeling. It dies with
them, and cannot be completely passed on to any school.
We only wait for the gift to reappear.

It is easier to account for the wrinkles in Swammerdam's face. He somehow contracted malaria in his youth,
and was never freed of it. It was not in Jan's nature, moreover, to get on with his family. If his father, an eccentric
rich apothecary of Amsterdam, wanted to control his son's
life, the son was certainly a problem for any father. He

showed no indication of ever supporting himself or marrying, and the worst of it was that he could work hard enough when he wanted to, at his blessed " flea-glass."

When his father would have no more fiddling with mayflies, and refused to support him further, Jan came down with another fit of ague. He was released to recuperate in the country upon a promise to give up his idle pursuits. But it was midsummer, the sweet, brief summer of northern Europe, where the day begins at three and one may still read a book by the after-glow when the clock hands lack but two hours of midnight. The butterflies were dancing over the blowing flowers; the bees were thrumming in the fragrant heads of clover. A promise given under duress is invalid; life is short of span, a fevered dream between two sleepings. The impetuous Jan deliberately plunged to a fresh breakdown of his health.

" It was an undertaking," wrote his editor Boerhaave, " too great for the strongest constitution to be continually employed by day in making observations and almost as constantly engaged by night in recording them by drawings and suitable explanations. This being summer work, his daily labors began at six in the morning, when the sun afforded him light enough to be able to survey such minute objects; and from that time till twelve he continued without interruption, all the while exposed in the open air to the scorching heat of the sun, bareheaded, for fear of interrupting the light, and his head in a manner dissolving into sweat under the irresistible ardors of that powerful luminary. And if he desisted at noon, it was only because the strength of his eyes was too much weakened by the extraordinary efflux of light and the use of microscopes to continue any longer upon such small objects.

The Lens Turned on Life

" This fatigue our author submitted to for a whole month together, without any interruption, merely to examine, describe,
and represent the intestines of bees, besides many months more
bestowed upon the other parts; during which time he spent whole
days in making observations, as long as there was sufficient light
to make any, and whole nights in registering his observations, till
at last he brought his treatise on bees to the wished-for perfection." [1]

So throwing health and honor to the winds, Swammerdam achieved a work that was epochal. Single-
handed he discovered half the secrets of the hive. Where
Aristotle had seen a king bee as the ruler of the apian
community, Swammerdam detected the matriarchy, and
proved that the queen is the only effective female of the
hive. He unmasked the infinitely effete drones as the true
males, and the workers as neuters. He put forth delicate
skill, such as the world had never seen, to reveal the anatomy of the eyes and sting and proboscis — that marvelous
tongue that dips in the deepest nectaries of the flowers.
Of the bee eye nothing escaped him; he saw the many-
faceted eyes which are largest in the drone, and the three
other eyes that no one else had ever noticed, simple eyes
like ours. He alone knew that the compound eye was not
a collection of such cameras as our eyes that have pupil
and iris, but that it is rather a window, admitting almost
all the light that falls on it. As for the sting, he knew that
it is curved in the queen, straight in the worker, and want-
ing in the drone. He experimented with its venom, thrust-
ing the darts into his arm, swallowing the poison, rolling

---

[1] English translation quoted from Locy, *The Growth of Biology*
(Henry Holt & Co., New York, 1925).

it on the sensitive tip of his tongue. With such a knowledge of bee anatomy as this, science was now for the first time in a position to generalize upon the economy, politics and behavior of the hive.

Greatest of the Dutchman's triumphs was his discovery of the metamorphosis of insects. The mighty Harvey, who on the prestige of one superb pronouncement was taken for authority, had looked down from man's royal position and asserted that insects had no true growth, nothing that was really reproduction — that is, the bearing of like offspring. To Harvey insects were spawning, writhing, equivocal vermin who melted diabolically in and out of each other. The caterpillar, he pointed out contemptuously, does not, like an honest creature, make more little caterpillars; it turns into a butterfly. Carrion flies, it seemed to him as to all men then, were bred spontaneously out of filth, without previous ancestry. So, in the insect world there were no real species, but only a breed of endless pest and corruption that had no logical form and no discoverable scheme.

Swammerdam knew these things to be untrue, nor was it his way to be gentle with ignorance. Sarcastically he demolished all previous misconceptions of insect life histories. The egg, the caterpillar, the pupa and the butterfly are all, he proved to an astonished Europe, one and the same individual in different growth stages. When Duke Cosmo of Florence visited him at Amsterdam, the arrogant clever northerner performed a showman's trick, slitting open the skin of a pupa and showing how, all packed away, the legs and wings and antennae of the full-fledged butterfly were already formed, ready to expand in the sunlight. Beholding this marvel, the Florentine was so enraptured that he offered twelve thousand florins for Jan's father's private museum of rubbish, provided that Jan himself go to Florence with the other curiosities. For princes have ever had to buy their jugglers and philosophers, like their rugs and pictures and young mistresses.

At that moment Jan was at outs with his bread and butter; he was weary and longing for a change. But religious scruples withheld him. So the Duke picked up a bargain in the Dane, Steno, and took him off to Florence where we have already met him at the gatherings of the Cimento. There he fell under the colorful spell of the old mother Church, foreswore his Lutheran faith, and became a show window exhibit for all those since who have labored to prove that the Church can attract a man of science. They forget to mention that Steno ceased scientific work and became a bishop.

Swammerdam had been taught, no doubt from infancy, to abjure the Pope. But no one warned him of Antoinette Bourignon, one of those women founders of new sects that are a phenomenon of the protestant faiths. Reviled alike by Catholics and Protestants, the Bourignon wandered about Europe, attracting broken souls, reveling in persecution, carrying Swammerdam in her train. Steno thought the moment had come to allure his old college friend to the cult that is mystic beyond all others, and he wrote to him urging him to find peace at the great bosom. The dying man — he was but forty-two — sent a tart reply, and passed away at last without moral certainties and with more than three-fourths of his great work unpublished. Many times the manuscript was sold at auction, and it did not appear until the next century, when the rich Boerhaave finally brought it out. It bore the title, both reverent and audacious, that the religiously self-tortured Swammerdam had wished for it: *The Bible of Nature*.

I am come now to the last of the three great microscopists of the age, Antonj van Leeuwenhoek. It will be a long time before any one gives a livelier account of him than has the nimble Paul de Kruif in his *Microbe Hunters*. But Dr. de Kruif was chiefly interested in the old man's discovery of bacteria — which Leeuwenhoek did not entirely comprehend. Wealthy, but self-made, an expert lens grinder who increased magnification up to two hundred and seventy diameters before he realized that more median lenses give the best results, unwilling to part with the secret of his art, shrewd with a sort of magnified common sense, gossipy, stubborn, ignorant of any language but Dutch and contemptuously proud of it, Leeuwenhoek of Delft was one of the most eccentric personalities of the scientific age, and you may be sure that his English friends in the Royal Society did not miss a wrinkle in his character. But those famous letters of his, full of chaff about his health and his neighbors' follies, were read with amazement for their precious kernels. They surpassed in wonder anything that even Malpighi or Swammerdam communicated, and sometimes it was well-nigh impossible to believe what this shameless *voyeur* was recounting — a bit of everything under the sun and much else which it is more delicate to keep dark.

For Leeuwenhoek did not methodically study a limited subject, like his two great rivals. He had, boylike, discovered the sheer rapture of looking at the whole world through a lens. Not only were his lenses more sensational than anything that had yet been produced, but the eye at the objective was shrewder, brighter, more restless. There was only one trouble, and that was that the mind behind the lens was not the equal of the crystal or the cornea. He was the consummate amateur, having an uninhibited good time, enjoying robust temperament and health, untroubled by that scientific conscientiousness that made of Malpighi a melancholy man and of Swammerdam a self-slaying maniac for work.

Leeuwenhoek's own title for his collected works (they were Latinized by his friends and correspondents to give them a broader reading) was as symbolical of his temperament as *The Bible of Nature* was revelatory of Swammerdam's last-moment pietistic scruples. The inveterate Peeping Tom of Delft called his opus *Secrets of Nature*, and some of the secrets he revealed were the human male's spermatozoa, the bacteria he found in his mouth by scraping his back teeth, the generation of fleas, the eggs of tadpoles, and the true nature of the red corpuscles of the blood. His minor discoveries are almost endless, though he never had the patience to tunnel through until fact met fact in a significant penetration. There was even a moment when he made an absurd pretension — he declared that he saw in the spermatozoön a whole tiny man, body and limbs and head.

But for all his faults, Leeuwenhoek belongs in the great chain that forges the cable of certain knowledge from age to age. He drove nails in the coffin of the spontaneous generation theory by his discovery that vermin are not bred

out of filth but come from eggs laid there by their predecessors. He revolutionized our view of sex, diminishing
the importance of the male, when he showed that plant
aphids reproduce parthenogenetically, by a sort of virgin
birth of endless fatherless generations. He found the true
eggs of ants, and revealed that what are called and still
sold as ant eggs are in reality ant pupae in their chrysalids.
One day he discovered the striated nature of muscles, and
another he dug out of his rain gutter those fascinating
dervish animalculae, the rotifers. He started enough lines
of inquiry to found a whole school of biology — and yet
he was so jealous of his knowledge that he never took a
pupil.

I find myself closing this chapter without a mention of
the gazers who through the lens discovered the cellular
structure of all living tissue. I have given no place to that
eccentric, cantankerous, deformed little pest of an English microscopist, Hooke, who always claimed to have
discovered everything before everybody else — and was
often right about it. Grew, who turned the lens upon the
sexuality of plants and made epic history in botany, I have
failed to mention, and now I shall never be able to retrace
my steps and honor Redi as he should be honored.

It was in this era, too, that men first worked on the
fascinating problem of the irritability and motions of
plants, stimulated to it by the arrival from the tropics of
a mere botanical curiosity, the sensitive plant. It was an
era when men began to suspect and assert — though they
risked the rack for it — the animate nature of fossils.

So it may seem to us that the colorful seventeenth century was almost within sight of our own, as it pursued the

nature of the cell and attacked the paralyzing myth of spontaneous generation, penetrated close to the heart of sex and unwrapped the mystery that clings around the seed. We have the feeling that the men of that age were coasting along golden shores that were hidden from them in thin mists, and that with a little more perseverance, vision and daring, they would have had a landfall of twentieth-century discovery.

But the first great days of microscopy were over when the aged Leeuwenhoek was claimed at last by death. And a sterility is always likely to fall upon those very branches of investigation where the greatest progress has been made, for the swiftness of the advance outstrips the flanking support of sister sciences. Now beyond the rim of the lens there lay a great world of Nature still to be found out. Investigation lifted its eyes from the microscope. I doubt if Buffon ever looked through one with more than lukewarm curiosity; the blind Huber did marvels without even his naked sight; Linnaeus, for better or for worse, seldom used anything more than a strong hand lens, yet he made order out of chaos. The centuries after the seventeenth were to write their odysseys of discovery in tropic islands and on arctic shores. They had the world of the complete, the living organism to conquer.

3

SCIENCE AT COURT —BUFFON AND RÉAUMUR

AFTER the great victory of Fontenoy, King Louis XV celebrated by dowering his pretty mistress with the title, Marquise de Pompadour. He allowed her to move his statesmen and generals about like men in a game of draughts, and it pleased her also to manipulate the savants with her pretty finger tips. Like new pieces for her cabinet, she acquired Diderot, Quesnay, Helvétius, d'Alembert, Voltaire and Malesherbes, those astonishing gentlemen who for their work on the daring *Encyclopédie* were popping in and out of the Bastille or exile.

It is not to be imagined that this engaging little parasite understood Diderot's article on mathematics or even Rousseau's wretched contribution on music, but learning was the mode. According to Voltaire, during a *petit souper* at the Trianon an argument arose on the subject of the making of gunpowder. The Pompadour pouted that for her part she did not know how her rouge or her silk stockings were made, and the Duc de la Vallière sighed over the ban on the unfinished *Encyclopédie*. But although officially confiscated, there were plenty of copies of it circulating about the court, and servants were sent to fetch them. The lackeys soon came bringing twenty-one volumes, and the king found the answer to everything he wanted to know. Boredom, that bitterer enemy than Albion, had been banished for an hour; once more the *Encyclopédie* was in favor and permitted to progress.

To this world of the *Encyclopédistes*, of powdered wigs and gold lace and ruffled shirts, there came a naturalist with an idea for a mighty encyclopedia of his own, something that was to sum up the world of the natural sciences for all time. Georges Louis Leclerc de Buffon, of the *petite noblesse* of Burgundy, was the rising star in the heavens of science. It is not often that a naturalist is a courtier too; learned men are apt to be bores in society, justly feared by the *salonnière* as by the modern hostess for their deficiency in small talk and for the difficulty of stopping them if once they break loose with their favorite topics. But Buffon knew society as well as science. Versailles welcomed him.

For the court of Louis XV was looking just then for a personable zoögrapher who would sumptuously catalogue the curiosities in the " King's Cabinet," describe the wild animals at the *parc* of Versailles, tidy up and make smart the long-neglected Jardin des Plantes on the left bank in Paris. He must also publish something voluminous, something full of praise for the king's hunting horses and hounds, with plenty of colored illustrations and no technical language. In short, what the moment called for was a gentleman naturalist who would add one more gleam to the most illustrious monarchy upon the globe.

There was, of course, old Réaumur, but you could not

catch his eye; it was bent on such vermin as ants. This young Burgundian, now, with his courtly bow, his exquisite speech, was the very man, and he received the post of intendant of the Jardin des Plantes, with a handsome stipend attached.

The next thing, of course, was to get him into the Académie Française. He was young, but, *diable*, Réaumur had crashed into it at twenty-four! Could not the Marquise de Pompadour be persuaded to use her influence? It was known that she practically controlled the seats, and only a last-moment whim of the king's, like his exclusion of Piron because in his youth he had written an *Ode to Priapus*, could prevent the election of one on whom she smiled. But Buffon discreetly retired from candidacy, because, it was whispered through the mirrored halls, he too had after his own fashion written odes to Priapus in his early days, and did not care to have them published. A little patience, a little time, and young men's follies and young women's beauty are forgotten.

And Louis was immensely pleased with his new zoölogist laureate. The man was a magnificent show piece, impressive to generations to come. Geoffroy St. Hilaire believed that Buffon was " one of those mighty men who with a bold tread cross the frontiers of their epoch, march ahead alone and advance toward the future centuries, carrying their genius as a conqueror carries his sword." Mirabeau stated that Buffon was the greatest man of his century and of many others. Cuvier was first directed toward the study of natural history by reading Buffon, and all his life regarded him as a god. Rousseau, before he entered the tower of the old château at Montbard where Buffon worked, fell down and kissed the threshold. Gibbon speaks of Buffon as one might of the Gibbon of natural history. Even Voltaire, after quarreling with him about the origin of fossils and the Great Deluge, capitulated at last. He wrote Buffon that he was a second Archimedes — which Buffon capped with gallantry by replying that there would never be any one called Voltaire the Second.

This charming young exponent of science, translator of Newton into French and close student of Leibnitz, was indeed a swift-witted phrase-maker. In an age when an epigram was worth an encyclopedia, when Diderot and Malesherbes and Voltaire were all epitomizing the sum of human experience in a couplet or a prose passage of twelve words, Buffon could still be called, even by an enemy, " *le roi des phrasiers.*" " The horse," Buffon charmed all chivalry by writing, " is the noblest conquest that man has ever made." To him we must credit the belief that " genius is an infinite capacity for taking pains," and that " *le style est l'homme même.*" He spoke like a scientist when he said, " The purpose of philosophy is not to understand the *why*, but the *how* of things." If this dictum had been more widely accepted, the world would have been spared many philosophers. When Buffon told the court that " all subjects are one subject, and however vast it may be, it can be encompassed within a single discourse," society sighed with relief. At least he would not be an interminable bore, this young fellow.

One could not but admire his way of going to work,

as he set out to write the natural history of the world, from its creation to the last wingless bird of the ultimate isles of Ocean. For it was his habit, whether in his château at Montbard, near Dijon, or in Paris at the Jardin, to arise precisely at six, dress himself with exquisite care in full court costume, donning all his rings and orders, flicking out his lace ruffles, tapping his snuffbox; he then walked straight to his table, where he usually stood at his work, and wrote steadily, saying precisely what he meant, never hesitating, never revising, never opening his ears to the calumny of his enemies. He worked eight hours a day, stopped as promptly as a Union carpenter, and threw away his exhausted notes as if he were getting rid of the shavings of a plane. " Buffon," wrote Mallet du Pan, " lives absolutely *en philosophe;* he is just without being generous, and all his conduct is based upon what is reasonable. He loves order, and makes it everywhere."

In this fashion, beginning at the beginning, that is to say, putting the most important things first, proceeding by the principle that Descartes had laid down — from the simple to the complex — a scientist might logically hope to come out at the end of a life's work precisely where he intended to, like an engineer whose mathematical calculations bring his tunnel out of the mountain at the predicted spot.

The training of Buffon, indeed, had been mathematical. Born in 1707 at Montbard, in the same year as Linnaeus, he had early shown an aptitude for the precise sciences. His stay in England had made him acquainted with Newtonian theories; his first published work had concerned the strength of wood. When he was made intendant of the royal gardens he had known little about animals and plants. " I have learned botany three times," he said with weary boredom, " and all the same I have forgotten it." Minerals appealed far more to his temperament. But Réaumur had already settled himself into that field, with his treatises on the drawing of gold wire, the crystallography of metals, the tempering of steel and iron casting, and methods of recovering gold from river sands. Still, Buffon meant to get around to disposing of the mineral kingdom too, when he had finished with the animal. For the present he proceeded to make a zoölogist of himself by a sort of cool and steady calculation, as a man today will lay his plans for reaching the North Pole.

The first sentences of his great encyclopedia are admirable. " One should begin by seeing much and coming back often for a second look." He goes on to refer to the self-evident chain of Nature, descending by imperceptible gradations from man, through the lower animals and plants to the minerals. Then he abolishes the systematists, with magnificent contempt for that fellow Linnaeus splitting hairs in Sweden. All groups, Buffon asserts, are abstractions. " In Nature there actually exist only individuals; genera and orders and classes exist only in our imaginations." So much for Platonic universals!

This promised a relief from the tedium of learning the technical definitions of the cat family and the dog family and every other sort of category, and Buffon's readers were further delighted to find that the arrangement of animals was to be as simple as grouping books in a library. Why introduce Latin nomenclature? *Un chat est un chat* — a cat is a cat; why call it *Felis domestica?* If *felis* means cat, as in classical Latin it certainly does, is it reasonable to call the lion *Felis leo?* A lion is not a cat, *parbleu!*

And those microscopists! Their eyes are so close to what they are looking at that they cannot see the flower for seeing the pollen grains. Buffon himself would approve informal descriptions, without tiresome details. The grouping should be that which naturally follows the train of human thought. Instead of following the description of the horse with that of its technical relative, the zebra, would not a reasonable man append the dog who runs at the horse's heels?

" The more one observes, the less one reasons," Buffon wrote, sharpening his quill for the attack, and that with a sublime disregard of consistency; there is a drop of acid now in his ink:

" Is there, in fact, anything more gratuitous than this admiration for bees, than these moral views with which they are supposed to be endowed, than this love of the common weal which they are supposed to have, than this extraordinary instinct which equals the most sublime geometry, an instinct recently attributed to them and in obedience to which bees solve without hesitation the problem of building their comb in the *most stable manner possible, in the smallest possible space, and with the greatest possible economy?* What shall we think of the excess to which the details of these eulogies have been carried? For, in the end, a bee should not occupy more space in the head of a naturalist than it does in Nature; and this marvellous republic of flies will never be more in the eyes of reason than a swarm of little beasts that have no other relation to us than to supply us with wax and honey." [1]

All France, reading this superbly royalist pronouncement on one of Nature's working classes, knew now what the court zoögrapher thought of Réaumur. The greatest naturalist in the Académie (still closed to Buffon) had up to this time produced six volumes of his careful *Mémoires pour servir à une histoire des insectes*, including many acute pages concerning the hive.

"These cells of bees," went on Buffon's depreciating voice, "these hexagons, so much extolled, so greatly admired, furnish me with a further proof against enthusiasm and admiration. This shape, perfectly geometrical and perfectly regular, is here merely a mechanical effect and a rather imperfect one at that, like those which often occur in Nature and are observed in her crudest productions. . . . If you fill a vessel with peas, or better with some other cylindrical seeds, close it tightly, after having poured in enough water to fill the interstices remaining between the seeds, and then boil the water, all the cylinders will become prisms with six surfaces. Obviously the reason for this is purely mechanical; every seed, whose form is cylindrical, on swelling tends to occupy as much room as possible in a given space; hence they all become hexagons by *reciprocal pressure*." [2]

But truly, as Buffon himself remarked, the more one observes, the less one reasons. If he had observed bees, as Réaumur did, patiently day and night, he would have discovered that bees do not build only the common hexagonal cells such as came to his plate. There are special

---

[1] Wheeler's translation quoted from Réaumur, *The Natural History of Ants* (Alfred A. Knopf, New York, 1926).
[2] Ibid.

cells for the queens, and others for the young. Peas in a pot will not explain these away, nor explain the shape of a butterfly's chrysalis or a spider's net. Some voices murmured these objections. But Buffon found it vulgar to quarrel. " One must let calumny fall back on itself," he said, throwing his day's notes into the waste basket, and flicking off his fingers one against the other.

Linnaeus and Réaumur thus disposed of, Buffon advanced another step, with his *Théorie de la terre*. This picture of creation owes a debt to the geological work of Steno the Dane, to Ray the Englishman, to Swedenborg's cosmology, and to the mathematical researches of Descartes, though if Buffon ever realized and acknowledged his sources, I do not recall it. But he astonished the noble and orthodox subscribers to his sumptuous volumes by suggesting that the world was not, after all, only six thousand years old, as the Bible might lead you to believe. Steno, after being made a Catholic bishop, had foreseen that this conclusion must be reached, and solved the dilemma quite simply. He gave up geology. Buffon stepped out more courageously. The earth, he said, was stricken off the sun's mass by a collision with a comet. (Sir James Jeans tells us that it was pulled out of the sun's mass by the too close passage of another sun.) And from that celestial accident were born the earth and sister planets. After the incandescent state there followed a period when the seas overlaid the rocks everywhere; behold the sea shell fossils found on top of the Alps. The waters having subsided, volcanic activity and mountain upheavals created the continents. There followed a period when the tropical animals roamed the regions that are now cold, where their bones are still found. And finally there set in the modern climate and fauna and flora, and man, last and noblest of God's creations, appeared upon the earth.

This pre-Darwin passage at arms with religious teaching is mildly startling to the modern mind. We seem to have come upon an unappreciated evolutionist!

" If one once admits," he points out, " that there are families of plants and of animals, that the ass may be of the horse family and differs only because it has degenerated, one could just as easily say that the monkey is of the family of man, that it is a degenerated man, and that man and monkey have a common origin, like horse and ass, that each family, among the animals as well as among the plants, has only one source; and even that all animals have come from but one animal, who, in the succession of eras has produced, while perfecting itself and degenerating, all the other races of animals."

From its context, this may well have been said sardonically, but greatly did it trouble the Sorbonne professors, still theologians and Schoolmen — this passage and the unorthodox history of the earth. So before he knew it, this very correct and courtly scientist, who had always been careful not to be too intimate with the Encyclopedists, was as thoroughly in hot water as ever Diderot. An indictment of fourteen points was brought against him. In vain Buffon protested that he had said in the next paragraph that every creature had left God's hand just as it was, and that he had not exactly said that the earth was formed by the collision of a comet with the sun; he had only suggested that it was theoretically possible, for the sake of philosophic discussion, to take that view. The Sorbonne remained adamant.

This censure was a deplorable setback to a golden career, and worse, it instantly quashed all hope of election to the Académie. And for the moment, by the devil's own ill luck, the Pompadour herself was in trouble. Her beauty was gone; the king was tired of her and had made her a countess as the price of getting rid of her, and raging and trembling, she had packed up and was ready to fly the court, quaking at every knock on the door.

There was nothing for Buffon to do but make a recantation, and promise to publish it in full in the next volume of his *Histoire Naturelle*.

" I declare," it reads, " that I had no intention of contradicting the Scriptures, that I believe most firmly all therein stated about the Creation, both as to order of time and matter of fact. I abandon everything in my book respecting the formation of the earth, and in general all that may be contrary to the narrative of Moses."

But no sooner had the courtier, fallen among thorns, disengaged his pale blue satin coat from one bramble, than another caught him in the face. All France was talking about the *Lettres à un Americain*, by the Abbé Lignac. There was, of course, no American ever destined to receive these letters, which caught the *Histoire Naturelle* out in countless errors and derided the whole undertaking as a welter of pretentious rhetoric.

Buffon flew to the Pompadour, who had come back to power and was punishing her enemies right and left, and behind her fan besought her to influence the king to save his book. The Abbé was silenced, but gossip declared that the attack had been instigated, out of jealousy, by Réaumur.

The very next year, following the recantation, Buffon was elected to the Académie without a canvass. In the same lucky moment of his life, at forty-six, he had the felicity to marry the rich Marie Françoise de St. Belin. People quickly forgot the *Lettres à un Americain*. The Marquise de Pompadour and the Comte de Buffon had both weathered out their storms.

But Buffon's friends kept warm the feud against Réaumur. The quarrel was alive in France for generations, with Cuvier's cold authority thrown on the side of the magnificent zoögrapher. Réaumur's reputation was so diminished that actual facts about him today are scant. But even upon Cuvier's chill testimony this was a man of glittering, many-faceted talents. The stories of the sciences are now so widely divergent and already so long, that Réaumur's fame is like a great diamond that has perforce been cut up into many smaller ones. It is divided among the meteorologists who remember him for his thermometer, the metallurgists who think of him as the inventor of a process for making steel, and the entomologists who know that he began a great work, *Mémoires pour servir à une histoire des insectes*, which he could not live to finish.

According to Cuvier his notes for further volumes in this series truncated by death, were found to be in hopeless disorder. Rubbish, really. Nothing to be done with them. A pity, but they were so much waste paper. Thus, Cuvier. And the papers lay dusty and forgotten on the shelves of the Académie des Sciences.

Nearly two centuries later, in 1925, William Morton Wheeler, our most distinguished student of the ants, when visiting Paris asked to see these notes. There were brought to him four large pasteboard boxes of papers inscribed in a bold if obsolete hand, with a lofty disregard of punctuation and endless interlinings and revisions. With labor a part of them was at last transcribed, and what emerged was nothing less than a superb treatise on ants. Réaumur, it appeared, had discovered the castes of the emmet society, the workers and females and males; he proved how the winged ants were not a separate kind of insect from the wingless, but sexual forms; he observed for the first time the marriage flight, upon an appointed day, of the queens and their consorts, and so led, or would have led, the way to a solution of the problem that neither Swammerdam nor the beemasters had been able to solve — the nuptials of the hive bee.

And all these brilliant researches upon the behavior and the social and physical anatomy of ants were as lost as if they had never been written. The two Hubers, Forel, McCook and several whole generations of naturalists had to learn all over again what Réaumur had written for them to read. He was the father of formicology, but as Maeterlinck had said, a father whose children never knew him and could not inherit from him. Of their heritage they were cheated by the proverbial wicked uncles, Réaumur's brother naturalists, Buffon and Cuvier. For there is something more than a suspicion that Buffon, through Madame de Pompadour, was able to prevent all further publication of Réaumur's works after the older man's death. And Cuvier at least furthered his master's ends by assuring entomologists that what Réaumur had left them was only worthless paper. Late, but not too late for our pleasure, Professor Wheeler published *The Natural History of Ants.*

"Perhaps I should have learned nothing," Réaumur tells us therein of his discovery of the nuptial flight, "from the first chance opportunity of seeing two ants mating, if I had been less familiar with the ways of these small insects. Being on the road to Poitou and finding myself on the levée of the Loire, very near Tours, on one of the first days of the month of September, 1731, I descended from my berlin, enticed to stroll about by the beauty of the spot and the mild temperature of the air, which was the more agreeable because the earlier hours of the day had been warm. The sun was within about an hour of setting. During my stroll I noticed a lot of small mounds of sandy and earthy particles rising above the openings that led the ants to their subterranean abode. Many of them were at that time out of doors; they were red, or rather reddish, of medium size. I stopped to examine several of these earthen monticules and noticed on each among the wingless ants a number of winged ones of two very different sizes. Some of them had abdomens no larger than those of the wingless ants, and to judge from unaided vision one of the larger winged individuals must have weighed more than two or three times as much as one of the smaller. Over the beautiful levée, where I was enjoying my walk, there appeared in the air in places not very far apart small clouds of large flies which flew about in circling paths. They might have been taken for gnats or craneflies or mayflies. Often the small cloud hung in the air at a height within reach of the hand. I used one of mine to capture some of these flies and succeeded repeatedly in doing so. All I secured were without difficulty recognized for what they were, for they were winged ants like those I had found at every step on the small mounds of earth. But I observed — and the observation was as important as it was easy to make — that I invariably captured them in pairs. Not only did I almost always find in my hand one large and one small ant, but most frequently I took them copulating and held them for some time before they separated." [3]

Here is a gentleman as well born as Buffon, or better, who descends from his carriage upon a fine summer day and bestows his whole attention upon the humble ant people. This man is not puffed with pride nor deviled by ambition; he is a self-forgetting scientist, and his portrait shows the wit and humor, the generosity and the divine curiosity of the man.

For forty years Réaumur was the dominating figure in the corps of the sciences; scarcely a year went by that the Académie des Sciences did not publish some new discovery of his in metallurgy or the making of precise instruments, in physics, in the manufacture of ropes or of porcelain or in the artificial construction of pearls. He discovered the mode of locomotion of mollusks, worked on the growth of their cells, brought to notice the light that is emitted by some of them, essayed a method of spinning spider's silk, improved the hanging of carriages, constructed his thermometer and at last in 1734 began the great memoirs on insects. He had turned to the subject of birds before his death at the age of seventy-four, not from a descriptive point of view, but in the hope of furthering the still backward study of animal physiology.

At the time when he began his work on the insects, most of Swammerdam's *Bible of Nature* was unpub-

---

[3] Wheeler's translation quoted from Réaumur, *The Natural History of Ants.*

GEORGES LOUIS LECLERC,
COMTE DE BUFFON

Portrait Bust of Réaumur,
advanced in years.

lished and unknown. Linnaeus was only a wild young
student off on a junket to Lapland. There was in consequence neither anatomy nor systematics to guide Réaumur. The part of his work that entomologists knew best
was his study of the hive bee, that marvelous irritable
busybody that has captured the imagination from man's
early days. The better to spy upon the golden horde,
Réaumur invented a special hive of glass plates held
apart by short props. So he discovered the pollen-collect-
ing hairs, the famous bread-basket and the special cleans-
ing combs on the legs of the worker bees, and found that
the sucking proboscis of the bee is not the tube that Swammerdam supposed it, but a gutter which can be cleaned
of obstruction. The cells of the comb, too, absorbed him;
he wrote to the geometrician Koenig to determine what
angles would be ideal for the rhombic plates that form
the pyramidal cell ends. Koenig's purely abstract reply
tallied with the fundamental plan of the little storehouse
of honey. Réaumur's small triumph of prediction ran
through France and irritated Buffon into emitting the
fatuous paragraphs quoted earlier. If Réaumur ever
made a reply to these, I do not know of it. In private
correspondence, however, he made the following remarks concerning the *Histoire Naturelle:*

" M. de Buffon's pompous manner will not persuade you to
accept his queer notions. Had you read his first volume you
would have been no more satisfied with it than with the second.
The three together can only impede the progress of natural history and physics in general, should the propositions they contain
be adopted. But I learn on all sides that one shriek of protest has
been raised against the work, and this may indicate that the sub-

sequent volumes are not to be feared. Moreover, there is little confidence in the facts reported by the author in so far as they are based on his own observations." [4]

Kind friends provoked and prolonged these differing viewpoints into personal controversy. Each adding a stone, Buffon's followers covered the grave and obliterated the memory of Réaumur. But thanks largely to Professor Wheeler, modernity has revived his honor. We cannot imagine Réaumur as undertaking anything like the *Histoire Naturelle*. He saw that a lifetime is not enough for the insects alone, not even for a family of insects or for one single species. Not his the boast that he worked by the clock and never revised. He revised perpetually, stopped work for months or years, when it was necessary to wait for fresh confirmations or deeper insights, and he published nothing before it was ready. He knew that a man has to go afoot to the living world; it will not wait respectfully in an anteroom with its hat in its hand. So for his seventy-four years he served his mistress Nature with the humility as essential to the true scientist as conceit may be to the creative man.

His rival gone from the field, Buffon shouldered the great task of trying to complete his encyclopedia. But his troubles, strangely, did not dissipate with Réaumur's passing. For there awaited him a final tribunal, not of Sorbonne professors but of reality itself. He confronted it on the day when he espoused the unlucky cause of the English naturalist, Needham, who was engaged opposite young Spallanzani in the battle of vitalism against

---

[4] Wheeler's translation of letter to Ludot, May 3, 1750, quoted from Réaumur, *The Natural History of Ants*.

spontaneous generation. Buffon had characteristically pronounced that flies were born of nothing but dung, and when Needham championed this cause, Buffon came to his side with his ready pen, his wit, his sarcasm, his ringing appeals to reason and that adored French *clarté*. The age was with him. Unfortunately, Spallanzani was of another age — the future. In experiment after experiment he defeated and disproved his opponents. With a terrible logic of his own, with a *raison* of which Buffon knew nothing, he simply crushed them. In the world of science, at least, Buffon's reputation never recovered.

Even his theory of regeneration in animals by means of primitive organic molecules which course through living tissue, is not as original as it seems. He owes it to the forgotten works of Réaumur. Réaumur called them " little eggs," Darwin was to call them " gemmules," and the modern names these still unproved messengers of heredity " genes." Buffon owed all he knew of regeneration to Réaumur, and for the origin of the philosophical concept of organic molecules one must go back, also, to Leibnitz and those monads of his; Buffon, it may be recalled, had studied Leibnitz in his youth.

So there is nothing left to Buffon but his gracile descriptions of animals in the *Histoire Naturelle*. Empty of significant fact and filled with the sonority of his mother tongue, they have evoked ecstasies from such a critic as Saint-Beuve. Here is the first passage from *Le Cheval*, which Buffon considered his masterpiece:

" *La plus noble conquête que l'homme ait jamais faite est celle de ce fier et fougueux animal qui partage avec lui les fatigues de la guerre et la gloire des combats: aussi intrépide que son maître, le cheval voit le péril et l'affronte; il se fait au bruit des armes, il l'aime, il le cherche, et s'anime de la même ardeur: il partage aussi ses plaisirs; à la chasse, aux tournois, à la course, il brille, il étincelle; mais, docile autant que courageux, il ne se laisse point emporter à son feu, il sait réprimer ses mouvements: non seulement il fléchit sous la main de celui qui le guide, mais il semble consulter ses désirs, et, obéissant toujours aux impressions qu'il en reçoit, il se précipite, se modère ou s'arrête, et n'agit que pour satisfaire: c'est une créature qui renonce à son être pour n'exister que par la volonté d'un autre, qui sait même la prévenir: qui, par la promptitude et la précision de ses mouvements, l'exprime et l'exécute, qui sent autant qu'on le désire, et ne rend qu'autant qu'on veut: qui, se livrant sans réserve, ne se refuse à rien, sert de toutes ses forces, s'excède, et même meurt pour mieux obéir."* [5]

Perhaps Buffon prepared his own epitaph when he wrote, " *Le style c'est l'homme même.*"

As the years went on, his task stretched out before him endlessly, the horizon ever receding. In desperation he

---

[5] "The most noble conquest man has ever made is that of this proud and fiery animal who shares with him the fatigues of war and the glory of battle: as intrepid as his master, the horse sees the danger and faces it: he accustoms himself to the clash of arms, he loves it, he seeks it, and takes fire with the same ardor: he shares also man's pleasures; at the hunt, in the lists, at the race course, he shines, he sparkles; but, as docile as he is brave, he does not allow himself to be carried away, he knows how to restrain his movements: not only does he bend to the hand of him who guides him, but he seems to consult his desires, and, obeying always the impression he receives from him, he charges, paces, or halts, and acts only to please: he is a creature who renounces his being to exist only for the will of another, who knows even how to anticipate it, who, by the promptness and precision of his movements, expresses that will and executes it; who feels as much as one desires and does no more than one wishes; who, yielding without reserve, refuses nothing, serves with all his forces, surpasses himself, and even dies the better to obey."

was driven at last to accept the idea of genera and families; "*nolens volens,*" Linnaeus chuckled, the poor Frenchman had to swallow his systematics. Buffon was obliged even to recant his recantation. That this passed unnoticed would indicate that people had stopped reading his books.

Yet there was nothing to do but toil on. He wrote to his collaborator, the Abbé Bexon, complaining that he had arrived at the endless, dreary, monotonous water birds — "*Ces tristes oiseaux d'eau, dont on ne sait quoi dire, et dont le nombre est accablant!* " To my ear this is the finest passage of prose style in Buffon's writings. It is the only genuine expression of the man's feelings, the only passage not intended for show, the one cry wrung from his heart.

The Abbé Bexon was not his only collaborator. After the faithful Daubenton left him, wearied out, we suspect, Montbéliard and his wife undertook to assist the great labor. Montbéliard is said to have had the trick of perfectly imitating his master's style, a convenience for Buffon, certainly, but an unanswerable commentary. Buffon was, in effect, operating a great literary factory, like Dumas, and as the task weighed more and more heavily upon him, he left increasing quantities of it to his ghostwriters.

And the sad years came, the years of empty honor and disappointment. His wife died. His son, " Buffonet," as he called him, was to have been nominated his successor as intendant, but the post was obtained by D'Angiviller, a tall, serenely impudent grandee who knew nothing about natural history. But, as he wrote to console Buffon, he came of an order superior to that of savants. Buffonet's young wife was corrupted by the Duc d'Orléans and became notorious throughout France. The Pompadour died, utterly worn out by the effort to be The State and to find new amusements for a king whom she herself had already taught every vice and folly. A generation was passing, a knell was sounding. And Buffon heard it. As if crushed under the weight of his own volumes, as if unable to breathe for the orders and medals on his chest, this ornament of science sank at last and died. It must have been one of the last royalist funerals that Paris saw; the eulogies were appropriately long, the cortège was sumptuous. One year later the Bastille fell, and the head of Buffon's son dropped under the knife. The mob opened the court zoögrapher's tomb, scattered his bones, and pulled down his statue. And time has not dealt less harshly with his fame. No other great reputation in science was ever brought so low.

Réaumur's findings in general remain sound. As for the man himself, his death brought these words to the lips of a friend:

" A true friend, always ready to seize every opportunity to demonstrate his affection, he neglected none of its manifestations. His influence and the acquaintances it had cost him so much to acquire, were in his estimation merely a treasure on which his friends might draw in case of need. He was so punctual in coming to inquire after their health, when they were ill, that some of them, who felt that they saw too little of him, said they would willingly have the fever merely for the sake of enjoying his attentions more frequently. The blows of fortune that prostrated his friends only strengthened the ties that bound him to them. He was by such sentiments rendered so worthy of their esteem that a list of them would include all the personages of Europe most distinguished by birth and talent. The greatest men vied for the honor of his friendship. If he had enemies (and what great man can fail to have them?) he was never the aggressor and never opposed them, except with the splendour of his fame and an imperturbable philosophy. Owing to the sweetness of his disposition he was gladly welcomed in society. He permitted none to feel the superiority of his genius, and while he never sought to instruct, those who left his presence felt that their knowledge had been increased." [6]

---

[6] Wheeler quoting de Fouchy in Réaumur, *The Natural History of Ants.*

4

THE GREEN WORLD OPENS

IN 1707, when Carl Linnaeus was born in a little red farm cottage near Råshult, no one, surely, expected that the greatest naturalist of the age would come out of Sweden. When continental Europe thought of that peninsular country at all, it was as a big icicle hanging from the eaves of the North Pole.

At the moment Sweden was enjoying a meteoric military ascendancy, but it had neither the men nor the resources to keep its Baltic empire. In a few years the fireworks were to come down as a dead stick, so that the whole land, during Linnaeus's youth, was anemic with debt and shaken in its self-confidence. The sense of decline was felt throughout the country, from its timid king, down through its contracting, listless universities, to the impoverished rural population out of which Linnaeus sprang.

Yet from this rocky, snow-bound kingdom was to come the man who would really create in science all that order that Buffon supposed you could make by being *raisonnable*. The babe in the red cottage was to become the thinker who brought the scholastic ideal of abstract concepts to some useful culmination. Now was born Nature's tender lover who would awaken all the world to intense

enthusiasm for his beloved. To the astonishment of all
the wise men, he was not a product of Wittenberg, or the
parks of Versailles or even of English country life, that
nurse of so much delicate feeling for natural beauty. But
genius so seldom grows where the highly born and the
members of the eugenical societies tell us to expect it!
Possibly there is a misconception about genius. If Buffon
was right in supposing that it is an infinite capacity for
taking pains, then bank clerks would be geniuses. But Sir
Isaac Newton could never add up the household accounts
either as correctly or as swiftly as his cook.

Nor will the advantages of good teachers or a well
equipped library or laboratory suffice in themselves to
make a naturalist. Linnaeus, born out of peasant stock,
never had more than a few hours' formal instruction in
the very subjects where his name was to be graved with
the immortals. The scientific equipment of his university
was inferior to that of a rural public high school in our
age. And as for books, he had frequently to write the ones
that he needed most. A stultifying environment — for
mediocrity.

But the making of a naturalist may well begin before
all formal tutelage. The gift, like a grass-flower, will
spring up almost unmarked in a country childhood, and
to the countryside that nurtured the childhood of this
man we must look back.

In after life Linnaeus remembered it with tender sentiment.

" Lake Möckeln," he says, " here extends in a quarter of a
mile long bay," (one of those appalling Swedish miles, seven of
ours) " and almost reached the foundations of the church. The

level farmlands surround the church on all sides except the west, where Möckeln displays its limpid waters. A little way off, the fine beech woods show themselves toward the south. . . . The fields are sheltered from the north by coniferous woods, and east and south are pleasant fields and leafy trees. . . . The meadows resemble more the most splendid groves and richest flower gardens, than their actual selves, so that one may sit in summer and hear the cuckoo with other different bird songs, insects piping and humming, and at the same time view the glowing and splendidly colored flowers. One cannot but turn giddy at the Creator's magnificent arrangement. . . . Stenbrohult parish is like a queen among sisters, she has predominancy of rare and scarce plants, which in other localities in the country seldom or never show themselves. Yes, the surroundings seemed as if they had been adorned by Flora herself. . . . I doubt if there is a spot in the whole world set out in more pleasant fashion." [1]

So he speaks of his *ljuve natale*, his dear birthplace, as he calls it in a characteristic blend of Swedish and Latin. And we might take it that an old man is merely remembering a childhood through sentimental eyes.

Mayhap, and yet is he not trying to tell us that, as a naturalist, he was born with a silver spoon in his mouth? That marching spruces, and not topiary, were the first impressions to print themselves upon the retina of memory?

Through the woods that swept down to the edge of the cultivated fields of Stenbrohult, the wild stepped lightly, and gazed with its bright, curious eyes at the garnered fields, the red farmhouses and the white church. Elemental forces were close at hand, and the child who

[1] Quoted from Benjamin Daydon Jackson, *Linnaeus* (H. F. & G. Witherby, London, 1923).

walked only a little way into those woods stepped straight into the most primeval part of Europe still remaining. Bear there were, and wolves, and tiny elvish forests of black moss, deep hangings of lichens, delicate ferns sprung high and green in the unexpected lushness of northern vegetation, and mushroom villages with their red-warted gables. Many children, of course, came there, to count the cuckoo's notes. And they were all a little awed, I suppose, with the solemnity of the forest, conscious that it stretched away without bound, to unknown Lapland, to give place at last to the tundras, where under the blazing midnight sun the reindeer sped and the boggy sward was enameled with the intense colors of the wide-eyed arctic flowers. But one child who wandered there, made preternaturally old, perhaps, by his father, took fire from the thought of the width of the green world. He had no need to think his home surrounded by a rose hedge, as some domestic souls would like to have it. It stretched away, on the north at least, toward a bit of infinity, where winter and summer, day and night, beauty and terror, life and death, were abrupt and imminent and absolute. One whole side of this boy's nature seems from the first to have tingled with the consciousness of such elementals.

And so, while all of central and southern Europe was being ransacked in the unreal search for some lost wisdom of the ancients, in the north a glistening, a stirring, a clear-eyed reality awaited the coming of an appointed seer.

The first clear picture that Linnaeus had of himself was of a child who ran about the rectory garden at Stenbrohult, telling off the names of the flowers. When he forgot the name of one, his father gently reproved him for shortness of memory or want of attention, and sometimes tears of mortification came to the little boy's eyes.

According to tradition the pastor used to put the year-old Carl on the grass with a flower in his hand, and on this the child bent such rapt attention that he would be good for hours. It is not necessary to believe the legends of a great man's babyhood, but in this case I am inclined to listen to the tale. Pastor Nils Linnaeus was himself a passionate lover of flowers. When a father sets out, pridefully, to teach his eldest little son that thing which he holds dear, that favorite hobby, that vocation which he gave up for a more practical calling, he may succeed in communicating all his suppressed excitement. And Pastor Linnaeus was more than an ordinary gardener; he collected what he believed to be rarities, and though his taste in horticultural design might now be thought atrocious, it was the pride of the parish of Stenbrohult.

In the long summer evenings that lasted until eleven o'clock, the pastor would take the listening child to walk over the flowering meadows by the lake, while he discoursed upon the plants, telling how each one had a name, a name in goodly Latin that had been bestowed upon it by the ancients, or by the wise herbalists — how this was an *Orchis*, that a *Rosa*, and this other a *Lilium*. So the father taught the son to see all things, the lake and the sky, the birds and the blossoms. He laid for him that indispensable foundation for a naturalist, the long view and the quick sight. By showing the child, repeatedly, that which is usual instead of trying to amaze him with the marvelous and exceptional, he taught him what is natural in the woods and fields, and that which was strange could be left thereafter to proclaim itself.

The name Linnaeus was a prophecy. For in old Sweden only the nobility had family names. The pastor's original cognomen had been Nils Ingemarsson, that is to say, Nils the son of Ingemar, whose name in turn had not been Ingemarsson, but Ingemar Bengtsson, Ingemar the son of Bengt. Such names are not familial but patronymic, and correspond to a Russian name like Ivan Stepanovitch, John the son of Stephen. But when peninsular Sweden became Continentalized, many persons elected a family name, and Nils chose Linnaeus, a Latinized form of *Linn*, the word for the linden or lime tree. There are few " flowering " trees in Sweden, but the linden is one of them. With its deep green shade, its gracious, heart-shaped, talkative leaves, and its honey-sweet flowers that bloom at the joyful northern festival of Midsummer, it was held by the peasantry to be sacred, and one majestic lime in particular was venerated by Nils Ingemarsson. From it he took his name, though you may know it in some other language; thus the great naturalist is sometimes put down as Karl or Carl or Charles Linnaeus, Carl von Linné, or Carolus Linnaeus. In after life, he said it mattered little to him what he was called. Probably he was glad to escape the ubiquitous name of Nilsson which would logically have been his if his pastor father had not had a bit of pagan tree-worship in his soul.

His good mother wanted to make a priest of the boy. Carl had no way of explaining that what he wanted to be was a naturalist. There were as yet no scientists such as he wanted to become, and perhaps not even any word for them. The only road to his half realized career lay through medicine, at that time the least reputable and certainly the most poorly paid profession in the country. But Nils Linnaeus, after a proper show of reluctance, consented at last to let the boy go as far as the university at Lund, where he had a rich relative on the faculty.

Lund at that time was as little likely a place for studying medicine and natural science as any small country academy of today, whose curriculum is ridden by trustees drawn from the body of Fundamentalist divines. At last the disgusted boy left it abruptly for Upsala, a rich man's college located near the wicked great city of Stockholm.

And there we find him, putting paper in the soles of his worn-out shoes, wandering the neglected, dusty, autumnal botanical garden, and nervously awaiting, as so many boys have had to wait, the arrival of his academic credits. He scuffed the dead leaves and wondered what he would do when his money was gone. He had made the usual miscalculation of country boys who go far from home to a big university, and was beginning to see that by spring he would inevitably find lodgings in the graveyard. His father had many other children to support; his mother was out of sympathy with the whole undertaking, and the rich relative at Lund was in a huff with him.

And even Upsala held disillusion. It had recently been razed by fire and though rebuilt it was still intellectually in ashes. The botanical garden, laid out in his youth by the famous Olaf Rudbeck, had suffered equally. It was shrunk to two hundred sorts of flowers, half of them commonplace. But Rudbeck, who had seen a lifetime of manuscript researches go up in flames, had no heart left to restore an herb garden.

Rudbeck it was, indeed, under whom Linnaeus had supposed he had come to study, and under Roberg. But both were aged, weary of teaching, weary of students, lost in abstruse research.

There was a surgical theater for giving anatomical demonstrations, but no one to perform them, and the religious temper of the regents was probably opposed to human dissection. So that both the faculty and the students were glad, on one occasion, to go to Stockholm to hold a public dissection on a woman who had been hanged. Linnaeus for this privilege spent the last of his money on the trip.

But if Upsala was not fitted to make a physician of Linnaeus, there were still crumbs of natural history to be picked up. The library at least was fair, and there Linnaeus forgot his hunger and wet feet as he read for hours, unconscious of the gathering dusk outside — one of those earnest boys with wrists grown out of their frayed cuffs, whom librarians still have to put out at the closing hour.

And a bursar of the university had once pasted up a "plant book" — probably an album of pressed specimens — which Linnaeus used to ask to see till doubtless the custodians were weary of lifting the massive volume down for him. Some lectures on birds were given by Rudbeck, though they never went farther than the domestic fowl. But they were at least an introduction to anatomy. Roberg occasionally expounded Aristotle and Descartes, and gave five medical lectures during the entire year, but

Linnaeus was not even successful in getting into the hall to hear these.

Bitterly lonely, Linnaeus in the first autumn quarter inquired everywhere for some one of similar tastes. The answer was always the same — Pehr Artedius, Artedi, as they called him and as he has since become known — a lad who had arrived from the borders of Lapland a *summa cum laude* divinity student who yet insisted on practising the hell-born science of alchemy and entertained a mad passion for icthyology. *Fishes*, forsooth! Even the medical students gave him up, yet by all accounts he and Linnaeus should get on together. But Artedi was at home, taking leave of his dying father.

In the winter quarter he returned, and Linnaeus found him, " pale, cast-down and tearful." But the friendship was like a chemical attraction; the two young exiles met together with a shock of surprise and happiness.

Is there any one who has so far forgotten his young self that he cannot remember that friend, discovered out of all the meaningless faces at school, that one right and consanguineous soul? Perhaps you can recall your excitement at the thought of meeting him again, the anxiety lest you fall short in his estimation, the honor you felt when you could loan him a farthing, or when he casually tossed you the necessary clothes when you were asked to dinner at the dean's house, and the dean's wife and daughter snubbed you. But where is he now? Have your wives separated you? Has he gone on in the impossible dream, the impractical calling that you so prudently gave up? Can you even recall what it was that you talked of so passionately?

OLOF RUDBECK,
benefactor of Linnaeus
(See page 92)

LINNAEUS IN HIS LAPLAND DRESS
(See page 96)

The Green World Opens

"The ideas which Artedi propounded were new to me," Linnaeus records, "and the knowledge which he disclosed astonished me."

Ah, yes, those ideas, those preposterous cosmogonies, those unearthly systems of thought, those wild young ideas you had! Yet in this case they were nothing less than the very grammar of the natural sciences as we know them today. They were not more Artedi's than Linnaeus's, for in a measure they had been Aristotle's, they were Bauhin's, they were Ray's, Camerarius's and Grew's. I have written thus far in vain if I have not made it plain that science grows layer by layer, like a snail shell, and that in natural history, at least, no discovery and no hypothesis come suddenly, or may be born at all without a long chain of parents and grandparents. Its beliefs must be perfected, polished, and pruned by many loving hands. They only become celebrated and accepted several hundred years after they are first conceived, or even several thousand.

Only the desperately young and brilliantly ignorant would have attempted what now Artedi and Linnaeus did attempt. Aristotle and Augustine and the great Ray had already failed gloriously at it, and in a measure Bruno and Spinoza too. But between them these two lads began to map out nothing less modest than all God's good creations upon earth. They sought to make a great schema or system of all the three kingdoms, animal and mineral and vegetable.

And they labored to invent a new language for it. Their *lingua* merely availed itself of the still universal language of Latin; it was not Latin in any literary sense.

This language was to enable men to speak in universals of Nature; it was to make an orderly community out of the staggering, slippery profusion of the tangible world. And withal, this categorical science must be provided with some finding-key, some intelligible syllabus, some Blue Guide that would make straight a path in the wilderness.

For every day that wilderness seemed to grow up with higher thorns and weeds. To all that natural science already knew of temperate Europe, Asia, and America, there was abruptly added the overwhelming influx of tropical proliferation. Knowledge of the floras of Malay and Brazil, the two largest in the world, had come almost simultaneously to swamp reason, and mounting upon this green tidal wave came a second wave, ten times as high — the tropical insect world, unknown, unnamed, unmanageable.

How this superabundant life was dealt with and made science, what was the language and what the great system of Nature conceived by Linnaeus and Artedi, and who the many were who labored before and after them at the great task, there will be time enough, I take it, to tell in the unwritten chapters before me. For the moment it was all only a shared secret, a dream conceived perhaps with the same abstract purity, the same scorn of its practicability, as Plato's rule by philosophers.

The two lads, like conquerors, divided up the kingdoms between them. Artedi took chemistry, fishes, amphibians and insects; Linnaeus elected the birds, flowers and minerals. The contrast in their temperaments he has recorded for us: the lad from the north tall, silent, deliberate and earnest, and a little melancholy, while Linnaeus himself was small and quick-witted, hasty and vivacious. He could not then foresee the deeper contrast that is apparent to us, for he was, all unconscious, destiny's favorite child, who was to grow rich in years, to be heaped with honors, to live a man's full-rounded life; he stood in sunshine, while close at his side Artedi was shadowed by his own young death. As brilliant as his friend, perhaps, Artedi was to leave behind him this epitaph — that, had he lived, he might have been the Linnaeus of zoölogy.

But the prospect that Artedi would die in less than ten years seemed less likely than that Linnaeus would starve before spring. It was late in April, on one of the first days of early spring as it comes to bleak Uppland province, that the old Dean Olaf Celsius, a flower lover and a friend to science, came for a stroll in the dilapidated botanical garden. He was presently aware of a young, unknown student sitting on a bench, with flowers in his hand, writing notes upon them in a book. So strange a sight had not been witnessed for many a year. Celsius drew near, and fell into talk with the student.

The answers came back so charged with significant enthusiasm, so knowledgeable of the neglected subject, that the oldster could scarce credit his ears. He supposed, no doubt, that Linnaeus must know with whom he talked. But in truth the young man had no idea that he was addressing the august Celsius, who had been long absent in Stockholm and was known to him only as a mighty name. It was not until, talking as they walked, and warming to each other, they entered the imposing door of the dean's house, that Linnaeus comprehended in whose presence he stood.

The upshot of it all was that Linnaeus was comfortably lodged in Dean Celsius's house, gratis, and by grace of his benefactor was made recipient of a royal scholarship. Later his patron secured for him a small position as a demonstrator in the botanical gardens. He had the run, too, of the dean's library, better suited, it may be, to his need than the university's. And there it was, no doubt, that he first encountered what other men had accomplished toward that great chart of creation at which he worked, and that grammar of science. His discoveries, he must have learned then, were not half so original as they seemed. And he must have perceived those holes and lacunae and blind-spots that are inevitable in every young man's early science. After all, it appeared, Bauhin had already devised a binomial nomenclature for plants and animals; Ray had already attempted a classification of plants by their flowers and fruits; Camerarius had done marvels in demonstrating the still half-unaccepted sexuality of the vegetable kingdom, and Belon, with his anatomy of birds, had long ago laid down the fundamentals of a schema for the animal world. Toward the delineation of natural families the patient Tournefort, the boy must have found, had mightily wrought.

But you are nowhere in science until you are humbled; the art of practising a science consists in a perfect willingness to learn, coupled with an assertive tendency to doubt, to check, to re-verify even highest authority. And these two temperamental tendencies are so difficult to wed and bed in the same human intellect that many promising careers, many geniuses, indeed, have broken up in wreckage because these two faculties warred rather than worked together, as they worked for Linnaeus.

In particular the work of Vaillant on the sexuality of plants allured and charmed the young man. I would almost venture to say that his predilection for this subject — which was to waft his celebrity to the ends of the earth — was at the start connected with the emotions, with something consanguineous with art and with love. It is not possible to analyze the psyche of the long dead, but we know today how far the choice of career is determined by some personal and chancy mental association. The wording of Linnaeus's youthful manuscripts on the ultimately renowned " sexual system " reveals traces, mere traces, of an artist's love of symmetry and perfection, bound up with an intellectual sublimation of the young man's very normal preoccupation with sex. Scientists who have forgotten where they first found their present impersonal vocations may frown or look away in embarrassment at this suggestion. Or they may snort that it is imaginative nonsense. And we shall have to endure their wrath as best we may.

In all events, history was made when on New Year's Day, 1730, Dean Celsius discovered on his desk a manuscript that bore the title (which I translate out of the Latin), *Preliminaries on the marriage of plants, in which the physiology of them is explained, sex shown, method of generation disclosed, and the true analogy of plants with animals concluded*, by Carolus Linnaeus. The introduction read:

[91]

" It is an old custom to awaken one's eminent patrons on New Year's Day with verses and good wishes, and I also find myself obliged to do so. I would gladly write in verse, but . . . was not born a poet, but a botanist instead, so I offer the fruit of the little harvest which God has vouchsafed me. In these few pages is handled the great analogy which is found between plants and animals, in their increase in like measure according to their kind, and what I have here simply written I pray may be favorably received." [2]

The errors in this tract, ineluctable in the state of knowledge then, stand out pathetically to us in our boundless wisdom. But the text shows at least that Linnaeus was striding down the right road. In that hour of fuddled theorizing and windy classicism, it was something so direct and convincing that the delighted Celsius went about waving the pages at every one he encountered. As there was only the one manuscript copy, students gladly toiled to handwrite copies of their own, or quietly lifted them from one another's desks — always a healthy sign for a book! And finally one of these transcriptions came to the aged eyes of the titan Rudbeck. He carried it close to his short vision, and having read, put it down with one of those half-sentences of mild commendation that from the old and wise means more than the rapture of court ladies. Presently, sighing and groaning with his senile aches and hypochondria, he pottered around to Celsius's door. Who was this Linnaeus, and what did Celsius mean by keeping him dark? And what was any one doing about him?

What Rudbeck did about him was to take him into

---

[2] Quoted from Jackson, *Linnaeus*.

his house and lodge him at a good stipend as a tutor; intellectually he adopted the youth. It was a mighty friend to whose home the lucky Linnaeus now removed — a man for whom the double doors at court swung open, a man who could grumble a word or two to a bigwig of either political party — Count Tessin or Count Horn — and secure reserved appointments, or set the dilatory presses to flashing, or pry money loose from miserly state coffers for traveling scholarships and exploration.

Not that Rudbeck exerted himself at once. He was too battered a veteran of life to trust any one very far. He bided his time, and while he seemed to doze at the fire, watched around the wings of his easy chair, as it were, with a sly old eye.

But bit by bit he relaxed, and, in the comfort of house slippers, he opened out the mighty storehouse of his memory. He too had been young once — a botanist, like his father before him, a zoölogist, an ethnographer and philologist. Forty years ago he had made a journey to Lapland — did Linnaeus know the north? Linnaeus did not; perhaps he spoke some prideful words of Småland. But we can hear Rudbeck snort. A tepid province, a place for invalids and women. He began to tell of the mighty miles of travel, over bog, over boiling rivers, past cataracts whose spume and thunder rose up to heaven like a forest fire. He remembered for the young ears the dark fierce men, the pagan girls, fair only for an earliest month of maturity, like the arctic wildflowers. And it all came back to him — the high geese crying, the loons diving, the wild swans drifting upon lakes so far from human ken that even the Devil had never found it worth his while to visit them.

Of that land-faring nought but a truncated fragment had ever been told in print, a fragment that carried the reader only along the first leg of the journey, and was disfigured (for all but the author) by windy philological digressions. The rest of the pages had risen to the sky as flames in the Upsala fire. But the diary — the battered old log of his travels — was still by him. And in this primitive Odyssey we know now that the young Linnaeus read, for, though its existence was unsuspected for a century or more, it was discovered some forty years gone by among Linnaeus's papers in the British Museum.

It was in 1731 that Rudbeck and Linnaeus began agitating for a scientific expedition to Lapland, petitioning the Crown and the Royal Scientific Society of Upsala. It is necessary to realize, in this day when you can pass the hat and somehow find the tens of thousands necessary to finance a useless submarine dash under the North Pole, that such a journey as the old and the young man then proposed had no precedent in history. Every previous scientific reconnaissance had been made in connection with a boundary survey, a diplomatic or commercial mission, a search for precious metals conceived in an alchemical or a purely gainful spirit. Or at best there had been a research after the legendary wisdom of the ancients, one more ransacking of exhausted Greece and the Holy Land. In the explorative field of natural science, Europe continued to be literally *oriented*, as late as the days of George III when John Sibthorp traveled and suffered in Greece and Turkey like a good medieval, a Don

Quixote of botany, in quest of the ambiguous herbs of Dioscorides.

But this project on the Royal Society's table in 1731 was startling because it was twentieth century in spirit. No wonder if the good gentlemen scratched their blond Swedish heads under their white wigs. But, tell it to their credit, they voted Linnaeus at last something nearly half as much as he would need in the way of money, and that delighted young fellow shortly after New Year dashed home to see his parents.

His father resigned all into God's hands. But his mother was too human a woman for that. Like every good Scandinavian, she quoted at him one of those sayings intended to prevent the young from doing youthful things:

> " In thy country
> Born and bred,
> By God's bounty
> Duly fed,
> Be not lightly
> From it led! "

Linnaeus might well have protested that he was not leaving his country. But Lapland was only politically Sweden. For Frü Linnaeus it was — rather accurately — a heathen land. In point of peril and obstacle, the land of the midnight sun in that age presented mountain barriers of difficulty such as today are buried in Tibet or in Antarctica.

So having kissed him an unforgiving farewell, this sensible lady marched into the gloom of the rectory parlor and began to mourn her son for dead.

At last, on the twelfth of May, Swedish Old Style

(the twenty-second of May by our calendar), in the year of grace 1732, Linnaeus, then twenty-five years old, lacking but a single day, rode out alone through the old north customs gate of walled Upsala town, his blood singing with adventure — rode past the three high mounds of the cemetery, symbol of the dead past and of all the wise and cautious of earth who are under the sod. He rode out of winter, out of all pedantry and musty book learning, into the springtide of science.

" My clothes consisted of a light coat of Westgothland linsey [woolsey]," he records, " lined with red shalloon, having cuffs and collar of shag; leather breeches; a round wig; a green leather cap, and a pair of half-boots. I carried a small leather bag, half an ell in length, but somewhat less in breadth, furnished on one side with hooks and eyes, so that it could be opened at pleasure. This bag contained one shirt, two pairs of false sleeves and two half shirts; an inkstand, pencase, microscope and spying glass, a gauze cap to protect me occasionally from the gnats, a comb, my journal, and a parcel of paper stitched together for drying plants, both in folio, and my manuscripts on Ornithology, *Flora Uplandica* and *Characteres Generici.* I wore a hanger (knife) at my side, and carried a small fowling-piece as well as an octangular stick, graduated for the purpose of measuring. My pocket-book contained a passport from the Governor of Uppsala, and a recommendation from the Academy. . . .

" It was a splendid spring day; the sky was clear and warm, while the west wind refreshed one with a delicious breath. The winter rye stood six inches high and the barley had newly come into leaf. The birch was beginning to shoot, and all trees were leafing, except the elm and aspen." [3]

There were dandelions, rye-flower, forget-me-not and pansy and sweet violet, primrose and water cowslip in

[3] Quoted from Jackson, *Linnaeus.*

bloom — pale, simple little flowers of early spring, common in many lands. But this time there was coming forth one whose eyes were clear, on whose fresh vision the commonest phenomenon would fall as marvelous.

The lark was his companion all the way, he said, quivering upon the air as it trilled its *tirra-lirra*. In the distance the dark coniferous forests rose up ahead of him in the north, and far away, in the changeable spring sky, a blue-black rain cloud unfolded its soft cumuli, while all about him the fields were spangled with dew and sunlight.

When the dark woods closed around his way, he left the lark behind, and heard instead " the amorous warblings " of the redwing. Almost at once he found himself in one of those gnomish forests of northern Europe where ancient spruces, centuries old, with thick and knotted trunks like twisted muscles, are still dwarfed as if under some curse of eld. Deep lichens hung upon their boughs, like sorrow upon an ill-fated castle. Black moss, ankle deep, closed about his horse's hoofs, and out of it peeped frail windflowers, shivering in the chill young day.

So it began, that great Lapland journey, the first of all its kind in the world. Like the south wind Linnaeus came to it; he came like an army of youth; he came with the spring, that surged, wave upon wave of greenness, flash upon flash of flowers; he came like the wild geese and the swans winging arrowy straight and sure, over the lakes and the tundra, for their secret rites in the North. He led the way for us all.

For have we not, all of us, had our young particular Lapland? For some of us it lay in the south, or the west, or east. Perhaps it was Colorado, and you knee-deep in lupine and columbine, with a breath of the glaciers cold upon you and the tingling western air in your lungs. Perhaps it was Florida, with the wealth of the King of the Sea washed up as iridescent shells on the strand at your feet. Perhaps it was the Blue Ridge, when the rhododen-

Linnaeus's own field sketch of the way in which he portaged his Lapland boat

dron petals snowed on the pool at the foot of the waterfall, and a redbird swept with a burst of song from a flowering dogwood to a flowering tulip tree. Wherever it lay, it is the living world as you came to it with the ardor of first love.

You know now that you wouldn't go, at your age, to see fabled Roraima, not if they came and besought you. You know too well when you are best off, nor would you endure again your young discomforts, for a princely purse.

But sometimes you will remember how you set out

once to see your first snow-capped peak. You will recall
how you struggled up the slopes, through briar, through
mire, the pack straining at your shoulders, and the adventurous wind freezing the sweat beneath your shirt.
Until you stood at last upon a knoll and waved your hat,
and shouted up the wind to see the clouds draw back, un-
veiling the longed-for, ice-cased virginity, glittering and
cruel. Just so Linnaeus saw, across the desolate bogs, the
first spearhead gleam of the Norway fells, flashing a pale
enticement to death, swimming like a moon through the
banks of drifting fog. Remember it all, back to the
high-hearted faring forth, and you may catch your old
self gazing after your young self, as Olaf Rudbeck once
watched a young man ride away, into the morning, into
the lark song, into the springtide.

5

THE LIFE WORK OF LINNAEUS

LINNAEUS re-entered Upsala after an absence of six months, brown as a Lapp, with all that exposure to the midnight sun, to the glare of the icy fells, and the wind.

He also arrived in debt, having had to borrow money on the way. And he came back confirmed in his revolutionary views on the great order of Nature, and the proper way to correlate and describe its multiplex abundance.

Now as he threw his mineralogical specimens down on the polished tables of the Royal Society, he cast a challenge at his world. He laid his magic drum, bought from a Lappish shaman, before them and asked them to take it as seriously as if he had presented them with a bit of the Parthenon. The actual number of his specimens was extremely meager, owing to the difficulty and cost of transporting them. But he brought back something else, and demanded that it replace the miscellaneous, useless curiosities that had been the desiderata and object of previous foreign travels. In place of souvenirs, he spread out the knowledge that he had gained — of the breeding grounds of the migratory birds, of the number of eggs to a clutch, of the juvenal plumage of the chicks. He had discovered the plant that for centuries caused a grievous disease of cattle in the north. He had learned the formula of the Lappish love philters. Without using the word (I doubt if it existed), Linnaeus was presenting an ethnological report on a portion of his native land that no one had supposed it worth while to investigate. At the same time he handed in the results of a mineralogical reconnaissance, and the brief of a biological survey. And the wonder of it is that the world was so quick to it all, in an age when savants were still poking in the ruins of the classic world.

Linnaeus's ethnological investigations are outside my province. But I cannot pass them by entirely, because they indicate the breadth of the man's interests; they bring him closer to us as a human and curious traveler, as a warm-hearted observer like ourselves (as we like to fancy ourselves). He was a man who would spend the money he didn't have on a Lapp costume, complete with magic drum and cap, a sojourner who could note with some tender care what games the wild children of the north played with their short brown fingers. He reacted with indignation to the wastage and dilapidation of the state forests, spoke with pity or with admiration when these came naturally to his lips, and rejoiced, as the perpetual daylight of the northern summer waned, at the first star he had beheld within the arctic circle.

Linnaeus might today be considered a poor ethnographer; he was probably inferior to Rudbeck. But he was a first-class naturalist, because he took his ethnography as he found it, and beheld it as part of a single great biological problem, the wild life of the arctic — no animal in it much wilder than the Lapps themselves. The scientific world was astonished at first by his more sensational discoveries, and applauded his personal adventures. There was a fine tale, for instance, in his ride on a frightened horse over a torrent spanned by a rotten and wet and perfectly circular tree trunk, or in the time that, clinging to the lichens on a cliff, he was the target of a Lapp's pot shots. But Linnaeus had brought back more than traveler's yarning. He had seized all the salient features of Lapland life. The attention that he gave to the reindeer, for instance, and to every detail of the growth of its horns, the injuries to its hooves, its parasites, its rutting, its foaling, and its different food plants on the summer and winter ranges, shows that he understood how in Lapland *Rangifer tarandus* and not *Homo sapiens* is the king of beasts. Where *Rangifer* wanders, *Homo* must follow or die, an obligate nomad. Linnaeus comprehended in all its implications that arctic biota or total life community.

Not, of course, that Linnaeus talks in this language; I am expressing in dull modern jargon what is imminently implied on every page of his journal, where the reader shares all his laughs and fatigues, and every glimpse of beauty.

The impression created by the Lapland report, even before it achieved print, was electric. Newspapers began to carry articles about the journey, albeit two years after the event. However, the newspapers of America, equipped with the transatlantic cable, were even slower in discovering Einstein, so we need not feel too superior to the intellectual alertness of the eighteenth-century public. The news traveled via Copenhagen and Hamburg to the rest of the world, and returning like the echo of a great shout, reached the inner rooms of the palaces

of Stockholm. Who was this native son, about whom foreigners were talking?

It was decided forthwith to send Linnaeus off on a well
equipped reconnaissance of the resources of Dalecarlia.
This is a province about which Swedes become sentimental. Dalecarlia is " picturesque," it is " pure Swedish,"
and its peasant militia twice saved the nation when the
regular army was prostrate. But to Linnaeus, remembering the fells and the tundras, the wilderness of birds, the
Elysian wildflowers, Dalecarlia was a tepid experience.
More can be accomplished when not too much equipment is thrust upon the field naturalist; most, certainly,
when the business is unofficial, and the heart runs faster
than the feet.

But there were features for which the province is especially famous, that did not escape the quick young eyes.
These were the mountainous, brilliant petticoats, the
dairymaid complexions, the pouting bodices and the ropes
of golden hair in which " Dalecarlia's sirens " rejoice.
In this respect, Linnaeus confesses, he enjoyed an eyeful;
his head was in a swirl when he got back at Christmas-
tide in 1734 to Falun, base of his operations.

Great festivities attended all olden Swedish Yules.
And any one who has read *Gösta Berling's Saga* will know
how the dancing whirled in one long rout, intermitted
only by a sleigh dash through the snow-bowed spruces,
under the northern lights, to another open house where
the long night was fiddled into morning, while miles of
candles guttered in their chandeliers and sconces. Punch
flowed like streams in thaw. And there were charades,
and theatricals, and on the twist of the dark stairs, kisses

taken and given. In the midst of all this, Linnaeus met Sara Elizabeth Moraea.

The diary of Linnaeus records that on January 2, 1735, he called upon his Sara Lisa in Lapp costume, and that upon the next day, finding her parents from home, he stayed all day with her. He was back on the tenth and the fifteenth, and on the nineteenth his friends were wagering two cans of Rhine wine that there would be a christening in four years.

Sara Lisa was the eighteen-year-old daughter of Dr. John Moraeus, a wealthy and learned physician. Some biographers have suggested that Linnaeus had determined to marry only a rich girl, for one of his friends had some time ago suggested to him that such was the road to his career. If that had been his aim it would in his age have been no disgrace; but I think it more likely that the young man, now twenty-seven years old, simply had decided to marry. His life seems to have been exemplary up to this point; his ideals of morality were always both high and untainted with asceticism. He had a tender, even a fatuous love of children, and pretty Sara Lisa — for she was as seductive as the Dalecarlia sirens and far better born — eagerly promised herself.

Not so susceptible was Dr. Moraeus. He promised to withhold his daughter, without a formal betrothal, from other men until Linnaeus made his fortune. In the meantime, Carl was to stay away for two years — then one would see what one would see.

Linnaeus had already laid plans for a tour of Europe. It was really obligatory for a Swedish physician to hold a degree from a foreign university. The Dutch universities specialized in routing Swedes, for a consideration, rapidly through the curriculum, providing they could pass certain examinations, and with the intention of availing himself of this diploma mill, and of seeing the learned world, the young naturalist set off, very poor, admittedly miserable in his unwed state, and wondrously full of hope.

In Lübeck for the first time Linnaeus saw streets illumined by lights on iron poles, that burned all night! In Hamburg he was dazzled by the size and wealth of the city, shocked by the wide-open doors of the *maisons de plaisir*, whence streamed out the sound of the lubricous dulcimers and oboes insinuating the immoral waltz. But it was a delight in this Babylon to read his own name repeatedly in the *Hamburgische Berichte*.

In June he reached Amsterdam, went sight-seeing, visited the rich Burman's splendid library, and the curious specimens in the learned Seba's apothecary establishment, and so continued to the college of Harderwijk, and was passed through the mill in a week, licensed to practice medicine and enjoy the barren privileges of his profession. Now he hastened on to the great university of Leyden, paid his last florin to be enrolled, and prepared to starve learnedly.

But his lovable personality saved him, and out of the machine swept down a god, the wealthy Dr. Jan Frederick Gronovius, a friend to science, who had read his manuscript of *Systema Naturae* with rapt astonishment. This is indeed the golden book of Linnaeus's life work, though like most of his great ideas, it had all been conceived and sketched in the earliest years of his maturity. Gronovius was quick to recognize its genius, and at once published it at his own expense.

Holland was full of notables in those days, and of rich men buoyed up in eccentric hobbies by the wealth of the Dutch East India Company. Amongst such was Hermann Boerhaave, the same who had re-discovered and published Swammerdam's *Bible of Nature*. So renowned throughout the world was Boerhaave as one learned in every science, that a Chinese sage had written a letter addressed simply to, " Dr. Boerhaave, scholar of Europe," and it had been straightway delivered. His reputation as a practising physician surpassed even his fame as a collector of the world's oddments and bitments of curious information. Great men, however, must render themselves inaccessible. According to report only those strangers who could oil his servants' palms could make appointments with him.

But a letter from Linnaeus sufficed to bring the kindly Zeus from the clouds. They met in Boerhaave's superb garden, stocked with exotic trees, amongst which Linnaeus walked, pointing out and naming everything that the learned botanists of Holland had not been able to identify.

The enchanted Boerhaave offered forthwith to send Linnaeus to the Dutch settlements on the Cape of Good Hope, whence were pouring back the strangest beasts, the most fantastic plant forms that the Creator in his whimsy had seen fit to bring out of the dust. When Linnaeus declined this offer, Boerhaave proposed Surinam, where the richest rain forest in the world bloomed with ten thousand kinds of flowers, and all the birds of two continents were gathered together to winter every year. From England came rumors that he might be sent to America, to see the last great stand of the temperate flora left virgin in the world, and to walk the untrodden prairies where flowers on which no scientist had ever gazed shone in the matchless autumns of the New World.

But the wealth of Ormuz and of Ind was, literally, not sufficient to bribe Linnaeus from his course. He made all manner of excuses, but underneath there was but one. He was afraid of losing Sara Lisa.

Such a consideration, excusable, even commendable, in mortals like ourselves, appears a weakness in an immortal. One leaps at the conclusion that Linnaeus turned down boundless opportunity in refusing to recognize that the world is full of agreeable young maidens. It is fascinating to speculate on Linnaeus in Florida, Linnaeus in California, Linnaeus on the prairies. But I shall leave it to the rest of the story to prove that Linnaeus accomplished more for science by remaining in Europe and sending out a host of disciples to search and preach for him, than would have been possible had he amassed any number of curious collections. Boerhaave asked him to nominate some one else to go in his place to Surinam, and he chose young Dr. Bartsch of Königsberg. Poor Bartsch arrived in Surinam in October, and was dead of fever by November. So with Linnaeus's " apostles," as he called them. The gifted Ternström, splendidly equipped, died on the way out to the East; Hasselquist was slain by the climate of the Holy Land; his favorite, Löfling, was carried off by fever in Guiana soon after his arrival; Kähler's expedition was fraught with shipwreck and illness and loss;

Forskål perished amidst his collections in Arabia Felix; Anders Berlin had no sooner reached unknown Guinea than he sickened and died.

Enough has been said, I think, to make us glad that Linnaeus took care of his health and preferred frankly to make his bed with Sara Lisa than with the maggots.

In spite of all these rebuffs, his patrons in Holland remained devoted to him, and he soon found others. Richest of them all was Clifford, a Dutchman of immense wealth who owned a private zoölogical garden and an arboretum and magnificent hothouses. There were menageries full of Indian deer, tigers and apes; an aviary where American snipe, hawks and crossbills mingled with Indian hens and every sort of diver, swimmer, whistler and game bird, all screaming or singing or stalking amidst the gorgeous poinciana trees and the mangosteens and coco palms. Here Linnaeus saw that which made his head swim, and through living plants and collections of specimens he gained such a knowledge of the flora of distant lands as surpassed even that of Lapland. The day was to come when he could, from these collections and a few others, compose a manual of the flora of Ceylon without ever visiting that gem of the Indian seas.

On the street one day Linnaeus encountered a long, lean, familiar figure. At first he doubted, then he hoped, then he knew — that it was Pehr Artedi. They embraced with tears in their eyes, and in no time at all Linnaeus had installed his friend as an expert in Seba's apothecary establishment, and Artedi's manuscripts were being waved about by excited scholars. Under the kindly treatment of the Dutch, Artedi, ever laconic, began to open out his heart. He went out in agreeable society; he was beginning to be happy; he and his friend were together again in the great work — when coming home one night, he stumbled on the dark wharves of Amsterdam, fell into the canal and was drowned.

Linnaeus hastened to the city at news of this disaster.

" When I saw the lifeless stiffened body and the froth upon the pale blue lips; when I recalled my oldest and best friend's unhappy fate; when I remembered how many sleepless nights, wearisome hours, journeys and expenses, the departed had undergone, before he attained such a measure of knowledge as to compete with any, I burst into tears, when I foresaw that all this learning, which should have secured for him and his country immortal honor, was threatened with annihilation; I felt that the love I cherished for my friend compelled me to fulfill my promise that we once mutually exchanged, namely, that the survivor should publish the other's observations." [1]

But an irate landlord held the manuscripts in fee. Seba did not come to their rescue; public auction threatened. Then Clifford paid the trifle, and Linnaeus saw Artedi's pioneering work on fishes to the press.

The flying trip that Linnaeus made to England brings his orbit into ours. Britain under George II is comprehensible to us, and we can almost fancy ourselves meeting Linnaeus as he walked in the famed Apothecaries' Garden, talking with Philip Miller, last of the herbalists, and winning him over to his system. True, we must think of him as speaking only in Latin; aside from Swedish he had no other medium of exchange, but he got on perfectly

---

[1] Quoted from Jackson, *Linnaeus*.

well with it; his was, indeed, the last era in which the dead language of titans was alive.

The most oft repeated story of Linnaeus in England is that when he saw the gorse in flower he fell down on his knees and prayed — or wept, I've forgotten which. Moderns are fond of spoiling this legend by showing that gorse was not in flower when he visited the tight little isle. However, all legends tell more than facts, and this one seems to show both how the English think of gorse, and still more how the character of Linnaeus was estimated. He was, praise God, remote from the temper of the modern botanical pedagogue who snorts at any esthetic weakness for his chosen subject. In Linnaean writings we often catch echoes of his emotional reaction to Nature; the gorse story would not have grown up around a man who liked his plants cut-and-dried.

Oxford of those days was a stronghold of medievalism. At the moment the very gifted but opinionated and rather confused Dillenius was professor of botanical science. The fame of the Linnaean system had reached his ears long ere this. And he hardened his heart against the newcomer. Their walk together through the gardens bristled with animosity. Dillenius constantly " broke out with angry gestures and little exclamations." Linnaeus asked the name of a flower. " What," cried Dillenius, delighted to catch this fellow out in ignorance, " don't you know what that is? " Linnaeus answered that if he might pick a bloom he would tell him. He deftly opened the petals, examined the stamens and pistils in the secret depths of the corolla, and at once gave its name. Could Dillenius have done the same for some plant he had never seen before? He could not and he knew it. This fellow had some devilish key that unlocked private stores of professional knowledge — that might, indeed, throw the whole science open to the public, and make what it was so wise to know, too easy for others. Angrily the professor stalked into the library, leaving Linnaeus outside, amidst the flowers. " There," said Dillenius, pointing him out with a shaking finger, " there goes the man who is bringing all botany into confusion."

But by the end of his stay, Linnaeus had completely won over Dillenius. The Englishman was so enchanted that he offered to share his salary with the Swede if only he would remain. Any professor today will appreciate the warmth of such approbation.

And now, what was it, this marvelous Linnaean system that had all pedantry by the ears? That was spreading through Europe like wildfire, making a popular science out of the most recondite and tedious subject on the list of useless endeavors? That men, fired by Linnaeus's name, were willing to die for at the antipodes?

First of all there was the matter of binomial nomenclature. This was the lesser of the two triumphs, since it was the least original. Caspar Bauhin had already pared the long rambling unintelligible phrases, the Latin abracadabra of the herbalists, down to two simple names, a clan name or genus, and a species name. Today we all think in such categories instinctively. I teach them to my small sons and they grasp them effortlessly. The suburban lady in her garden employs the concept of both genus and species, expressed in universal Latinity, without any thought that she is learned. The different sorts of *Rosa* are perfectly distinct to her, and not only does she visualize their differences; she grasps their resemblances that jointly make up the genus.

Not thus in the eighteenth century. Very mature intellects boggled then over these ideas. Réaumur had so faint a notion of different species that he often fails to make clear what insect he is talking about, and we are not always sure that he has not confused two or three. However, the times were riper than in Bauhin's age, and without more than a normal amount of old-fogy resistance, binomial nomenclature triumphed. In the case of common creatures a monomial terminology is adequate; it is still sufficient to call a cat a cat, as Buffon scornfully put it. But animals were brought to Buffon's feet, out of the wilds of the ultimate jungles and deserts, for which the French language contained no word. Flowers there are, tens of thousands, that would be nameless, so that we could not even speak of them and in consequence scarcely entertain them in our minds, were it not for Linnaean nomenclature.

But Linnaeus's unique contribution toward the popularization of natural science, toward the unlocking of the gates of knowledge, was his sexual system. There are many perfectly clear and very uninteresting ways of explaining this system. With slight effort a merely competent pedant can turn it into something rather more depressing than the aoristic tense. There is that telling incident of a little girl, in the era of hoop skirts and pantalettes, who declined the gift of a flower which she admired. " Grandfather would make me analyze it," she explained.

The Life Work of Linnaeus

So most of us have learned a kind of Schoolman's botany, something as withered into formulae as textbooks can make it. Pistils and stamens were all part of a lesson, and more happily forgotten. Or, if the sexual nature of these organs is comprehended, some loveliness, for many people, goes out of the flower; florists often find that they can sell Easter lilies more readily if they emasculate and defeminate them; ladies, it is said, do not like the untidy way that the stamens have of spilling pollen on the virginal purity of the lily petal.

But Linnaeus, who thought in flowers, who must have dreamed them in his sleep, saw with the bee's eye. The gleaming petals merely lead the bee to the significant interior. And straight as a bee Linnaeus went to the literal heart of the matter. He it was who, after all that had already been done in the morphology of the flower, discovered the existence of the nectaries. To his eye the tiniest wayside blossom leaped upward, enlarged as a lily brought so close to the face that the cheek is wetted by the gleaming stigmatic liquid on the pistil. He saw the stamens, rising out of the corolla's filtered light, and he saw that they were no merely ornamental tassels as the herbalists supposed, but upraised organs of generation. Under Linnaeus's simple hand lens, worn tarnished by long use in thumb and finger, the filaments arose as strong young columns lifting up the golden anthers charged with golden dust. Now for the first time man saw a flower as the insect sees it, that at once despoils and fecundates. And penetrating this cycle of male organs ranked round within the petals, he recognized with certainty the pistil, that always rises gleaming at the flower's very core. This

[113]

is the female element, the very axis and hub of all florescence. For this the plant has grown; it is the purpose of root and stem and leaf. Linnaeus knew the ovary at the pistil's base, the long, lifting style, the stigma upheld to receive the pollen, dust of life itself, that shall find the other half of life hidden in the heart of the nodding bloom.

This is to describe but a single type of flower. And there are blossoms of every conceivable form, and more that only mad fancy would imagine. Flowers with a golden fringe of scores of stamens, flowers with pistils past counting, flowers with numberless petals, with petals united into a corolla like a trumpet, like a salver, like a dragon's mouth. Orchids that pass for humming birds or a flight of gorgeous butterflies; aroids of the calla family, with spikes laden with hundreds of minute flowers, the whole wrapped not in petals but each in a single colored leaf. There are flowers of the duckweed family so tiny that they can only be analyzed by the compound microscope, and others, in the jungles of tropical Africa, that are three feet across.

There is the mighty composite family, where social flowers are united into a city, as snug within their tight green bracts as ever a medieval fortified town, and divided for different sorts of labor, into various forms, like guilds in their costumes.

Some flowers bloom only at night; others to allure the moths exhale their odors at night but are infragrant under the sun; many will close at the threat of a passing cloud; some bend downward to shelter the pollen from the rain, and others, like the orchids, are turned upside down, by

[114]

a twist that passes through the ovary, so that we see their curious faces forever in a sly inversion.

Flowers there are with elaborate devices for fertilization, for clamping a pellet of pollen on the head of the passing bee, whilst another device on the female parts as neatly hooks it off the insect's head. So finical are some floral mechanisms that only one insect, with a preposterously long tongue, could possibly fertilize them. Others are open to all the winds, and scatter like largesse their pollen which is particularly adapted by air sacs to such carriage. Many are sought out by hummingbirds only, others by tropical bats with dainty nectar-tippling habits. Some will employ the lowly slug to mate them, or the greedy ant. Or again a flower is found provided with mechanisms for fencing off ants, preferring to reserve itself to the refinements of butterflies.

Flowers there are that bloom but once in a score of years, or fifty, or never. A man may pass an Oriental lifetime in its high wooden grass forests, and never see the bamboo come to blossom. And when its does, that species blooms at once in every land upon the earth, whether in Calcutta or in the greenhouses of Leningrad. And then that bamboo dies back to the root. There are flowers that bloom in the sea; others that bloom, as it were, on the inside of the fruit, like the fig, and others still that chose to blossom under the ground, where daylight never sees them, and no bee may find them out.

And above all, and beyond all, and first and last and forever best — there are simply flowers, the common kinds, the little ones, the wild ones, tiniest blue speedwell peeping out of the lawns in early spring, eglantine flinging a spray of laughter over the dusty roadside hedges, gentians burning with their intense blue, on the last day of Indian summer.

And for each and every genus or clan of flowers, out of some ten thousand, there is a separate basic floral symmetry betrayed by the arrangement of the sexual organs — the stamens and the pistils — and more secondarily by the form of the petals and sepals and the structure of the fruit. It is incredible what variations are possible upon a few basic plans. For there are but a few. Yet within these severely simple and mathematical limits Nature can ring exquisitely subtle changes. This outpoured wealth, this staggering profusion, was composed by Linnaeus into an order with which men could deal swiftly and reasonably.

Once he knew, and could not be shaken in his knowledge, that all plants having a given floral pattern were akin, the great systematist had first to name his genera and after that the species could be distinguished. So he triumphed first at the great game of playing Adam to green creation. Classical names, like *Quercus* for the oak, he employed where such existed. But outside the classic flora he had to devise generic names, and this gave him the opportunity to honor many friends. *Moraea*, a genus of exquisite flowers from the Cape, akin to iris, was dedicated to his sweetheart; *Artedia*, a group of plants in the Queen-Anne's-lace family, *Rudbeckia*, our black-eyed-Susan, commemorate others who were dear to him. And finally a genus was named by Gronovius in his honor, *Linnaea, Linnaea borealis*, the twin-flower, his favorite. A modest choice, this dainty pink and fragrant thing of the deep moss and the north woods, but his own.

The Life Work of Linnaeus

Perhaps I have failed, through too much love of it, to give a sensible idea of the Linnaean system. I will sober down into pedantry, then. Linnaeus lined up all floral symmetry first by the number of stamens, and then, within these headings, according to the number of pistils. Thus:

MONANDRIA (1 stamen)	*Monogynia*	(1 pistil)	Canna. Cardamom.
	Digynia	(2 pistils)	Sea Blite.
DIANDRIA (2 stamens)	*Monogynia*	(1 pistil)	Lilac. Verbena.
	Digynia	(2 pistils)	Sweet-grass.
	Trigynia	(3 pistils)	Pepper Vine.
TRIANDRIA (3 stamens)	*Monogynia*	(1 pistil)	Crocus. Iris. Valerian.
	Digynia	(2 pistils)	The majority of grasses.
	Trigynia	(3 pistils)	Carpet-weed, etc.

This system is continued up to twelve stamens, and then follow many separate classes for special cases, including such peculiar groups as orchids, aroids, mallows, legumes, and composites. And finally, unable to do much with them, Linnaeus lumped together all the flowerless plants — the ferns and mosses, fungi, seaweeds and slime-moulds, into a group at the end, the *Cryptogamia*, or " hidden-sex " plants.

So we are come back again to the dry manual of botany, and perhaps after all I have failed to show the magnificence of the life work of Linnaeus. But the manual that looks so dull is, to the man who knows how to read it, a brief of everything growing. Any plant he picks he can find in it, or if he cannot, he knows that he has found something new. Thus all that Linnaeus found did not close discovery as a task finished, but on the contrary he, who traveled so little, opened wide the book of Nature for the ultimate isles.

In another chapter I shall go afield with his passionate disciples. It is May now, Linnaeus's lucky month, his birth month, and the month of his entry into Lapland. Let me make a period here, and myself go forth. Linnaeus was as eager to cut short his visit to foreign parts as I am to terminate the account of it, for as the cardinal is calling me, so the thought of Sara Lisa beckoned to him. Worse, a rumor reached him that his friend Browallius, the very one who had urged him to marry a rich girl, was amorous of Sara Lisa, and that her father, considering that Linnaeus had stayed away over-long, felt himself no longer bound to shelter his flower from the bees.

So Linnaeus tore himself away from Clifford and Boerhaave and all of Holland. Up to the last minute golden suasions were flung before him, to remain at any stipend, and do exactly as he pleased. But he left, made a hasty tour of France, visited Réaumur, and Antoine de Jussieu who was laboring even then upon a mighty classification of all the families of plants (something that the Linnaean system makes no attempt to delineate). He visited Versailles and Fontainebleau, was elected to the Académie des Sciences and told that, did he choose to become French, he would be appointed by the Académie with an annual pension. It was as if Athens had invited a Goth to be a citizen of the Periclean era.

But the Goth fled home. He went straight to Stenbrohult, and tumbled into his father's arms all the many learned volumes he had written and printed in Holland,

LINNAEUS'S MUSEUM AT HAMMERBY
(Courtesy of the Brooklyn Botanic Garden)
(See page 129)

LINNAEUS AS A COURTIER AND PROFESSOR
AT UPSALA

(See page 130)

and then he hastened on to Falun, to claim Sara Lisa for his own.

What he encountered at Falun was Dr. Moraeus, who was willing to acknowledge that his future son-in-law had great renown abroad and was the author of many learned works. But what fortune had he amassed? Had he not, rather, refused magnificent stipends in Holland for this mad career as a naturalist? In his infinite patience, the learned physician was willing to continue to promise his daughter, but only upon condition that Linnaeus should repair forthwith to Stockholm, set himself up as a practising physician, and if, by chance, he did as well as he, Dr. Moraeus, in that calling, he might come back, if the time were not too long, and claim his bride.

Linnaeus took himself away with an aching heart. The conditions were hard. But Sara Lisa was still there, as fair to look upon as ever, and she was, at least, no other man's. There was still hope, and Linnaeus hung out his shingle in the snowy capital.

Nobody cares to be a young doctor's first victim, and as no patients knocked on his door, Linnaeus went down into the dubious quarters of the town, and began saving the doomed — men from the breeding grounds of consumption, young blades whose excesses were shortening their days, women worn out with life's biological ruthlessness toward their sex. When smallpox knocked on the doors of poor patients, doctors of established reputation counted the risk not worth the problematic fee. But Linnaeus went into noisome horror chambers and fought with death.

He had little enough skill, if we think of the equipment of a modern medicine-man, but he had courage, and he made himself well liked. In no time at all his practice went soaring. Even a court lady consulted him about her bronchial wheeze; Linnaeus gave her some tragacanth pastilles for her throat. Seeing her put one in her mouth, the Queen asked what it was, and being informed of the excellent physician's name, she herself, the proud Ulrika Eleanora, sent for Linnaeus. In a short time he was a court physician, physician to the admiralty, and assayer of metals to the government, also president of the Academy.

Now indeed it was time to go back for Sara Lisa, and this time that man of parts, her father, was humble before Linnaeus. On the twenty-sixth day of June in 1739 Linnaeus was greeted in the morning by some verses upon his having obtained in Dalecarlia " a monandrian lily " — that is, a " one-man " flower, and that very day his Sara Lisa came to his side at the altar.

Happy are those nations that have no history; happy is the marriage about which all that the public ever hears is that from the altar to death all went well. Lucky Linnaeus, concerning whose wedded life there is so little more to say. Sara Lisa was not a faultless wife. She never understood his science; she wanted him to keep on with his fashionable practice, and when he gave it up for a position at Upsala, she was sure he had made a grave error of judgment. But when she was wrong (or when he was wrong, for we can be sure he must have been, only history has forgotten to record it), they remained forever lovers. If she was a one-man lily, he was a one-woman man, a great man who was in reality very simple about the most vital thing in life. In his quaint maxims written out for the benefit of his son, he summed up morality in a single injunction: Dishonor no woman.

6

GLORIES AND FOLLIES OF THE LINNAEAN AGE

IT was long the custom that on Linnaeus's birthday botanists in all countries should take down from the shelf their vascula or plant boxes, and set forth for a ramble in the great old style of the Linnaean field trips. These commemorative excursions seem to have been held at first upon the twenty-first day of May, owing to a misconception about the date of the anniversary. And it is said that even when the error was pointed out, many of the older men refused to change their *mumpsimus* for the new-fangled *sumpsimus*; they held, and probably rightly, that the traditional day of the celebration was more important than a barren truth.

So they set forth, in little companies, to re-discover the modest floral treasures of the countryside, as if they returned to their origins; as if they would recapture a lost delight in the age of innocence of their science. Men who knew things that Linnaeus could never have known returned to the fresh surface of experience; they cut through the bark, as it were, down to the green cambium layer that is found in every living branch. It was as if they needed to reassure themselves that still, under the arc of the sky and in their niches in the rocks or their stations on the moor, good green things grew and kept their faith with spring.

And what more natural, you ask, than that botanists should collect plants? The public conception of a botanist is little other than a man with a vasculum, who can name on sight any and all plants. Alas, what antiquated notions one may retain! Modern botany has almost ceased to concern itself with living plants. In many places, particularly in Germany and in the Germanized American universities, the " amiable science," as Goethe called it, is become an affair of titration tubes, spectroscopes, microtomes, chromosomes, and the mathematics of genetics. The botanical faculty are practically vassals of the physics and chemistry departments. Through their mills, vegetable tissue passes as the raw materials of the laboratory. It is in many cases of so little apparent moment to know the names or the life habits of the living plant which furnishes forth the experimental material, that it is possible now to be a bespectacled young doctor of botany without having a speaking acquaintance with half a dozen living plants where they grow.

In fact, it is a matter of some pride, especially to the young instructors, to profess a joking ignorance of Linnaean science. " Linnaeus could not now be considered a botanist at all," is a statement that I have recently read. Its author doubtless conceives of Linnaeus as the one who invented Latin names, a man who betrayed the essential frivolity of his character by devising the floral clock — a plot where diurnal and nocturnal flowers, opening at their different and appointed times, told off the hours in the

garden of his country estate at Hammerby. And there was
an emotional strain in Linnaeus's character, a candid love
of beauty, an impetuous enthusiasm for Nature (whose
very name is now in poor repute), and a partisan insistence
upon his great artifact of a schema, that intensely embar-
rass the thin-lipped and the ardorless.

Who that has passed through college has not had the
pleasure of one or two field trips with a grey-cheeked
biologist of today? You must surely remember it — how
the class straggled behind, harkening listlessly, feeling as
ill at ease out in the open, in all that sweet natural chaos,
as the instructor looked in his business suit with his Phi
Beta Kappa key sparkling unnaturally on his vest, while
he pointed out a few organisms that it is not feasible to
bring into the laboratory.

And all the while a beseeching wind was passing
through the grasses whispering an eery *see, see!* Somewhere a meadowlark flashed his song about in the sunlight; and you stooped to pick a flower that leaped up
from the earth on a tense slim stem and fell in a burst of
blossoms. Perhaps you admired it openly, and others were
embarrassed for you.

I tell this much of our modern wisdom, our fortunate
freedom of all that might be construed as eighteenth century, because we need to orient ourselves when we relate
the history of a movement. We have, after all, no triangu-
lation point from which to survey save our own age and
our own methods, and so perforce I must set down the
contrast with others, not in malice, but in the offices of
clarity. I must point out that we have returned natural

science to the indoors, out of which Linnaeus led it joy-fully forth upon those high-hearted farings of which I purpose now to tell.

Let me not say that what we have done is not all for the best, or more precisely that it is not the best we can do. But I wonder if our age will not be known as the renaissance of Scholasticism. In our age of doubt we are tending to reintroduce philosophy, to question how we know what we know, to analyze the nature of matter down to something that is no longer material but energic only, and to realize the poignant limitations of human comprehension. Perhaps opposing philosophical atti-tudes revolve in cycles. Perhaps we best approach abso-lute truth by alternating between schools that believe only what they see, and those that believe less than they see.

But the age of Linnaeus was one of simple-hearted dis-covery. In its naïve, poetic empiricism, it was, with what it could see, content. And it saw with the marvelous fresh vision of childhood.

I always think of Linnaeus as a student has described him in the years of his greatness, waiting under a tree out-side the walls of Upsala, joking with his students as they came up, speaking Latin with the foreigners, while he smoked and attended on the late ones. Two hundred fol-lowers were sometimes gathered at the rendezvous.

Never were there field trips in the world like those, so ceremonious and so high-spirited. A whole convention of procedure was laid down. Every student was to carry a lens, a botanical penknife and dissecting needles, a lead pencil, a notebook, a Dillenian vaculum of sheet copper for plant collections, and an insect box. He must be provided with Linnaeus's *Systema Naturae* and other useful books, and even the dress was prescribed; pupils in the field must go clad in thin linen trousers, with a broad-brimmed hat upon the head.

Once all were assembled, an *Annotator* was appointed to take dictation, a *Fiscal* or monitor to keep order. And then with a shout and a fanfare, the horde was loosed upon a world still largely unexplored.

How we should like to go off with them, we as moderns, conscious of the coming greatness of those students then mere boys, or distinguished foreigners come from Russia and France, England and Germany, Switzerland and Holland! We might have wandered the Baltic strand with Peter Thunberg, aware that beside us strode the man who would penetrate forbidden Japan, the first naturalist ever to see the flowers upon Fujiyama's slopes. We might have started a lark from the low meadows beside the Fyris River, and listened to its song along with Johan Falck, foreseeing for him how he would capture the hunting eagles of the ranges. Have you found a fossil, and do you pass it over into the curious palm of a field companion? He is Forskål, who will penetrate Arabia Felix disguised as a Bedouin, and die for science, under a vulture-filled sky.

A young man has plucked a sprig of rare white heather, amidst the intense abundant purple. His name is Solander, and he is a Thursday's child. Far to go, he has, far to go — in good Captain Cook's voyage round the world; he shall discover breadfruit of Tahiti, tree ferns of New Zealand; eucalyptus of Australia. At Botany Bay there will fall to his hands the first specimens of the flora of an old continent newly found, when in a single day's haul hundreds of new species, scores of new genera and whole families will be brought to light. He will tumble out of his vasculum forms of flowers so bizarre, so unpredicted in the modest little *Systema Naturae*, that to accommodate them within the Linnaean system, great breaches will have to be made in its quaint walls. And here we see him, happy because he has found a sprig of white heather.

The tall positive fellow who climbs up the steep sides of Jumkil hill beside you is Dr. Adam Kuhn of Philadelphia, the only American student at Linnaeus's court, who has journeyed all this way to bring a living specimen of a little flower of the New World, which he could not identify in Linnaeus's system. Today, in his honor, it bears the name of *Kuhnia*.

Then, when at last you stand on Jumkil's summit, where blue distance aches away into infinitely ulterior horizons, while the sweet cool wind of the long summer day whistles in your ears, the master comes. On his right is Löfling — he who will make of all Spain his Lapland, and die in the Spanish New World — and on his left tramps tall Peter Kalm, the Finn, envoy extraordinary from Linnaeus to America, for whom our mountain laurel bears the name his master gave it, *Kalmia*.

Linnaeus, the accounts all tell us, walked with a quick, almost a shuffling gait; his brilliant brown eyes, says his student Acrel, blinked perpetually; his head was large, his stature medium; his nose, like that of many a great man, was big, and (Linnaeus sets it down himself) he bore a small wart on his right nostril, a large one on his

left cheek. So we see him, coming up into the midst of
his students, the wind of health and confidence about him,
as he marches to the spot that is the trove of the innocent
foray. A tall plant, laden with a spire of brilliant golden
two-lipped flowers, rises, startling and almost tropic-
seeming in the northern air. It is *Sceptrum Carolinum* of
the students' books, a *Pedicularis*, we should call it now,
wood betony of the foxglove family. Here, long ago,
when he was a boy, Linnaeus had been brought by Celsius, to gaze on the mysterious, stately inflorescence. And
both of them, in their pre-Linnaean science, puzzled then
what plant it was that could be named in no herbal and
no classic.

Now on the wild turf boxes are emptied, and every find
of the day displayed, discussed, discoursed upon — fossils
and mosses, fungi and birds, newts and insects. Where it
is a matter of insects, Linnaeus politely takes off his cap
and bows to Fabricius the Dane. " You are the master, I
the pupil," he says. With mosses he turns deferentially to
the pale Zoega, who stands beside him breathing delicately in the fashion of a dying man; Zoega must name
them.

Would we smile now at Linnaeus's lectures? But certainly. Who has not heard of his childlike piety, referring
all causes to the great First Cause? What student does not
know that in zoölogy he was inferior to Ray? That his
classification of minerals is untenable, his conception of
the lower plants quite slipshod? The whole of his System
of Nature, unillumined by any notion of evolution, was
capable of expressing none of Nature's true relationships.
But it is not the little that Linnaeus knew that captivates

us. It is the wisdom in his ignorance, the wisdom to aim so purely, to learn so joyfully, to care so deeply.

When the sun was turned toward afternoon, the whole company would march back again, Sparmann, who shall see Cathay and the incredible flora of the Cape, linking arms with Rolander, who was to return from tropic heat a madman, clutching grey seeds that he fancied precious pearls. Rotheram the Englishman, whose father wrote Linnaeus complaining that he had bewitched his son, on the way back talks fluent Swedish with Hasselquist, who shall die leaving the curses of his widow upon Linnaeus for having lured her husband to his death in Syria.

Back to the old botanic garden of Upsala, where once Linnaeus had wandered forlorn amid neglected plots, his pupils would march, to the sound of French horns and kettledrums, with banners fluttering. And there they all disbanded, giving the rousing cheer of *Vivat scientia! Vivat Linnaeus!*

Great days. Wonderful golden years, when all of natural science was polarized toward the most northerly university in the world, when to the little farm at Hammerby trooped the wise of earth, and the worldly great no less. Lord Baltimore rolled up in a coach and four of such sweeping proportions that all the gate posts on the way had to be taken down to let him pass. Some one whispered to Linnaeus that the English lord had come straight to Hammerby without waiting to see the king. " Why should I go to see the King of Sweden," asked Baltimore, " when I have never even cared to look at my own monarch? "

Fabricius the Dane (Linnaeus of insects, he was

called) has left delightful recollections of his student
days at Upsala. In the winter the foreign students were
lodged close to the master, Fabricius, Zoega, and Dr.
Kuhn bunking together. Of an evening Linnaeus would
present himself at their door in a short red dressing-
gown and green furred cap, his pipe in his hand, and,
promising to stay but half an hour, would grant his audience two, while he chatted of his travels and his correspondence — that great correspondence with all the
learned of earth. Or he would answer his pupils' questions and doubts. His laugh rang up to the rafters; his
face, between pipe whiffs, beamed with enjoyment.

In summer the foreign students adjourned to Hammerby, Linnaeus's country estate. In that season it was
Linnaeus's habit to rise at four in the morning, when the
blue convolvulus was just opening; he usually break-
fasted with his pupils at six, and lectured informally
until ten. In the evening they strolled in the prim of his
garden; perhaps they even told time by his floral clock;
I cannot say; great men are boundlessly frivolous at times.
But when a shiver ran through the great horse-chestnut,
and the night-blooming cereus opened its petals, they
would all go inside and please Sara Lisa by playing at
trisett, her favorite card game.

The Lutheran Sundays at Hammerby were not too
blue. The students were permitted to send for a hurdy-
gurdy, of the old-fashioned sort such as one still sees in
old corners of Europe, a kind of lute most hideously
vibrated by a wheel turned with a crank. The music for
the polkas and minuets was bad, the old barn floor was
worse, but how distinguished the company! Immortals,

with no laurels yet but the crown of youth on their heads, capered with Linnaeus's three daughters and squeezed the waists of the country girls. Linnaeus himself sat apart, contentedly pulling on his pipe, talking with the frail Zoega who dared not dance. But at rare intervals he would arise and step a polonaise that no youngster there had breath for. Unless he saw that every one was cheerful, and even uproarious, he feared they were not enjoying themselves. " *Interpone tuis interdum gaudia curis*," he laughed to them — Mingle sometimes your joys with your earnest occupations.

Ennobled, Linnaeus went to court. At blindman's buff it was not etiquette to catch the queen, the majestic Louisa, sister of Frederick the Great. Yet Linnaeus clapped a big hand on her shoulder. " Clap, woman! " he chuckled. " Who plays at this game may expect to be caught."

Old age advanced. His teeth fell out; he could not hear so well the skirl of the hurdy-gurdy; he must hold the specimens from world's end come to his door far from his blinking old eyes. Even in summer he hugged the comfort of the fire. He slept the sleep of the old — cat naps in which he snored, from which he awoke with a start and fell at once to work.

Senility. The tender indulgence of his pupils. A scene at court where he upbraided the king, magnificent Gustavus III, and wept. Others saw — he could not — that Sara Lisa was grown a shrew, a clutch-penny, that his son on whom he had lavished such doting love was pettish, a frenetic spender and boundless egotist.

And finally, in the dark of a December night in 1777,

he did not return from the sleigh drive on which he had stolen away like a bad child. The search was scattered far and wide, until he was found, on his sleigh where it had been drawn right into a peasant's hearth room. He lay there with his pipe at his mouth, half conscious. Upon the tenth of the following month, with Rotheram, the English student, at his side, the end fell.

Upsala, under young Linnaeus and Sara Lisa, became intolerable. But the flight of the students was like the dispersal of winged seeds out of a ripe pod. Not only his own pupils (of whom I have mentioned only a handful) but learned men the world over set out upon the great search. There had been scientific exploration before, and collecting before. Sir Hans Sloane, called the greatest collector of all time, had by his own labors and what his fortune could procure, laid the foundations of the British Museum's collections. But the Linnaean system revolutionized the way of looking at categories of things, and things themselves. It not only permitted a systematic method of naming that which was collected; the names themselves implied relationships; they automatically distributed Nature into a pattern that, if the times were not ripe for reading its full meaning, was nevertheless the most significant pattern yet devised. Aristotle, with all his cosmology, had been able to think of nothing better than alphabetical order for the enumeration of particulars.

In still another way Linnaean system stimulated research; collecting came to subserve the end of enhancing the system, of filling up the gaps and lacunae, of presenting what (it was mistakenly hoped) would soon be a complete series illustrative of a definitive exhibit of the whole of Nature.

So the land masses of the world were crisscrossed in every direction by Linnaean exploration. The oceans were coursed for the tiniest of unmapped coral atolls or the last, ice-swept islets of the Antarctic. At last scientific exploration had turned its face away from Greece and Palestine (actually two of the most sterile and uninteresting fields for biological field work of which I can conceive), and even from a preoccupation with the directly useful.

Men were converted now to a new point of view, antithetical to that of the herbalists. They were content no longer to devote attention only to that which happens (most fortuitously) to be good for the human digestive tract, or to serve human comfort. Such lines of inquiry are almost as sterile as alchemy. Nature is a whole; she must be approached along every line of investigation at once; she must be viewed as the mother, not the drudge, of man. She is greater than we, and the purely human point of view will not comprehend her.

Knowing for the sake of knowledge is the true Philosopher's Stone. In the times immediately post-Linnaean this credo was fresh and new. Its converts, in the way of converts, went to excess. Collecting reached fantastic lengths, collecting for collecting's sake — an end which Linnaeus, we can be sure, would have deplored, could he have foreseen it.

The joys of collecting, some wise and some foolish, are many, and the adventure tales of the great collectors are more. But the telling of them would lead me far afield, so I pass swiftly over that princely gentleman, Sir Joseph Banks, famous now as the instigator of the search for breadfruit that culminated in the mutiny on the ship *Bounty*. Around the world with Solander and Sparmann, Linnaeus's pupils, went Banks, under the sails of Captain Cook, skimming the cream of collecting on new-found continents and isles, from New Zealand to Iceland. At home in his beautiful mansion in Soho, he kept open house each Sunday night for the naturalists of the world. His purse, his friendship, his boundless enthusiasm carried on the great tradition.

And I can but notice the voyage of Sonnerat to the East Indies after its gorgeous-plumaged, screaming birds. Or the marches and countermarches of the mighty Pallas through the new Asiatic dominions of the Tsar, from the crumbling cities of Turkestan to the frozen tundras of the Samoyed. Or the penetration of Andrew Smith, the ornithologist, beyond the Orange River, into the heart of central south Africa, or the wanderings of Robert Brown in Australia, continent of missing links. Into Abyssinia, that last Eden where great beasts walk in the gentleness of innocence, journeyed Rueppel. The Portuguese friar, Louriero, single-handed gathered out of the jungles of Cambodia the material for his great *Flora*. And for every illustrious name that I have mentioned, ten must pass without notice. The world is so wide.

And so richly stored with wonders! A great light began to break upon men's minds; it was, after all, not the age of man, they saw, but the age of birds, of fishes, of orchids, of composites — to judge by abundance of species, by endless adaptation of form to environment.

There was, of course, a belief that the number of species in the world must be finite, just as the land areas of the world are finite. True, Linnaeus's *Systema Naturae* looked, soon after his death, naïve in its ignorance. But even so, it seemed, it should be possible to chart the whole of Nature.

Yet collectors and systematists were astonished to find that a definitive knowledge even of mere species receded like the horizon. For they had no conception of evolution, no idea that new species are in the making. Nor were they conscious that their own ideas of species were undergoing constant refinement and fractionation. Almost every old Linnaean species was turning out to be in fact two, three, fifty or a hundred species. Indeed, any artificial concept of Nature's slippery prolificity, of its thoughtless melting of form into form, can lead to no other result.

But of this men had no notion. They were haunted by the illusion that, with just a little more discovery, all gaps in knowledge would close up. So the collecting went on and on, and so, back in the museums and universities of Europe, did the systematizing.

In all this amassing of specimens, until they filled miles and miles of groaning, sagging, dusty, cluttered shelves and drawers in the museums of all Europe, there lurked a danger — that the collections should fail, at the last, to *think*. That, after all, they would represent nothing. And that scientists would begin to conceive of Nature as existing in order to give grey old gentlemen of a philosophic turn something to identify and classify.

BOTANICAL EXPLORATION AT THE HEIGHT OF THE LINNAEAN AGE
From an old Danish print. (*Courtesy of the Field Museum, Chicago*)
(*See page 132 and ff*)

MONUMENT TO LINNAEUS
in Lincoln Park, Chicago;
replica of another in Stockholm.
(Courtesy of the Chicago Daily News)
(See page 140)

What useful end classification served was not questioned
— except by the sound good sense of the public.

For what, of course, these mighty collections cried
aloud (or so it seems to our ears) was the concept of evolution, to give them meaning. Connected series of specimens would then take on significance, prove or disprove
something. But though the idea of evolution was already
nearly two thousand years old, though some one propounded it upon the average, at least once every two hundred years, it was not heeded. Even in times immediately post-Linnaean it was put forward once again, more
appealingly than ever, and was greeted with ridicule by
the very men who needed it to justify the refined futility of their life work. But the time to tell of Lamarck,
Cuvier and their contemporaries will come later.

All the while the collecting went on, ever mounting
up; the describing fed upon itself and could lead only
to more describing. Here was the same dilemma in which
Buffon found himself, but Buffon at least makes better
reading; he actually has more to tell than those tedious
Germans and Englishmen who practised their Linnaeanism like the grammar of a dead language.

Or they drew up schemes for " Natural Systems " of
their own. (The Linnaean system had not pretended to be
more than a finding syllabus; Linnaeus knew that he had
not established natural families, and beyond a few very
obvious ones he did not know what such families were or
how related.) But lacking any idea of evolution, the ar-
chitects of these systems could only pattern them on royalist lines. The noblest beasts were put first. Thus our

old manuals of ornithology all open with the eagle (our ancestors admired its rapacity as the highest virtue, it seems), and they ended with the booby, stupidest of birds.

In the passion for collection lay another evil, one that was realized to the full and reached ultimate follies. This was the danger that commercial exploitation should set in, to purvey specimens to people not remotely interested in science, but avid only of prideful and personal arrays, with emphasis, of course, upon the rare. It seems impossible to make people realize that the rare is of trivial biological interest compared with the common. The very commonness of any living thing is the most miraculous and meaningful fact about it. But now the rare was searched out, and the pretty or the bizarre. Shells, butterflies, beetles, hummingbirds, ferns and orchids have for their loveliness suffered from the attentions of persons who happen to collect them instead of postage stamps or autographs.

Some commercial firms maintained their own collectors of orchids and butterflies. The brothers Verraux of Paris were famous for their clearing house of rare bird specimens, which they bought up all over the world, received from sea captains and globe-trotters, or had collected for them by men as athletic, intrepid and slaughterous as they were ignorant. Books too responded to the collecting mania and frivolous curiosity. The stuffed-bird fancier's delight was John Gould, who in endless folio volumes illustrated the birds of India, the birds of Australasia, the birds of everywhere, in the most insipid attitudes and the most exaggerated coloration.

The research after the rare, a quasi-commercial, quasi-scientific research, is typified, glorified and carried to the point of exhausting the fun of the game, in the career of the excellent Englishman Hugh Cuming, a wealthy amateur, who set out in a private yacht to cruise the world for new shells, something to tickle the jaded fancy of the European collector in his castle or parsonage or shell-shop. In the Philippines Cuming sent native collectors into the jungles after tropical tree snails, and saw one fellow returning with a sack full from which specimens (every one possibly a genus new to science) were dribbling carelessly along the jungle floor. On a reef in the South Seas (which has since been destroyed by a hurricane) he came on eight living shells of the " Glory-of-the-Sea." Almost fainting with delight he took all eight away, and it seems unlikely that the world will ever see any others. Anyone who understands the commercial value of such singularities will not need to be told what a bull market in conchology set in when Cuming's molluscs reached the auction rooms. Shells the size of the finger nail went for five hundred dollars a piece; others could be purchased only by Rothschilds. In such romances — and orchids and butterflies have had similar ones — the part played by science is naturally limited.

But the *scientia amabilis* was not the property of the pedant and the collector only. Linnaean clarity had popularized all the natural sciences. They were available now to every good intellect. Rousseau gave lectures on botany to classes of ladies; Jane, the daughter of the urbane Cadwallader Colden of New York, was taught the Linnaean system by her father, and by it described the " parts " of four hundred flowers of the New World. Country doctors, driving or riding on their rounds, became ornithologists; priests on their solitary walks stopped to notice the ways of the insect people; ladies pressed ferns; small boys spitted *Lepidoptera*.

A patronizing manner toward these amateur efforts is usually assumed by the professional naturalists. What museum has not had to turn away Great-aunt Lucinda's parlor album of orchids, the abalone shells that Uncle Abner gathered when he went out to California, and Willy's taxidermic efforts?

But at its worst, amateur science could never have sunk to such abysmal depths as professional Linnaeanism. It was stigmatized — it still is — by endless guesswork as to what Linnaeus meant, tedious squabbles over priority of publication, ungenerous and quibbling little reviews, parochial lists of Latin names. Such, and not the well-meant and sometimes very important work of the devoted amateur, have made modern science ashamed of Linnaeanism.

Linnaeus himself has not escaped the blame for the sterility of his followers. It has been said, and truly said, that he was too often content with naming and classifying. That he took no interest in the physiology of plants and animals; that he neglected the microscope; that he never experimented; that he was in effect the most scholastic of all the Schoolmen, entirely preoccupied with abstract categories. He was, in short, no modern.

But is this really a reproach to Linnaeus? Is it not enough that he accomplished what he did? That, however superficially, with however many slips and errors as to detail, he conquered those provinces that he set out to conquer? His was a triumph, a first necessity. It held the ground for science until the modern artillery of attack could be brought up.

The life work of Charles Darwin has had to endure quite as much destructive criticism as Linnaeus's. So have the cosmology of Aristotle, Newtonian physics, and the anatomy of Cuvier. Their claims to finality have had to be retracted and retracted; their reputations have receded from point to point. Until it seems as though nothing is left them — except their greatness.

And I am not alluding to the obvious fact that such men were great in their age, which is all we may ask of mortal flesh and blood. They were great in an absolute sense, great for all time. That we have, today, new methods of apprehending scientific truth does not necessarily mean that we have better methods. The years three thousand and four thousand will judge better of that. Whatever truth is, whatever life is, or matter, we shall never know more of them than some purely human concepts, and by a concept we mean a reduction into artificial terms such as we can talk of, such as we may shift about conveniently. Ideas are like money — small, round or symmetrical symbols (some dross, some gold) that stand for large, irregular, unmanageable values. In the natural sciences no one has yet minted any coinage more practicable than the Linnaean, and still, all over the world, it passes on its face value.

There is another way in which a scientist may be great, and that is in his personality, his magnetic power to sway his followers. Some great scientists have lacked this quality entirely. A general may also lack it, and still win battles. But Linnaeus was dowered with a temperament so glowing that across the years we may warm the heart at its geniality. Most of the historians of science have been at pains to efface personality from the individaul humans whom we call scientists. They regard this peculiar expunging as part of their duty, a sort of rule of public decency. They are applauded in this by the modern scientists, themselves a prudish lot, constantly afraid that you will discover that they are human. The eulogies that scientists write of each other in the black-leaded obituary pages of their tedious little journals are like country photography, where every wrinkle is touched out. To judge only from these accounts the same scientist keeps dying all the time; I defy you to tell the difference between his incarnations.

The city of Chicago — rather surprisingly — boasts a statue to Linnaeus, in Lincoln Park. Under its stone gaze pass nurses and men out of work, little girls on roller skates, a lethargic white-wing, a tall, ragged boy earnestly studying *The Elements of Chemistry*. Such, at least, was the public I beheld there when yesterday, on a delicate, high-arched day of spring (that languid, awkward spring in the city that puts such torment into the bones of adolescence), I hunted out the memorial to the sage of Hammerby. I found him at last as a rotund gentleman in stone cape and stone wig, standing on a pedestal where, rather trustingly, I thought, no inscription but his name proclaimed him. Two girl children, that grown boy knitting his brows over the periodic table of the elements, and a nursemaid sat at his feet quite unconcerned with him. The whole city, no doubt, is equally oblivious.

The Linnaean Age

But in the statue's out-held hand, confidingly, a sparrow had built its nest.

Long ago it happened, long ago when the world was younger — the Lapland faring, the boy scuffing the leaves in the sleeping botanical garden, the child in the sunlight naming the flowers in the garden of Stenbrohult parsonage. But still out in the woods, beyond the city, the trillium and adder's tongue carpet the woods; the birds still build, under the eaves, in the marsh, in the hollow of a stone hand. And there are many of us left to cry, with Thunberg and Kalm and Kuhn, *Vivat scientia! Vivat Linnaeus!*

7

A CHEVALIER IN SCIENCE: LAMARCK

BAZENTIN-LE-PETIT is a hamlet of Picardy — in the modern Department of the Somme — and it stands upon the great plain of northern France, its heavy stone church too large for the congregation, its school too small for its children, those generations of black- or blue-smocked, sturdy-legged children that come on perpetually, faster than any one, except the French army, desires. The Mairie or town hall looks rather like a bad château, and the château Lamarck rather like a gaunt meeting-house — a symmetrical building in the style we know as Georgian, rising, unshaded, four-square and perpendicular out of the vast, logical lines of the plain. A sea of black earth — that same mud that the World War ploughed into a welter of flesh and agony — surrounds the château, and on it thrive a million glaucous blue cabbages, gigantic, slow-footed horses, and a realistic and skeptical people, plodding through life under the grey sky's high pessimism.

But it often happens that the interior of such a house has, or once had (as we must say in the case of the château Lamarck) more refinement than would be suspected either from the exterior of the building or the impecuniosity of the *petite noblesse* in the reigns of the last two Louis. The wanderer in the empty shell of this house still remarks the wide halls, the elegant staircase, the double paneled doors, the high wainscoating and, above the hearth, a painting of a shepherdess and shepherd embracing, while in the distance graze their neglected sheep. Its delicate colors faded, this ikon may still be taken for the altarpiece of the family, the symbol of that tender, insistent religion that carries forward the generations. In those days love kept the cradles full, and the child Jean Baptiste Pierre Antoine de Monet de Lamarck was the eleventh and the last to wail in that house, and suckle, and grin and duck his chin.

There was practically nothing in the family estates with which to dower a youngest son, and Nature therefore took a hand and, touching his small brow, bestowed upon him immortal genius. She wished for him that he might speak out the truth. And then, apparently, some unbidden fairy, arriving late and angry at the christening, added that though he spoke the truth, it should be his destiny that no one who heard him should believe him. A third, unable to undo the curse, capped it with the wish that he should be honored after he was dead.

The family de Lamarck, or la Marck or Lamarque, had a long martial tradition. The chateau was one of those halls where the servants have not been paid for an age, but there is always money for a new saddle or a new blade, and its inhabitants, drinking wine and eating pride, have rigid, almost Castilian notions of honor and courtly bearing. Not, perhaps, an environment for producing much more than a tilter at windmills, except that in the case of the future naturalist Lamarck it early bred him to accept the poverty from which he never escaped; it taught him to endure mockery without deigning to descend to it in riposte, to serve the state regardless of reward.

Young Jean Baptiste was destined for the clergy, but he wore his student's bands with scorn, and on his father's death he bought a miserable old horse, hired a wretched village boy for a groom, and set off across the country to join the army campaigning in High Germany. It was the disastrous maneuver of the Prince de Soubise against the Prince of Brunswick. The officer to whom Lamarck bore a letter of introduction was annoyed at this seventeen-year-old recruit, and place him in a company exposed to the direct fire of the enemy's artillery. They had orders to hold their ground, and they continued to do so when there were no more French troops left in sight. The officers having all been killed, the boy Lamarck simply took charge of the fourteen men. In spite of the entreaties of the oldest grenadier, he held his ground until his marshal, perceiving them, sent out an orderly commanding him to retreat. When Lamarck marched into camp he was made an officer *sur le champs*.

After peace was made, Lamarck's regiment was sent into garrison first at Toulon and later at Monaco, and here, if tradition speaks aright, the soldier first became the naturalist. The principality of Monaco, where chance has made and broken so many men, included in those days not only the Rock of Monaco itself, with its fantastic, murder-haunted palace and its toy-like harbor, but a tiny stretch of coast that embraced the mountains to the north, and the sleepy fishing village of Mentone, and the hillsides were not gay then with villas, terraced to the sea. There was only a monastery on the hill of the Annunciata, at La Turbie the broken pediment of a great monument built to the glory and folly of Augustus Caesar, a medieval castle at Roquebrune, and a few villages nestled into the mountains, Castillon and Castellar and Gorbio and Eza, whose slow bells chimed out the endless sunny years to the valleys deep in olive and ilex and laurel and myrtle, and to the bare mountain summits, covered with wild thyme and mother-of-thyme, frail rock-rose and dancing narcissus.

Here it was the habit of the young lieutenant to walk alone, and according to the story, his walks made him thoughtful, as he strode across the harsh, sun-bitten, aromatic vegetation of the heights of Mont Agel. In the distance, to the north, he could see the flashing summits of the Alps. To the south the sea stretched level and wrinkled, a shimmering bed of blue and green and silver silk. In the dry, golden air there was distance, a sense of height and peace, a contemplative religious glory, not so Christian as Grecian, where there was place for Olympic thought, Empedoclean reasoning.

Perhaps he remembered flaccid water-weeds waving in the rivers of the rainy plain of Picardy, the dark coniferous forests of Germany, as he gazed thoughtfully down upon the wiry Mediterranean weeds at his feet, armed with harsh hairs, or thorns, very small and chary and thick of leaf, very large and brilliant of flower, where the wild bees darted and chanted, busy about progenitive matters. And he began to wonder how it comes to pass that the world is clothed in such varied sorts of vegetation. The thin, watery, delicate leaf of a Norman oak would soon shrivel and die in the arid southern climate. And so, in their place grow ilex oaks, with small, thick leaves, spiny and glossy above, like holly, and deeply felted on the under surface with a white wool. Everywhere, in every tree, in every humblest weed, he saw the evidence of adaptation to a special environment. As the limp leaves, the flexuous stem of the water-weeds exactly suit the endless motion of the brooks of Picardy, so the spines of the spurge bush defend it against the devouring goats of Provence.

No one can say how far these reflections carried him then, nor what seeds they sowed. The boy at the moment was twenty, thirty, forty years from a formulated concept that evolution is possible, is real, is more characteristic of life than motion or breathing. He had, in fact, no training as a naturalist, no ambition to become one. It is possible he had never heard of the profession. But destiny was keeping an eye on him, nevertheless, and in a short time his military career was brought to an end. A brother officer attempted to lift him by the head. This gave rise to an inflammation of the neck's lymphatic glands and, greatly suffering, he was sent to Paris for an operation. His treatment occupied a year — a year of dire want and a long enforced leisure in the capital.

It may mean many things to be twenty-one, and alone in Paris. The usual connotation is amatory adventure. But Paris is amatory chiefly to those who seek for nothing else in it. Paris is also the city of the Sorbonne, the city of a thousand little shops; the city of haunting streets, of the

A Chevalier in Science: Lamarck

manifold poor, of students, of workmen, of palaces, of
violet lights shining through the winter mists, of tender
and rather weary springs, of despairing autumns. A city
with a long ache at the heart of it for the young and the
poor and the very eager. A city of endless attic stairs, of
miles and miles of roof-tops, and garret beds.

Up such stairs each day climbed Lamarck; his roof
was right beneath the eaves, and his window, a skylight,
gave him no view save spires and gables and an opening
into the depths of the sky. Ill, and ill-shod and without a
warm coat, he lay for hours upon his back in the bed,
gazing up at the clouds, forever passing, forever changing. But where a mediocre mind sees silly faces, and forms
of fish and ships and beasts in them, the mind of the young
scientist, still quite unconscious, of course, that his was
such, began to sort out the different kinds of clouds, to
study the connection between their forms and the following weather. Having nothing else to gaze at, he became
at last an expert in these matters. Whether or not he had
any nomenclature of a standard sort I cannot say; but
certainly he soon learned every type of cloud, the black
sheets of the nimbus that bring snow, the galleon cumuli
that ride east at the end of a long summer day, the delicate
feathery cirrus clouds that promise fair weather, and the
cumulo-nimbus thunder-heads. Before long he had noted
every sort of vaporous body that comes within ordinary
experience, and having learned what to expect, having
the most precious gift of a scientist, an infinite patience
with the repetitions of normality, he was able to detect
the unusual when it occurred. Thus it happened that one
day he discovered an entirely new sort of configuration

in the sky, the mammato-cirrus cloud, a formation so rare that it has seldom been observed since.

When at last the cure was effected, the young man was faced with the prospect of living on a pension of four hundred francs a year. He might perhaps have re-entered the army. But Paris had done its work; or, more truly, the long hours under that mansard roof had changed him. He had made friends, here and there, other young thinkers, or older men. On one of his walks he fell in with a fellow who introduced himself as Jean Jacques Rousseau. Rousseau was botanizing along the banks of the Seine — he had a quite trivial taste in Linnaean science — and they struck up a friendship that changed the course of Lamarck's life. He was then working in a dreary bank, and hesitating between a musical and a medical career. Rousseau, acquainted in all the scientific circles in Paris, generously introduced his friend, and before long Lamarck, quite without funds, determined upon a career which consumed, but did not produce, money. He went to the best instructor that France, or perhaps the world, could have provided, Bernard de Jussieu, the botanist. In no time at all he knew about the amiable science what Rousseau would not have had the application to master had he had the opportunity.

But before the great sentimentalist, confessor and parlor revolutionary passes from the tale, it will be worth a glance to discover what his inchoate thinking may have contained for Lamarck. Rousseau seems to have understood very well how far the environment influences the organism, and how needs are the distinguishing mark of the living being, needs that must be satisfied, needs to which the living creature responds with all its being. He pointed out the influence of natural selection in Sparta, where the weak children were exposed to die, leaving only the strong to breed.

One does not know how far he communicated his nebulous conceptions of evolution to his friend, but it is certain that what we call Lamarckism, and Lamarck called *transformisme*, was not born whole out of Lamarck's brow. All ideas have forebears, and France, in those days, France the skeptical, the liberal, the explorative, was filled with the suggestions of evolution. The materialism of La Mettrie — we would call it mechanism now — the negatively stated, pusillanimous, groping speculations of Buffon, Geoffroy St. Hilaire's views upon the history of life upon earth — these were in the air, and much more fantastic guess-work beside. Across the Channel in England Dr. Erasmus Darwin, in his crazy, involuted, perspicacious way, was announcing, to an unbelieving world, that living animals have descended from quite dissimilar creatures in the past, and the poet Coleridge expressed public opinion on the grandfather of Charles Darwin when he scoffed at Darwinizing as the opposite of sober biological thought.

We must really remember to come back to the excellent Dr. Darwin of the what-not-cabinet mentality. But in spite of Samuel Butler's guess (in *Evolution Old and New*) Lamarck never heard of Darwin or his *Zoönomia*, and there is no evidence that he ever read the French translation of *The Loves of the Plants*. More to the point it is to know how far men had wandered from the Mosaic picture of creation. In France particularly, the science

of geology had half turned from the pursuit of evidence
that would prove some absurd Babylonian legend (borrowed by the Jews of the Captivity) about the Deluge.
A great suspicion was creeping into the French mind
that Time — ages and eons of it, quantities undreamed
of by Moses — was required to explain the rocks. The
organic nature of fossils was now more than suspected
by a few madmen like Steno the Dane. It had been
maintained by Réaumur and Buffon (for once they were
agreed on something) that fossils are not mere whimsies
of the Creator, stone patterns precisely imitating animal
forms, as frost on the pane or agate fortuitously resembles
fern or moss. These two, and other thinkers, perceived
that these prints were effigies in calcium or silicate rock
of obliterated Medusae, crinoids broken at the stem,
conchs for a Triton to blow, choked now with the dia-
tomic ooze. Or here were the very bones, turned stone,
of beasts that once breathed, devoured, excreted, roared,
mated, foaled (or whatever) and fell at last in the cease-
less harvest of death, the mute unshriven death of beasts.
Here in what is now rock they buckled and sank, the pre-
diluvian ooze rising swiftly to the dark eyes that always
seem to gaze not on the stainless future in which humans
hope, but with a backward, vitrified longing for life itself.

Oddly enough, the resistance to the organic concept
of life came not from the clergy so much as from " sensible men." Voltaire, for once, was just a shade too clever,
too reasonable, and Buffon surprisingly bold and imaginative, in their controversy over the presence of the sea-
shell fossils upon the tops of the Alps. The wit of Ferney
imagined, no doubt, that he was pricking one more bub-

LAMARCK AT THE AGE OF 35 YEARS
(See page 153)

ble when he asked why it was necessary for some savants
to sink the Alps under the sea in order to place a sea-shell
on a peak? One had only to suppose that pilgrims on their
way to Rome had carried shellfish in picnic baskets to
the mountains and after feasting tossed the shells away.
But Voltaire soon realized that he knew nothing of the
subject he was talking about, and tiptoed rapidly away
from the scene of one of his few intellectual humiliations.

And from every side rose now a murmur of voices —
a studious abbé in the provinces, an old man behind a bone
pile in Göttingen, a young enthusiast hanging about quar-
ries watching for signs of the unmistakable thumb print
of life — voices proclaiming that life has changed, that
the living creatures of today did not swim in the vanished
seas of the past, and the monsters of long ago that trod
upon great ferns are not on the earth today. The continents had been once beneath the sea, and tropic animals
padded across the tranquil plain of France. Time, suddenly, seemed to give way at the back, and what had been
thought the ultimate horizon of this dimension was found
to be nothing but a painted backdrop; lifted, it revealed
a wild and unfamiliar landscape, fabulously populated
and receding into a perspective unbelievably deep.

All this I recount with no other purpose than to tell the
temper of the times — to waft what was in the air in those
days. My hero — for I admit to a predilection in his favor,
conceived when I heard his memory mocked by a very
tedious professor — was many years from his confession
of faith, his nailing of the articles of evolution to the doors
of orthodoxy. Long young thoughts in strange places —
these had sown the seeds in his mind; as they were to do in

the mind of Charles Darwin. But a shock, a change, a co-incidence, a " disadvantage " (as it seems at the time) may be needed to crystallize, to cast down as a brilliant, salty precipitate that which drifts invisible in solution in the mind. So it was to be with Lamarck as with Darwin.

In the meantime the life of young Lamarck was pro-ceeding along the most modest and inconspicuous run-ways, so that Paris, the Court, the world knew as little what he did with himself as if he had been a sparrow. Lamentably, those few — the coterie at the Jardin du Roi where Buffon was intendant — who knew anything of Lamarck's personal life failed to write home about it, never conceiving that future ages should wish to know whom he married and when. Who, after all was La-marck? A student of Jussieu's, the tutor to Buffon's son, the author of the *Flore Française* (a mild best seller since botany had become " *une science à la mode* "). One saw him every day, *voyons*, a poor devil of a hack, without any definite salaried position, married to — well, heavens, who had she been? One of those girls, perhaps, one had to marry for love, since there was nothing else to marry her for, one of those patient, cheerful, unfashionable women who put up with artistic or scientific husbands and, in-finitely self-sacrificing, infinitely complicate matters by their weakness for having babies.

All this seems to have been so commonplace that the private life of Lamarck passed without record in an age when it was the rage to keep diaries and write letters about the most trivial affairs. So that the joys and the sorrows of Lamarck are not preserved for the same reason that those of the pastor of the nearest Swedish Lutheran church or the assistant taxidermist of your state Natural History Survey are no more than mentioned by you, if you write neighborhood gossip and happened to speak to these acquaintances on the street. It never occurs to you that they could possibly be more significant than yourself, or that the ages may just forgive the tinkling futility of your existence because your correspondence contains a mention of those great men.

So I have to confess that though Lamarck was married four times, no one today knows to whom, nor when. All four of his wives died — but no one knows which was the love of his life, nor what last gaze that woman turned upon him, nor what tears of his fell on the tumult of her hair, that still seemed upon the pillow to live its own adorable life. Now and then we hear how the Chevalier Lamarck petitioned the Crown, or the intendant, or the Academy of Sciences for a pension, an appointment, a larger house — the said Chevalier being charged with a numerous family, the wife of the Chevalier " being again *enceinte*," the servant having labored long in the service of the state and having a son in the fleet. Or, later, the citizen Lamarck petitions the Republic that a room be allowed to his son, a painter. We discover that from the moment of his election to the Academy of Sciences at the age of thirty-five, he seldom missed a meeting in thirty-five years; we know that he spoke occasionally there; that he lived, after Buffon's death, in the Buffon house, still standing in the quarter of the Jardin des Plantes, a typical old Parisian house with its green shutters and false window spaces, and, in the rear, the great, round, familial tree, and the eight-foot wall with the broken glass on it and the white cat putting a circumspect paw among these ineffectual cruelties. Whatever else there is of Lamarck's personal history, you shall have it, if it has any significance, and now that I have exposed the poverty of my materials, I proceed.

Lamarck's career began with the publication of the *Flore Française*, an admirable long labor that enjoyed many editions. This, and a wave of Buffon's ringed hand, brought Lamarck the title of Botanist to the King and election to the Academy of Sciences. Here was a tidy small success, and if Lamarck had never gone beyond it, if he had never done anything but revise editions of his book, adding species here and correcting genera there, like our own Asa Gray, he would have enjoyed the epithet of " the French Linnaeus." (It has dwarfed every one who ever wore the name to be called " the Linnaeus of " something or other.)

When d'Angiviller got himself made intendant after Buffon's day, that gold-braided grandee, ignorant of natural history but mindful of the claims of the clan, appointed his distant connection Lamarck to be Keeper of the King's Herbarium, at one thousand francs a year. Long service augmented this salary to eighteen hundred francs, and this might have been the very top for the intendant's poor relation, if the terrible footsteps of the Revolution had not come thundering into the lives of the little group of savants huddled, waiting, bewildered, at the Jardin du Roi. " The Republic has no need for savants," was the famous dictum of the Directory. Lavoisier, the great chemist, had gone to the guillotine; Abbé Haüy, founder of crystallography, had been barely rescued from prison by Geoffroy St. Hilaire, and Latreille the entomologist was snatched at the last minute from a traitor's exile.

True scientists have never been nationalists, nor do they vaunt political creeds; even in times of civil war and revolution they may be looked to for aloofness from the passions and reprisals of strife. The band at the Garden of the King included a few petty noblemen, like Lamarck himself, but none of them seems to have been seriously disturbed by the frightful events of The Terror, owing to the fact that all of them had been singularly free of intrigue with the royal government. What a fate might have befallen the men of the King's Garden had the storm broken in the day of the courtier Buffon!

Lamarck's associates, beside Jussieu and Haüy, were Daubenton, the aged ornithologist who had supplied Buffon with all the science the latter possessed, the boy Étienne Geoffroy St. Hilaire, embryologist, anatomist, and amateur evolutionist, Desfontaines, the botanist who had ransacked Barbary and the Atlas for the strange, and (most astonishingly) the sentimental and amorous author of *Paul et Virginie*, Bernardin de St. Pierre, appointed the new intendant because he was a friend of somebody at the Court-that-was. Nor will I forget gentle, loveable Thouin, the royal gardener, for I once owned a first edition of Linnaeus's *Genera of Plants*, on the flyleaf bearing in crayon Thouin's signature and the words " Jardin du Roy."

Dangerous words those, when heads were falling because their owners had once offered an arm to the Queen. It was Lamarck who proposed the change to " Jardin des

Plantes " — the name by which today you visit the Paris zoo. The timely proposal brought a change of heart to the Convention, and the chairman of its committee on education being himself a scientist, saved the gardens, museum, and the salaries of the little band. Every one eagerly fell to his new duties (except the literary intendant), and, strangest of all, Lamarck found that he was occupying the chair of invertebrate zoölogy, a subject about which no one in the world knew much, and Lamarck nothing at all. Indeed, invertebrate zoölogy was not a term that then existed (since Lamarck was to be the first to distinguish vertebrates from invertebrates). What he was occupying was the chair of all the zoölogy that nobody wanted. Birds, mammals, reptiles, fishes, comparative anatomy and paleontology — there were men eager to profess them all. What was left over — in God's good creation and the dusty museum drawers — was a lot of vermin in the way of snails, squids, spiders, insects, scorpions, worms, and such *coquillage* as oysters, lobsters, shrimps and the like. This protean rubbish had baffled Linnaeus and all the other systematizers, and it had neither been classified nor seriously examined in what were then modern times. In short, it was limbo — the midden of God's lowlier efforts. And it was nineteen-twentieths of the animal kingdom.

Into this jumbled storehouse of creation — actually the richest in the world — went the fifty-year-old botanist, unconscious (or had he just a faint premonition?) that he had come to the crossroads of his career, and that when he emerged after nine years of silence, of wrestling with the gigantic invertebrate world, he would have a master key to natural history. At least his theory was the skeleton of a concept that would unlock the shut away significance of those miles of museum shelves.

For these were groaning with the spoils of the world. France at the moment had the lead in scientific expeditions to the ends of the earth — Geoffroy St. Hilaire and Savigny were off to Egypt; Lamarck's friend Bruguière was sending back all the wealth of Poseidon in shells of the Pacific. Bory de St. Vincent was emptying the Indies of their treasure. Le Vaillant was a maniac collector of everything from everywhere, Lesueur, sole survivor of the La Perouse expedition, was a merchant in corals, in nacre, in fishes, peacock-arrogant in beauty, margaritiferous shells and Venus' baskets and Portuguese men-o'-war.

In nine years of increasing application, Lamarck made order out of chaos assigned to him, establishing the natural families and super-families or orders of most of the marine invertebrates. If he knew little enough about insects, he at least defined them so as to clear them from centipedes, scorpions, spiders, lobsters, shrimps, and sowbugs and even the snakes and crocodiles that Réaumur had seen no difficulty in calling " *des féroces insectes.*" He was an authority among corals and shells, a pioneer much of whose work stands unsurpassed today.

All this would be creditable, even remarkable in a man of Lamarck's years who had abruptly switched to another science. But he had made of himself the foremost zoölogist of his age and he was ready with a conception greater and farther reaching than the Aristotelian, the Baconian or the Linnaean. Was the world ready to hear it?

Green Laurels

What Lamarck had to say was just as startling as anything that Charles Darwin announced some fifty years later. Its implications were just as upsetting and exciting, and churchmen and authoritarian scientists ought to have snarled and arched their backs when Lamarck declared that the species of the animal kingdom form a connected series, a graduated chain from the monad (one-celled organism) to man. The public might have read on page seventy of his new book on invertebrates that there has been in life an ascent from the most simple to the most complex. But the public of 1806 was following with its eyes the dust of Napoleon's columns. Europe was full of sound and fury; very few realized how little they signified. And the men of science who actually read through a work upon such offal of creation as the invertebrates, could permit their eyes to travel over Lamarck's declaration without receiving the shock that lay waiting for them there.

His connected chain of species was far from a new conception; Aristotle had suggested it; Buffon had certainly coasted by the idea though he was afraid to land at it. Careful looking has shown that Darwin had about a hundred forerunners. In all ages and in all languages sages have tried to put over the concept of evolution. They found no takers until the angelic origin of man himself was assaulted; the storm that this created in Victorian England gave the concept all that an idea, be it a Red Cross drive or a California cult, requires for success. That is publicity.

Lamarck in his age had no real organs of publicity to serve him. He was temperamentally indifferent to their

[158]

purposes, and he failed even to make himself odious to the Church. He was amiable, gentle, serious, and when an enemy would charge down upon him he would step aside with the grace of an *espada* in a bull ring. He never intended more by his conclusions than to expose a zoölogical fact. To his reasonable French mind, essentially skeptical and uncolored, supposing that that which hurts no one is no sin, no human moralities were involved in this discussion of origins. Obviously it contradicted Biblical cosmogony, but the Catholic French have ever been able to hold simultaneously to pure faith and intellectual clarity.

So Lamarck, who had gone from the seminary into the army, had nevertheless the freedom of mind for a tree of life of his own planting (*See Figure B*). Only those who know how bad have been many phylogenetic trees since Lamarck's day can comprehend how good is this one. To derive the insects from the worms, the reptiles from the fishes, and the birds and mammals from the reptiles is dazzling. There are other happy thoughts in the diagram — and some not so fortunate. The class of amphibian mammals is a hodge-podge based on a habitat, not on anatomy. But Lamarck at least perceived that many lines of development have led nowhere, that evolution has taken a wandering course, has tried, as it were, innumerable experiments, has gone where it could, or rather where it must. He did not try to see some logical sort of evolution such as Buffon groped for. He seems to have sensed that a logical explanation would not do; no one could have predicted in advance the course that life would take or indeed have imagined, in the delirium of fever,

LAMARCK'S TABLE

To Show the Origin of Different Animals

❖

WORMS *(Flatworms)*

INFUSORIANS
(Microscopic Animals)

POLYPS *(Corals, Sea-anemones)*

RADIATES*(Jellyfish~Starfish,etc)*

INSECTS

ARACHNIDS *(Spiders, Mille-pedes, etc)*

CRUSTACEANS

ANNELIDS *(Earthworms, Seaworms)*

CIRRHEPEDES *(Barnacles)*

MOLLUSCS *(Snails, Cuttlefish, Octopi)*

FISHES

REPTILES *(incl. Amphibians)*

BIRDS

AMPHIBIAN MAMMALS

MONOTREMES
(Duck-billed Platypus & other egg-laying mammals)

CETACEANS
(Whales)

[*Figure* B]

UNGULATES
(Hoofed Mammals)

UNGUICULATES *(Clawed Mammals)*

anything so hideous as a hippopotamus, so exquisite as some of the sea worms, so sheerly mental, naked and ungainly as a man. Lamarck's tree of life, with all its faults, is nevertheless a living tree, irregular, individual, like the silhouette of an actual oak; it is as unlike the symmetry and reasonableness of Greek cosmogony or Scholastic schematism as the shagbark hickory in my woods is unlike the Parthenon.

To the modern mind it seems impossible that a picture so vivid as the tree of biological descent could be drawn for the first time, without its self-evidence appearing. But the trouble with truth is that we never call it that; we call it " the views of Mr. So-and-so." I am not saying that matters should not stand thus. Not everybody with the light of conviction in his eye is speaking the truth. And if you have a message for science you will have to file your idea with the ages, and some time in the course of them, your posterity will be notified what is thought of it. If the answer comes back too soon, you should be skeptical of the judges, more particularly if the reply is favorable. So it is not surprising that the bare postulate that life forms change, one into the other, should have been received simply as what our colleague Lamarck imagines.

But Lamarck had enemies. And they were doubly dangerous, for they passed as his friends. This means, in short, that they were personally fond of him, politely acknowledged his help in prefaces to their publications, would have helped him also had he asked it, but they thought his views pernicious or childish and they did not intend to have him admired with themselves.

I think I sensed this when I first heard about Lamarck.

[161]

It was from that tedious professor I complained of earlier, who, after exposing Lamarck's views, proceeded to demolish and ridicule them. He then swept on to Darwin, whom it is so easy to admire, and whipped out Weismann, the invincible champion of Darwinism, as the final confutation of Lamarck. It was only long afterwards that I was allowed to learn that under the name of neo-Lamarckism the Frenchman's theory has come back for celebrity, and that the implications of Weismann when carried out to their logical end seem to testify for Lamarck. All this runs far ahead of my story, but I suspected from the first that there was an agreement to misrepresent Lamarck. Suspicions are not very logical, and I have always had a preference for the heroes of the losing side; who admires Scipio as much as Hannibal? But we must reasonably suspect that the extant accounts of the loser will emanate from the victor; the fallen are silenced or censored, and if we can go behind the official report of things we may discover that victories cannot be won without some help from chance, and every lost siege is accompanied by great heroism and labor and invention such as are not called forth from the conquerors.

Darwin was open in his hostility to Lamarck; he was objecting purely to the Frenchman's explanation of the means by which evolution might take place. But there sat at Lamarck's table, strolled in and out of his office, borrowed his authority and his pencils, one who resented the whole notion that the living world was not a rigid and immutable exhibition intended as material for the profoundly interesting subject of comparative anatomy. One who, consciously or not, could only work and be agreeable

[162]

if he were the captain of the game. His name first appears in the acts and memoirs of the Museum when in 1795 Lamarck arose to second a proposition that a young Monsieur Cuvier be invited to leave his jellyfish on the Normandy shore and come to the Jardin des Plantes to pursue his anatomical studies where his confreres might further and enjoy them.

8

ANATOMIST AGAINST DREAMER: CUVIER AND LAMARCK

Mᴏʀᴇ new truths concerning the external world," says Buckle, historian of civilization, " were discovered in France during the latter half of the eighteenth century than during all the preceding periods put together."

No one was more aware of this than the French, but they were not aware that across the Rhine the physical technique for the discovery of truth had begun to overtake the entirely cerebral methods of their own thinkers. Lamarck was one of the few Frenchmen who visited Germany and Austria; he knew what had been going on there since that youthful tour. He had probably met, at Freiburg, Werner the geologist, and he was aware that the great school of anatomists headed by Pallas, Camper, and Blumenbach was probing the structure of this house which we animals find that we inhabit. Anatomy *per se* is only sib to natural history, only, literally, the dry bones of it. But bones determine why a man walks and a bird flies and whence comes the deep roar of the gorilla. And bones and flesh and blood were just what lacked in natural history in those days when periwigs were going out and the heroics of the Empire were coming in.

[164]

Anatomist Against Dreamer

France, all unconsciously, needed a German. In Georges Cuvier there appeared in Paris an Alsatian of Swiss descent, trained at Stuttgart, protégé of the sister of the Duke of Württemberg, fluent in French and German, brought up on Gesner and Buffon, the very man for the day and hour. Twenty-five years younger than the studious chevalier, just the age of the brilliant Geoffroy St. Hilaire, his future foe, he had been tutoring a noble boy at the shore of Normandy. Shores seem to be fateful places for anatomists and thinkers; the shell in the hand challenges the imagination; the radial symmetry of a starfish has a look more perfect than our own bilateral shape, and the very amorphousness of the drift is provocative.

Cuvier had some anatomical training, but he knew nothing more about natural history itself than Gesner and Buffon had to tell him. As a child he had colored the plates in Buffon's books from descriptions in the text. Now in Normandy the strand-world awoke in him an intense interest in life's meaning and glory, design and law. He began to write, quite simply, about what he saw and knew. Without the least pushing or self advertisement, he came to the attention of the Jardin des Plantes, and arrived there one day in 1795 so uncertain that the great savants were really offering him a post that he brought his pupil with him, quite confident that when they had talked with him he would be thrown back on his old job.

For their part, they saw, I suppose, what I see now when I look at the portrait of Cuvier as a young man. He has great warm dark eyes, a dangerously jutting chin, strong lips, a vital shock of carelessly kept hair, and the coat and white stock of a poor young student. He had no idea then that he would one day dominate that group and indeed the whole world of science for a long generation, but if those who welcomed him at the Jardin had looked well enough at the jaw they might have guessed it.

I am not trying to tell the whole story of Cuvier's life, for he was scarcely within the camp of the naturalists. But his views and his personality affected men not only in the scene I now depict, but swayed naturalists in the field who had never seen him, and an adverse word from Cuvier was to injure the reputation of Rafinesque, who, unbalanced though he may have been, gleamed with genius. So I will let his second portrait tell the tale of his years; here he is, covered with his orders, the fine snows upon his head, his face at once more refined and more unyielding. George Bancroft, the American historian, saw Cuvier in 1827; he thought him one of the most magnificent-looking men he ever met, and one of the least agreeable. Audubon, rather used to being the handsomest man in the room, says that Cuvier had tusks which are omitted from the flattering portraits; he found him imperious but disposed to be merciful. A Mrs. Sarah Lee who visited Cuvier at home, chatters that the great man was a beautiful husband and father, and all the world knows that his life was utterly upright, industrious, capable, worthy of authority. He managed to stay in favor with all the changing governments, but he was a favorite of Napoleon, who felt, as we all feel, that here was a man. " *Ce qui caracterise partout M. Cuvier, c'est l'esprit vaste,*" it was said of him, and we need to remember here that *esprit*, so prized by the French, means intellect; his

GEORGES CUVIER AS A COURTIER
(See page 166)

PORTRAIT OF LAMARCK,
when old and blind, in the costume
of a member of the Institute.
Engraved in 1824.
(See page 176)

contemporary does not imply that he had a " generous nature "; he means that Cuvier ruggedly assaulted great subjects.

And this he did in addition to conducting a great school of anatomy and playing the part of inspector general of education, a post which he carried out so thoroughly that he usually reformed a school as soon as he had inspected it. A Protestant, he was put in charge of Protestant affairs by the Catholics when they came back to power with the Bourbons.

These are only high lights in his busy career. Nor is this the place to tell everything that he accomplished as an anatomist, but I can tell you at least of the astonishing way in which the thorough work of a lifetime, exploring animal structure, could somehow obstruct the progress of ideas. It would be too much to say that Cuvier even unintentionally obscured the truth; nothing is literally truer than anatomy correctly reported. It has a fascination for many minds, and even those who do not ordinarily respond to it can hardly resist the impact of a great hall of mammoths and whales, dinosaurs and rheas reduced or restored to ghostly skeletal essence. They are architectural; they are near solutions of fantastic problems in mechanics — the only real solution, of course, residing in the life force which keeps these impossible systems erect or afloat or aloft. Or, leaving the vertebrates, there are other structures, fundamental plans less plausible still, and Cuvier, unlike almost all the anatomists who had preceded him, respected those creatures without bones. A young man came to him crowing with a supposed discovery unique in birds. " Are you an entomologist? " asked Cuvier. " No?

Then go and anatomize an insect, and if you still think you have made a discovery, I shall believe you."

According to Cuvier, there were four great types of animal structure; he pointed to the vertebrates, to the jointed creatures (crustaceans and insects), the mollusc form, and the radiate such as starfish and jellyfish. Essentially, of course, he is right about it, but the unpredictable result of his classification was that he deprived zoölogy of a concept above classification. In those days they called it " scale of being "; we would now say, steps in evolution. It is hard for us to see why you cannot recognize certain types of structure and think like an evolutionist at the same time. But in those days absolute creation was an idiom that you acquired before you were ten years old. Men conceived the animal world in a royalist way; Buffon's lion was still king of the beasts. You could no more suppose that one of Cuvier's great sub-kingdoms gave rise to another than that Italy gave rise to Spain; they seemed to have sharp frontiers, and Cuvier was certain that there were no connecting forms. He saw the invisible lines between his realms, and unconsciously patrolled them. One has to look back into his life to see why he was so militant about it. And now appears the disadvantage attendant upon being a German, for so he considered himself. He seems to have been at one time under the influence of the poet Herder who had mystical views of Nature and sought divine archetypes in form; Herder did not suppose that these actually existed any more than a perfect circle exists.

But I am beginning to think I shall have to take a whole chapter to tell the wonderful and fearful consequences of German Romanticism; it is enough to say now that every one even slightly affected by this viewpoint was well-nigh emotional about it, especially those who considered themselves the most rational.

Springing up at last in irritation, the handsome Geoffroy St. Hilaire flung a direct challenge to Cuvier at a meeting of the Academy of Sciences. Friend to Lamarck, with his own notions of evolution more nearly like those of Erasmus Darwin, he cried that there was but a single plan that ran through all animal structure and knew no frontiers; it has developed from the simple to the complex, it has had offshoots that led nowhere, it is, in its history, at once the most erratic, wandering and chancy performance, and as a concept the most unified, deified and profound fact. The insected body of the lobster, declared the impassioned Parisian, the articulated joints of the vertebrate, are manifestations of the same thing, and science would be recognizing it, were there not one in this room who uses his authority as a teacher to obscure the truth.

Rising slowly to his feet, Cuvier expressed astonishment that a purely philosophical question seemed to have turned into a personal matter. But he would not take it personally. He would reply with the chalk and the blackboard. Adding to these great powers of oratory, he steadily and relentlessly demolished his opponent's wild analogies.

We know how far Cuvier was right, and yet we realize today that St. Hilaire was right even when he was wrong. He was trying to express what we mean today by homologies, that is to say, that the arm of a man and the wing of a bird are the same organ, while the wing of a bird and the wing of a butterfly have no relationship to each other but the analogy of similar function. And beyond this, he was trying to find some door of escape in Cuvier's all too perfect, royalist and static world.

The excited scene in the Academy of Sciences was the climax of a long rebellion against finality. The true thinker knows that when he seems to have come to a goal, he must begin again. What are called biological laws, for instance, are often very useful, but the first thing to inquire about one is, what is the matter with it? What are the exceptions? What temperamental predisposition had its author toward just such conclusions? Take, for instance, Cuvier's famous law of the correlation of parts; it is by means of it that, holding in his hand a thigh bone, the scientist is traditionally able to reconstruct a mammoth for you. Cuvier called the world's attention to the fact that the browsing animals with heavy hooves do not have wolvish teeth, and carnivores with clawed feet have not the dentition for the difficult task of breaking down the cellulose skeleton of vegetable food. In actual fact, of course, the brilliant reconstruction from fragments is possible only where the bones are recognized as closely similar to those of some species about which we know almost everything. Even Cuvier, from the teeth of the fossil bird Archaeopteryx, would never have been able to guess a wing; indeed, he would have forbidden you to imagine such a folly.

Luckily for Cuvier, he did not know too much about fossils and connecting links. He lived in an age when men had just recognized that the stratification of the rocks indicated different zoölogical ages. He knew that the fossils in one stratum were unlike those above and below it. But when Lamarck pointed them out as time's pictures on the rocks proving the story of evolution, Cuvier was ready with another story that was far more convincing to himself and a host of others. Quoth he, these stratifications which begin and end sharply, mind you, are records of great catastrophes, when the existing scheme of things was wiped out and a new page turned over. Writhing with seismic colic, the earth convulsed the mountains and belched the ocean upon the plains. Why else should we find such immense numbers of animals fossilized at a given level? Destruction overwhelmed them, he declared imperatively; the land animals were drowned in an instant; starfish were flung to the tops of the Alps; in Egypt, Chaldea and Palestine there are traditions of a Deluge, but it was only the last of many. This is the great " cataclysmic theory," and it was almost universally held to wipe out the claims of the evolutionists to any aid, comfort and abetment the solid rock might give them. Agassiz was a cataclysmist; practically, you had to be; you could not have been seriously considered for a responsible teaching post without accepting anything so obvious or so pleasingly moral.

I am telling much of the story backwards, because only when we realize the strength and the triumphant course of the opposition to Lamarck can we comprehend in how weak a position he stood from the first. That old die-hard pedagogue in college days gave me the false impression that people first believed Lamarck a while and then, coming to their senses, hailed Charles Darwin. As a matter of fact, nobody, not even his good friends, believed Lamarck. Even St. Hilaire preferred pet theories of his own. I find scoffing references to Lamarck, direct or otherwise, in Alexander Wilson's *American Ornithology*, in Nuttall's charming bird book, in the learned literary remains of Mr. Biglow, James Russell Lowell's correspondent.

So far as they were known at all, the principles of Lamarck made their way fairly rapidly through the scientific world. But it seemed morally repugnant that any creatures should, by themselves, have improved their status, or even adapted themselves to their circumstances. The wise Father of all would have attended to all these matters in the beginning which was the Word. But worse than this was the method by which Lamarck suggested that adaptation had taken place. It is odd that his century so objected to it when it is now the favorite theory of those who know nothing about biology.

Lamarck (if I can compress him into a nutshell, and I'm quite sure I can't) believed that the need that an animal experiences to be adjusted to his environment forces the mechanisms of the body to take on new forms in order to function in a new way. In this way a new animal results. When mammals entered the strange new environment of the sea, they took on, as we can all behold, fish-like forms. Lamarck does not suggest that they consciously willed to do this, but he implies at least a will that is not conscious. He believed that purely mechanistic powers within the organism rose to meet a need because they could do no other. He remembered those ilex oaks by the Mediterranean and how their leaves were reduced in size, thickened and felted to cut down the loss of water in the fierce southern sunlight. He pointed out how in the north most animals are white like the snow, the polar bear, the arctic hare, the snowy owl, the ermine. Just when a harsh tongue is needed to rasp tough food, the animal possesses it; the hooves of the mountain goat are dainty for climbing upon narrow ledges; the foot of the horse is adapted to the steppe. And — most classic example — the giraffe, from long browsing upon leafage overhead, has acquired such a long neck that he can enjoy pasturage denied to all creatures less absurdly fashioned than he.

The classic rebuttal is that the giraffe, being so long of leg and neck, cannot conveniently browse anywhere else than upon the tops of trees; in order to reach the grass he has to spread his legs most inconveniently apart before he can bring his muzzle to the earth. Lamarck was aware of this objection, but it simply struck him as absurd to suppose that without a reason a giraffe could come into being, and then, rather fortuitously, find some environment that would fit its peculiarities. He brought up the case of the ai, that feeble South American sloth that is practically unable even to stagger a few steps without falling down exhausted; in his opinion slothful habits make a sloth. Disuse of an organ through generations, he reasoned, will result in its atrophy, perhaps its disappearance; constant development of some part of the body will result in the exaggeration of that organ, like the blacksmith's arm, until in the course of time such change is stamped upon the race. Remember that Lamarck did not stint time to Nature; he granted her unlimited amounts of it. In his belief living tissue was plastic, just as we know the rocks to be. Give me a brief geological era and with natural forces only I will so change the look of your neighborhood that Tibet will seem nearer to home. Even so with the strange, colloidal protoplasm (these terms were not yet ready for Lamarck) that is identical in the fin of a fish and the fingers of your hand.

Such is the thread of his thought, the famous " inheritance of acquired characteristics." He believed it, he announced it, he supposed that men would find it true. But aside from a small following he met with little more than ridicule. It was remarkable how he bore up under that. He never replied except by adducing more evidence. When offended, it was his way to be more than ever courteous. Walking from his house across the park to the museum, he seemed to be cutting old acquaintances, but the truth was that he did not see them. As a dingy Parisian mist seemed to him to be settling upon the landscape, his inward visions of the epic history of earth engrossed him. Presently he realized that the mist was permanent. Years of peering through the microscope at the structure of the minute had impaired his eyesight. In those days microscopes were no whit improved beyond the products of the seventeenth century; lighting was bad; the sections sliced from the material to be examined were thick, opaque, confused, unlike the incredible parings of the modern microtome. So Lamarck was one of those pioneers who pay the highest price for their discoveries, like the early workers in X-ray.

Even the barren minutes of the Academy and the Museum contain references to this tragic infirmity. In April,

1825, we read, his failing sight no longer permitted him to fulfill his duties as a lecturer, and Latreille was requested to take his place. The following year: " In view of the blindness with which M. de Lamarck is afflicted, M. Bosc will continue to carry on for him." (We shall meet Bosc again — in America — Bosc the excellent successor to Thouin the head gardener.)

Debts — debts had never left Lamarck; there were moments of amelioration, when he sold his great collection of shells to the government. There were hopes that were never fulfilled, when he petitioned that he be given a sum of money to enable him to write a monumental *System of Nature*. There were small stipends, special sums that sometimes came his way after all the bigwigs of the Jardin had had their share of appropriations. But Lamarck was nothing of an executive; he did not have that indispensable determination and authority that obtain appropriations; he missed business meetings, though never scientific ones, nor was he one of those who simply commandeer and keep the best secretaries and assistants. Where Cuvier had the happy faculty of getting his students and associates to work for him, handing him their research to synthesize, collate, and put forward as his own, Lamarck was the type of odd, nervous, gentle gentleman who closes the door so that no one shall see that he is sharpening his own pencil. As he never barked, people supposed that he had no teeth to bite with. He lacked a nose for advantageous turnings to take in this life; he was as reckless of personal interest as he had been of his life on the battlefield. He was so faithful to his duties as a keeper of the educational exhibits and the menageries, that the institution could really not have afforded to part with him for any lighter duties; neither could it afford to raise the honoraria of one whose services became curtailed with the years. Least of all would it recognize that the boldest and the noblest intellect amongst them resided in the long, narrow head with the thinning hairs that was seen sometimes at the third-story window of the old house called " La Croix de Fer." A tall old man standing there to feel the sunlight that he could not see.

His last wife in her grave, and four of his children dead, Lamarck was attended by his daughter Cornélie, who read to him by the hour, from the novels of the day — always the best, it is said — who accompanied him at first upon his walks, and described to him the sky, the clouds, the trees he could no longer see. And later, when the great old man could no more go abroad, she never left his side, so that when at last the end came, in 1829, in the eighty-fifth year of his age, and the poor woman stepped into the fresh air, she was nearly overcome by the change.

The tall thin body was borne from the church of Saint Médard, through the slush and damp of a Paris December. It was the last day of the year but one — a season of graveyard weather in northern France — and in all the world there is nothing so final, so mortal, so purple and black and oppressive as a French funeral. The clangor of the bells seems to lap you in lead. The plumes of mourning on the heads of the horses fantastically checked as if for some tragic circus performance, the inevitable thin priest and fat priest, the arrival at those appalling cemeteries, so ancient, so densely inhabited, the first clash of

December sod on the coffin — how they all proclaim:
Dead and gone! Dead and gone!

But in the vast city of Montparnasse cemetery, Lamarck was not laid away in a permanent plot; there was
no money for such a luxury. His lodging was his for five
years only, after which, there being so many demanding
it for themselves, his bones were destined to be dug up
and carried to the catacombs, that immemorial ossuary of
paupers. Today the site of his resting place is obliterated,
and a half dozen crowded sleepers lie across his long bed.
There is not an inch left for a monument to honor him,
however modest or small.

At his grave spoke Latreille and Geoffroy St. Hilaire.
" Attacked on all sides, injured likewise by odious ridicule, Lamarck, too indignant to answer these cutting
epigrams, submitted to the indignity with a sorrowful
patience," said Geoffroy. " Lamarck lived a long time,
poor, blind, and forsaken, but not by me; I shall ever love
and honor him."

The only recorded words of Cornélie were prophetic.
" Posterity," she told the dead man, " will honor you."

The Jardin found the grey, lonely woman a small position — that of pasting plants to sheets in the herbarium.
This is how it is done: you smear a glass plate with glue,
and then picking up in tweezers the crushed brown corpse
of a member of the Sapodilla family from Nicaragua, you
drop it on the plate, lift it up at once, drop it in the center
of a stiff white sheet, paste on a label in the lower right-
hand corner, and add the whole to an ever-growing pile,
pressed down by an enormous iron plate which you must
lift each time. Then you give the glass plate a fresh lick

with the glue brush and begin on another plant. There are people — women, mostly — doing this today, six days a week, fifty-two weeks in the year, an unpromised number of years in a grey lifetime.

We search the records of the Academy of Sciences in vain for an obituary notice of Lamarck. For two years there is nothing but silence. Then, in 1832, Baron Silvestre arose and read Cuvier's "eulogy." It will be remembered that Cuvier had belittled Réaumur, in order, perhaps, to add stature to Buffon. Now, at last, the pent-up scorn and dislike which Cuvier must all these years have felt for his elder brother scientist appeared, concealed only by the half-mask of satiric courtesy. With a circuitous grace, Cuvier approached his silent victim. There are a few men, he remarked, who have brought to light nothing but sure and certain truths, never advancing anything dubious; their writings will enlighten the world as long as natural laws persist. Whereas, there are others who have " laboriously constructed vast edifices upon wholly imaginary bases, resembling those enchanted palaces of our old romances, that one may cause to vanish in thin air by shattering the talisman upon which their very existence depends. . . .

" It follows that once these principles are admitted, only time and circumstances are needed for the monad or the polyp to finish by transforming itself, gradually and indifferently, into a frog, a swan or an elephant. . . . A system resting upon such bases may entertain the imagination of a poet, but it cannot for a moment support the examination of any one who has dissected a hand, a vital organ, or a mere feather."

Anatomist Against Dreamer

The Academy of Sciences showed at least some spirit when this false eulogy was pronounced, by refusing to allow it to be printed as read. But Cuvier still dominated the field, just as Buffon, outliving Réaumur, was able every day to bury his rival a little deeper. Indeed the parallel between Buffon and Cuvier is striking. Both held practically laureate positions, had influence in high circles, never voluntarily retreated or revised, were given to making only *official* utterances, brooked no rivalry, and, like the men of the world that they were, masked their envy under urbane manners and cultivated a reputation for kindliness. They were kindly to those they considered beneath them. I would not for a moment say that Buffon was the scientist that Cuvier was, but Cuvier, at least, was reverent of Buffon. He felt himself bound, perhaps, to carry on the obliteration of Réaumur's reputation. For his own part, he seems to have been one of those persons who do not feel quite secure about themselves unless just once, at least, they crush some other career. Or like a dictator, they are never content about the opposition until it is shot down, thrown in a trench, and all its estates confiscated.

For Lamarck had dared to oppose the cataclysmic hypothesis. " A universal *bouleversement*," Lamarck had written, " a catastrophe which necessarily regulates nothing, mixes up and disperses everything, is a very convenient way to solve the problem for those naturalists who wish to explain everything and do not take the trouble to observe and investigate the course followed by Nature." Cuvier could not forgive this; he had been struck in his weak spot when Lamarck charged that he knew more about anatomy than functioning, living Nature, and it is a serious thing to strike a man in his faults. All his life long Cuvier carried on the well-bred, the silent war — never mentioning Lamarck, treating his ideas as if they had been uttered in a madhouse, burying him deep, deep, in oblivion and pity. Had you asked Cuvier if he remembered Lamarck, the answer would have been no tirade, no sneer. Certainly he would have recalled Lamarck for you — a lovely fellow — beautiful character — touching blindness — got off on the wrong foot with his ideas and never got straight again — a pity. It is the method we all use: praise, a certain false heartiness, one lasting, acid drop of compassion, a showy absence of personal animosity — that is to say, we have hastily thrust the animosity behind the bureau.

So the years went by and went by. Cornélie died. Every one who could remember Lamarck died off, and still posterity did not come to honor him. Darwin wrote: " Heaven forfend me from Lamarck's nonsense of a ' tendency to progression,' ' adaptation from the slow willing of animals,' etc. But the conclusions I am led to are not widely different from his; though the means of change are wholly so."

August Weismann, with his " continuity of the germ plasm," was supposed to have proved once and forever that, no matter what happens to the body, the germ cells, the messengers of heredity, remain untouched. They transmit immutable commands to their progeny. Weismann cut off rats' tails for generations and mated these poor creatures together without ever discovering a tailless offspring. He might have saved himself the trouble;

every one already knew that no Jews are born circumcised and no Chinese at birth have " lily feet." Mutilations are not inherited. Neither, perhaps, are the effects of disuse; some blind cave salamanders develop eyes when brought out and raised under red light, and pigmentation returns to colorless cave dwellers of many sorts. It is doubtful, too, if development of one organ through use is inheritable, even after generations.

So there would seem to be nothing left to Lamarckism except the possible effect of a vague general environment — climate, sunlight, temperature, rainfall — in short, wind and weather and soil. These might have some effect upon the organism, but Darwin hardly believed it, and Weismann had ruled it out forever — so they taught in my young student years.

But if the germ plasm hands down to posterity indelible written commands that the son shall be like the father, how does any variation, Darwinian or other, ever take place? It is possible that Weismann's theory proves entirely too much, and some like the late Professor Bateson who have accepted it, and the fact of evolution, have arrived in all honesty at the sterile solipsism that they see no method by which any variations ever could have arisen. If Lamarck is out, so is Darwin.

But Lamarck was not so dead as he was thought to be. Here and there voices were raised, tentatively, in his defense. Huxley and Haeckel, iron-clad Darwinians, honored Lamarck's speculation, at least his pioneering. Herbert Spencer championed Lamarck against Weismann. If acquired characters are not inherited, he asks, how has any human progress been possible? How has instinct arisen if not by transmission of a pattern of behavior which must certainly, once, have been a new thing in the experience of the race?

And in France, where Darwinism, being English, has never been too warmly received, there has been a tendency to go back, rather, to a native son and one who antedated that Englishman, and take up with his *transformisme*. Giard in France, Haeckel and Pauly in Germany, and in America the paleontologist Cope and the entomologist Packard have all been neo-Lamarckians.

And, in truth, if unconsciously, Darwin himself was a Lamarckian. He implies or constantly relies upon the influence of the environment in producing changes in creatures, changes on which his natural selection works its will. He assumes the inheritance of these changes, and could not do without such an assumption. And, at the last, even Weismann (who had started out a Lamarckian) came back to the inheritance of acquired characters — though this fact is carefully suppressed in Darwinian books. If an organ is not used, he says, the gene or determinant within the sex-cell for that particular organ will itself wither away; thus, Weismann thinks, has the whale lost its rear legs.

However, the fact that even Darwin and Weismann could not get along in the end without a Lamarckian concept is not enough to prove that Lamarck's hypotheses are correct, and that evolution actually takes place in the way Lamarck supposes. We may, philosophically, need Lamarck's theory; we may for the present be obliged to think as if it were true. But this will not make it true. The support for Lamarck, however, appears to be com-

ing from a most unexpected and most convincing quarter. Take, for instance, the new case of smoke-blackened
moths of certain industrial cities where powerful chemicals in the air make dark deposits in the pigments of the
wings. When these moths are removed to the country air,
their descendants continue to produce melanistic or dark
offspring. So, after all, purely external factors, the environment, the very air we breathe, can reach fateful
fingers into the germ plasm, change the orders in them,
affect heredity, produce new races.

Or there are the now famous experiments of Prof.
Muller of Austin, Texas, who turned loose upon the
chromosomes of the long-suffering fruit fly the incal-
culable power of the X-ray, and produced such a host of
new variations, inheritable in good Mendelian fashion,
as the world had never witnessed before. The possibility
looms that cosmic rays, falling on the earth from immemorial time, have all along been shaping the course
of evolution. As they penetrate to the hidden sex-cells,
they may be writing there what is, literally, written in
the stars. The possibility that factors more earthly, air and
soil and water, are able in their way also to mould life,
returns for a more respectful consideration than it has
had for a long time.

I have told this story — the strange epic of the fall
and rise of Jean Baptiste Pierre Antoine de Monet de
Lamarck — from the vantage point of modernity, for
indeed there is no other just way of relating it. When he
died the tale had scarcely opened; we are only witnessing
today the beginning of what may be his ultimate triumph.
In the end this man about whom no one troubled to re-

cord one-tenth as many details as are public about the chef at the Waldorf-Astoria, will be known as the true founder of modern evolution, the first to proclaim evolution in words that had no ambiguity in them. He enunciated a truth comparable with Galileo's and he went almost as far towards proving it. As a theory — considered philosophically — it is far more effective for explaining the origins of evolution than natural selection. And the actual proof of " Lamarck's nonsense " is at hand. It is no reproach to Lamarck that the proofs that he summoned to his own aid were flimsy or quite erroneous; that was due to the science of his age. The support arrives from a quarter he could never have suspected, yet this does not indicate that he made but a lucky guess. His apperceptions were intuitive.

Intuition is not a quality which every one can understand. As the unimaginative are miserable about a work of fiction until they discover what flesh-and-blood individual served as a model for a Becky Sharp, or a Heathcliffe, so even many scientists scout scientific intuition. They cannot believe that a blind man could see anything they cannot see. They rely utterly on the celebrated inductive method of reasoning: the facts are to be exposed, and we are to conclude from them only what we must. This is a very sound rule — for mentalities that can do no better, and you and I will be well advised never to depart from it. But it is not certain that the really great steps are made in this plodding fashion, and mere facts are stale cake to put under your pillow to dream on. Dreams are made on quite other stuff, and if there are still any left in the world who do not know that dreams have remade the world, then there is little, at this late date, that we can teach them.

You will have heard how Einstein, working in a patent office, suddenly perceived that energy equals mass multiplied by the square of the velocity of light, quite without any knowledge of how he knew it. First he dreamed it; then he knew it; then, rather for others' sake, he proved it. This, I take it, is a blow to Francis Bacon. But is it not time that some one presented again the case for the opposition? For Hamlet against the maxims of Polonius?

It would be a blow, too, for Cuvier if he could see where Lamarck stands today. Cuvier, who knew a thousand facts, was the author of the worst theory of the history of life that was ever suggested by a great scientist. The true explanation — or the most nearly true — began with Lamarck as an intuition, became a conviction, and, unsupported by proofs such as we could give today, went down in apparent defeat. No one fails so completely as a genius.

9

WILDERNESS PLANTSMEN:
BARTRAM AND MICHAUX

Now let me sing a new song. Now forget the smallest of the continents, the most long-loved, the most richly inhabited, and let me go far away and far back into time. There will be no Padua, no Göttingen, no Upsala, no museums, no academies. And no systems and no theories.

But there will be a land slowly buckling, rising, portentous and naked, a whale-back out of the sea, shouldering the brine away, and for the first time taking on its face of rock the rain from heaven. Many times the great whale continent rolls and turns, but the backbone ridge, the Appalachians, never again goes under. There are no sea-made fossils in those hills, and life, microscopic and protean, has never ceased its breathing there, its growth, decay, renewal. After millions of years, a warm shallow bay is emptied by a gentle uptilting of the land, and where the waters rushed out, leaving their vast lime silt, a stream began to run, watering deepest fertility, gathering other streams to itself, gathering like a great chief mighty sons to its council. Mississippi, the river, brown serpent, carrying water to the sea, winning it back again at the source, serpent with its tail in its mouth, closed cycle, life-giver.

And westward, the young steppe, great New World meadow, sunset prairie that flowers not in spring but in autumn, a land without echoes. By insensible gradations it rolls up, a thousand feet, two thousand, four thousand, six thousand, still a plain, climbing the sky till it meets the first broken arid buttes thrown out by giants when the rock was raw. Then in the sharp air the red and yellow features, lined with blue shadows, of the Indian-faced Rockies. Here are no flowering trees, no Appalachian mist or wistfulness, no perfume and no mossy age. This is youth, this is maleness, with the lodgepole pines, the incense cedars, Gothic spruces, lakes lifted quietly near the sky, and canyons where a silver thread is a thundering river. Then a burning desert, and abruptly out of it peaks capped and carved with the purity of ice, Sierra Nevada. Alpine meadows spilling out mariposa lilies, and marching out of Time the mighty columns of the redwoods. And rolling up to meet this land, another ocean, a greater, tumbling the giant red sea-kelp lazily in tempered waters.

This is the continent I sing, not ours by a million years, not named, one of the six great blocks of the world, the most intemperate, with a heartwood the hardest. For ages without number it stood grandly, indifferently empty of men. While Asia was filling with humans and human debris, it was still empty of them, the sun shining only on grass in the valley, the night finding beasts in the forest. It was full already with roots in the soil, and armies of birds sweeping northward, going southward; it was already perfection; nothing in it knew a lack.

Then, where the most northerly islands lie like stepping-stones on the blue sea map, came a leak out of Asia, of the little, erect, intentional species called men. The continent absorbed them; they were few in it; they were of it, a people erasing even their campfires.

But the continent lay athwart the roads of destiny. Not more so than its neighbor, South America, but the southern continent, mostly tropic, rich in precious metals, had first to play a long rôle, both vassal to European civilization and climatically repugnant to it. North America seems fated to upset the balance of power in Europe. A new temperate world rich, young, intractable, surpassing, it throws all comfortable European nations out of joint. From the first, when Renaissance appetite was ready for Indian spice and found instead upon its palate the strange fresh flavor out of North America, there was disappointment, a failure to appreciate the taste. The first animals and the plants that the colonists sent back to England found but a rare interest in the learned world. The great gardeners of earls and princes, the amateur fanciers of gorgeous fowl, were inclined to reject the fauna and the flora of the New World with some contempt in favor of birds of paradise and camellias out of the East.

But there were some noble exceptions. The Duchess of Beaufort was graciously pleased to grow scores and hundreds of American trees and shrubs in her gardens at Badminton, and there was a rich English patronage of the early collectors Josselyn and John Bannister. Linnaeus did not lack for learned American correspondents, John Clayton in Virginia, Dr. Alexander Garden in South Carolina, Cadwallader Colden in New York.

Wilderness Plantsmen

And Lord Petre entertained a most unusual passion for all that came out of His Majesty's turbulent American Colonies. Wealthy, generous, urbane, curious and whimsical, he was minded to pay well if some fellow could be found over there who would purvey to his curio cabinet, menagerie and garden. He had a friend, Peter Collinson, a Quaker who stood high at court and was in touch with co-religionists in Philadelphia. Did Collinson know of no one to collect for him? Good Peter did; he could recommend Friend John Bartram. And forthwith he entered into correspondence with the man whom Linnaeus was to call " the greatest *natural* botanist in the world." It seems an ambiguous phrase, but as one gets to know Friend John, it is the aptest expression conceivable.

The first preserved letter from Collinson is dated January 20, 1734, and found John Bartram when he was thirty-five years old. The story goes that Bartram had been an honest ploughman who sat down under a tree to rest one spring day, and idly plucked apart a daisy; very slowly he began to think about the object he was destroying. He could scarcely read and write; used all his days to heavy labor, his thoughts came not nimbly and logically but upon a wave of emotion which he called inspiration. Presently he threw the plant aside and went back to plough; when he got home he told his wife what he had been thinking. But Mary shook her head. It was true, she knew, that somewhere learned people made out of these little miracles of God strange and wise truths. But they were not for John; he was not rich enough to spend his time in such pursuits; he should stick to his farm which, being but newly hewn out of the wilderness, could not be kept clear unless he gave it all his care.

One begins to see why John was a " natural botanist." He was also the first native-born naturalist in the New World. There had been great fellows here, Father Labat and Plumier in the West Indies, Hernandez, and Moçiño and Sessé in Mexico, Mark Catesby in Carolina and Florida, John Josselyn in New England — they came and they reported home. Generally they also went home, finding these high void skies not their own. It had been an experience; they had done something for science. But nothing essentially for America. John Bartram's science was unlearned, instinctive, applied. Like a good American, he wanted to make it hitch on to something, to make it work; he was both an American and a Quaker in wishing it to pay. He had little grasp of theory, no capacity with foreign languages, no end of good humor and obligingness. In every way he was a " natural botanist," and not a bad natural ornithologist either.

Bartram was typical thus of all the early New World science, preoccupied with doing, exploration, feat, what in the days of chivalry they called " *gestes*." If Linnaean science was in the position of Adam naming the beasts, the first American natural history was pre-Adamite. When I give you now John Bartram I do not imagine for a moment that he was a naturalist of the first magnitude. But he was a great old fellow, and to men like Linnaeus and Gronovius who were great in the bookish sense, he supplied, in effect, what it was so very wise of them to know. With him Nature was a personal affair, a direct impact like weather on a bird.

Wilderness Plantsmen

For four days after the incident of the daisy, plough-man John wrestled with his temptation. Presently he succumbed, saddled a horse, and rode a few miles into the great and to him iniquitous city of Philadelphia. Not knowing what to ask for of the bookseller, he simply told him about the daisy; the pedantic old bibliophile sold him a botanical treatise in Latin, and thereby compelled John to buy a Latin grammar as well. With these extravagances in his saddle bags, he jogged back to Mary, abashed and elated.

This is the legend as it is supposed to have come from Bartram himself, but his son denied it, and relates a more dignified story of how his father's interest in medicine led him to take up the study of plants. The excellent James Logan presented John with a copy of Parkinson's herbal, and with it he began to botanize all over the farm. It does not sound to me like a promising book for the purpose, concerned as it is with the gentle productions of Flora in the English countryside, but there was nothing else to go upon but the Latin treatise which was probably even more exotic.

In the year when Logan gave him the herbal, God bestowed upon him a new spouse, Mary having died. Ann Mendenhall appears to have been an excellent help-mate who was simple in the days of John's simplicity but graced and perfectly understood his latter life when Friend Franklin and Friend Washington came visiting him in his rôle of philosopher and naturalist; perhaps, even, she assisted him with his letters to the amateur entomologist Queen Louisa of Sweden and her brother Frederick the Great.

Prophetically, John got ready for success long before those golden days. He bought at a sheriff's sale an excellent farm on the Schuylkill, and there with his own hands built him a house of stone; into the walls he set a stone inscribed in faulty Greek and with the names John — Ann : Bartram : 1731. Here it was that in 1735 Collinson's letter was followed by the first reward, a suit of clothes from London. (What worldly vanities, Ann! And how they become thee, John!)

John's patron, the " noble lord " over in England, was interested in fossils, as they were evidence of the Deluge, in the " poison-stick," that upas of America, the lady's slipper, the may-apple, good physic withal. Presently we hear from Collinson that the skunkweed John has sent to England " hath put forth two noble blossoms, very beautiful." He writes to thank Bartram for the *Magnolia glauca*, and we begin to realize which were the flowers that struck the English as strangest and fairest, lizard's tail of the pepper family, purple blazing-star, ground cypress, and the sensitive pea.

With the sum of twenty guineas John started off on a collecting trip in the south. Collinson earnestly recommended him not to go in his old clothes; those Byrds and Custises of Virginia to whom he bore letters of recommendation were a snobbish lot. Lady Petre asks especially for hummingbird's nests with eggs; her liege wants to see the famed pawpaw, and cannot Bartram's children capture a redbird alive?

The trophies of that first foray down the Atlantic seaboard were the sassafras and spice bush, the tulip tree and swamp rose-bay, the exquisite pensile nest of the Baltimore oriole, the great papery grey arsenal of the white-faced wasp. Fresh out of a fresh land they reached an English drawing-room, and back to John went reams of writing paper, Tournefort's books, funds and orders without stint. Honest John found himself in correspondence with the Duke of Norfolk, Sir Hans Sloane, Phillip Miller and Mark Catesby. Then came a letter from Collinson: " *All our schemes are broke.* Lord Petre died this twelfth of July, 1742, of the small pox."

But really Friend Collinson carried on admirably. He kept all his great English friends interested in Bartram, and lacking one perfect patron for him, found him many substitutes. But these great folk — he means the Dukes of Argyll, Richmond and Bedford, the Duchess of Portland who was an amateur of shells, and the proud Seymours, Smithsons and Hamiltons — are wondrous slow about paying, and not agreeable about being reminded. However, Dr. Dillenius " is delighted with thy last seeds, they are so good; says that thou art the only man that ever did things to a purpose." " The curiosities for Dr. Gronovius are gone for Holland. I have sent both to him and Linnaeus, not to forget the pains and travel of indefatigable John Bartram, — but stick a feather in his cap." " I have sent to Linnaeus a specimen of one leaf of the sensitive vine. Only to him would I spare such a jewel." " I have a sprig (in flower) of the Kalmia in water, and it stares me in the face all the time I am writing; saying or seeming to say, ' As you are so fond of me, tell my friend John Bartram, who sent me, to send more to keep me company.' "

There are today journals and organs and forums and

media of exchange that with technical efficiency take care of the traffic in scientific knowledge, the commerce of specimens when they are still necessary, the subtle perfections of modern horticulture, and every week in the year some learned publication carries new notes on the nesting of the osprey or what have you. And the whole business of natural history is carried on in an impersonal and I think on the whole uninteresting way. I mention it only because it is possible that others will smile as I did when first I read the Collinson-Bartram correspondence. But with time I came to see that this was the vehicle in which science made its progress. There are great theories, there are great synthetical minds to give meaning to museums of facts, but I said in the beginning that I knew how far the little men have built up the great, and I sometimes think now that I have rather more affection for the little men. We are less afflicted by awe in their presence; we are permitted to love them, as men have come to love Gilbert White, who was not by any means a great naturalist or indeed so captivating a personality as John Bartram. I have not space to tell of more than a few of these men who do so much of the actual labor of science, that labor that is the source of intellectual wealth at the capitals. They have lifted the plant from the ground while it is still wet with the spring rain; they climbed the tall dead pine for the unknown nest.

There was every reason to appreciate the labors of Bartram. He had no training, but a marvelous fresh eye, a knack of finding what he was asked for, and a sense of the unusual. Of all Linnaeus's correspondents he furnished the most original material and the most abundant. He traveled from Lake Ontario to Florida, and visited the fashionable Dr. Garden (for whom gardenia is so appropriately named) in Charleston; the polished doctor was much amused and at nothing so much as at John's new title, Botanist to the King. Again John would be under Cadwallader Colden's roof, learning the Linnaean system from the sweet lips of Jane. He generally made his expeditions in autumn, as this was the best time to take up trees and collect seeds, and so it happened that, wandering through Georgia's woods, he came upon a tree most astonishingly in flower. They were very gorgeous flowers, like to the camellia or the blossom of the tea plant. This vegetable, singular enough since it is autumnal and a member of so tropic and oriental a family, was the great prize of Bartram's career, and he brought it back to his garden in triumph. It has been called Franklinia, in honor of Friend Benjamin, the same who presented John with one of his new-fangled stoves, but the mystery of this species is that it has never been seen again in the wild. Many times scientists have combed the banks of the Alatamaha, and there have been cries of " Eureka! Eureka! " But all were false, and if anywhere in the woods, when autumn comes, those blossoms open on the air, no one knows where it is. Only in a few gardens grow cuttings from Bartram's original tree.

There was one spot that Bartram loved best of all, a flower-filled rift between the mountain ranges, two hundred miles long; he called it " my valley," and " my great vale," and " my Kashmir," and where it was he told no man. But out of it he brought his chief treasures,

that American cyclamen the shooting star, our cis-
atlantic herb-of-Paris the trillium, the dainty, enchanting fringe tree, the silver-bell tree and the calycanthus
whose dark red blossoms have the fragrance of sun-
parched strawberries. Then the vale was uninhabited
Elysium, creation in its innocence, and no one but John
abroad in it. Today we know it for the Shenandoah.

It was a great day when, in 1763, Collinson could
write that the young Lord Petre sent herewith his order
for a ten-guinea box of plants. Honors came flowing to
Bartram, a silver cup from Sir Hans Sloane, founder of
the British Museum, and a gold medal from a " society
of gentlemen in Edinburgh." And Bartram earned them
up to the last, astounding his friends with fantastic insectivorous plants of the south, with the American lotus,
like the sacred flower of Buddhism but yellow instead of
rosy, and with our showy lady's-slipper, the most beautiful orchid of the temperate zone, that is poisonous to the
touch. There were mishaps in his shipments, of course;
on several occasions the rats ate the cargo, and the French
privateers were on the sea. While " our Philadelphia
people seem at ease and dissolved in luxury," so that John
thought that two twenty-gun ships could take the town
with ease, his shipments were falling into the hands of
the foe. John proposed to send his consignments addressed
to Buffon or Jussieu, so that if the French must have
them, they would at least go to the right people. Collinson's garden was twice robbed of his friend's treasures,
and not seldom the two old gentlemen were at outs with
each other. Collinson had to explain that when King
George III, in a moment of good humor, granted a sti-

pend, there was no certainty that he would be prompt about paying it. Kings are apt to be the biggest debtors, and the least accessible to a dun. " Thou vexes thyself and me with perpetual complaints, thinking it is in my power to redress them, but really it lays at thy own door, in being so hasty for the expedition. Thou shouldst have stayed and got two or three hundred pounds beforehand, and then set out, but as I told thee before, if the King lives and thou lives, thou wilt be no loser, so pray do not tire me with repetition of complaints, but return home as soon as thou can and set down and gather strength, and receive thy income." John for his part thought of his stipend as something very like interest due him, nor could he understand why the King never wrote him about all the fine things he sent him. But it is a very long way from any throne to the Shenandoah.

They say that the shock of fear that Bartram felt at the approach of the British army, a fear for his darling garden, not for his aged body, caused the death of this master plantsman. Ann survived her husband for six years, mother of seven children which included a set of twins, Elizabeth and the famous William who carried on his father's tradition. William was a " natural " botanist in quite another way; he was generally regarded as more than a bit daft. Many people consider William, however, as the greater. He was the first, perhaps, to catch the unique feeling of American scenery, and in much the same way that the world traveler Humboldt had an eye for the scene — that is to say, knowing well of what a view is composed, what geological formations, what species of trees, what associations of grass, he read significance into types of landscape. He was also an excellent ornithologist, perhaps the best upon these shores, between the times of Mark Catesby and Alexander Wilson. Of all the plantsmen, botanists and mountaineers who have penetrated the southern and highest end of the Appalachians, Bartram was the first, and he bore out of it as many treasures as ever his father from the Shenandoah. It would sound like a nursery catalogue if I were to recite them, but any one who ever saw flame azalea of the Blue Ridge can guess what the plant lover would feel who found it for the first time, afire in a green pocket of those ancient hills.

The Bartram house, the Bartram garden, have had many periods of neglect alternating with loving care. At the present time as part of Fairmount Park in Philadelphia they are officially cared for but perhaps all too little loved. Every one in Philadelphia knows something about the Bartrams and is proud of them, but feels an inevitable decay creeping over the place no longer lived in, no longer alive. There are still a few trees standing planted by the hand of John, but no matter who adds another now, it will not be the same thing. It is charming to see Ann's pretty china closet, but no one drinks tea out of her cups any more.

So we leave them, these loveable Bartrams, only too conscious how dead they are, how little like our age. But this is no reproach to them; they were in their day a green growing tip of science. And to my taste there is just one moment in the past when I would as gladly have lived as in the present. In the era of our aristocratic, elegant Georgian civilization, in the days when European science was just available but not too easily come at, and in that forever irretrievable moment when wilderness began at the Blue Ridge, the American naturalist was luckier than he is today. Now he has everything he could wish for, except the virginity of his love. No one man can call the Shenandoah his own. And there is left no longer any beyond. You could think once how beyond the Blue Ridge rose the Great Smokies, and beyond them in turn green Tennessee, unknown Kentucky, unbroken forests of beech trees larger than Saxony, Navarre, Galicia. To the civilization at the mouth of the Mississippi, there floated down logs of sycamore and gum and cypress that told of an unexplored world of giants to the north. There were true tales of caverns where the fish and beetles had no eyes for eternal darkness, pine-ringed lakes where the swans were drifted like the snow, and one great meadow like the empire of the Czar where a wild cattle snuffed the flowers and stamped until the earth shook.

There can be no exaggerating the importance of the wilderness in the natural science of early America. It haunted the mind, it magnetized every one who came near enough to smell it on the western wind. It was the whole of the story. And the very nature of the wilderness — its thoughtless random abundance, the toilsomeness of all progress through it, the thirst to go on and look over a rim — this stamped the men who came to it. Science in the wilderness is never precise; you simply cannot see those first naturalists taking the temperature of bog water at different levels when an unknown whistle teased them from the swamp. Theirs not the patient tame exactitude of modern science, nor the philosophy of their contemporaries like Lamarck or Haller. If you are of the temperament interested but little in details of Nature and respectful only of the highly cerebral scientists, you may think it a pity that the grand masters of science were so homekeeping. If, you may exclaim, instead of these simple fellows like the Bartrams, over-awed by some animus dwelling at the back of the forest, we had but had an encyclopedic philosopher to confront all this ravishing green disorder, this Babel of bird song! Yet can you imagine Buffon by the Alatamaha? The distinguished describer of man's friend the horse looking the confident white-mouthed water moccasin in the eye? If he had lived through it all, he could only have emerged one of those rather taciturn, personally careless, realistic believers in the marvelous because they have seen so much of it.

So you are asking too much if you want the early naturalists to be " great men " in the marble-bust sense of the words. And I have not lost all sense of proportion when I give them this chapter and some of its successors. For I am speaking now of the greatness of Nature, and the littleness of man appears thereby. It would be the same if I were to tell the story of pioneering in natural history in Australia, in South Africa, in the new-won Asiatic dominions of the Czar, or in the Peruvian Andes. There are heroic sagas of these continents and of the days that correspond to our era of Daniel Boone and Thomas Nuttall; they have their own individual flavor, racial and environmental; they make more highly colored reading than our own adventure. But they are not our own, and I have no authority to tell of them. My song is of our kind in our country.

Wilderness Plantsmen

On all the horizon of the early American scene there is only one naturalist who appeals to me as highly as John Bartram, and that is André Michaux.

When I might write about such a worthy as Thomas Nuttall, the ornithologist and botanist, or such a journeyman naturalist on our shores as Frederic Pursh, or that great old tree lover, the Pennsylvania pastor, Gotthilf von Mühlenberg, I dare to select André Michaux upon the grounds of a personal affection. He loved flowers as Audubon loved the birds; he too came from the strict graces of France to woo the American wilderness, and his high and selfless adventuring led him at last to a grave in far-off Madagascar.

Michaux has never yet had a biographer, and it is probable that he never will. Like Lamarck, he was known to many people who might, if they had thought of it, have left rich reminiscences. He turns up in George Washington's diary, in an occasional reference amongst the memoirs of the Académie des Sciences; a statue was once voted to him at the Jardins des Plantes, but never set up; nor is there left to us a single tracing of the furrows or the smile wrinkles that may have been his.

The one presentment left to us of the man is the text of his journal. It is full of abbreviations; it is no more than jottings, shorthand accounts of the day's adventure in living. It is full of reminders to himself to do this or that little thing. It is abrupt, terse, often tense, and bald of details save analytical notes on the parts of some new flower, by which he hopes, back in civilization, to identify it. But through such a narrow-necked bottle we must drink at the personality behind it.

Green Laurels

The original manuscript is no more than a small pocket diary, dog-eared with travel, stained, they say, with salt-water and bear's grease; stained too like most explorer's logs with loneliness and weariness. It was written on his knee, by the flickering of his camp-fires. It is fragmentary — full half of it lost by shipwreck — and it ends abruptly, as your journal would do if, unconscious that life will not thus go on forever, warm-blooded, full of the impact of living, you were suddenly to die. But, as it happens, this scrap of Michaux's memoirs concerns his American years. It breathes the air of the same Nature that all breathe who live on the Atlantic seaboard, between Labrador and Florida, but it reports an age lost to us, the age of the black bear and the elk, the cougar and the ivory-billed woodpecker. An age when the North American trees seemed to belong to a different race than those of today — so tall they grew, in such prodigal abundance they produced their nuts and seeds, their sugar and their turpentine. The beech tree, shy of fruit today, furnished with food the incredible hordes of the passenger pigeons; the loblolly pines, anemic in our times, oozed then with centuries of untapped pitch, that in the days of the *Constitution* gave the richest naval stores in the world.

André Michaux was born a farmer in 1747, in a little village near Versailles. At fourteen his schooling stopped; at twenty-three he had married Cécile Claye, the daughter of a rich peasant. He came of, and had settled into, the class of Frenchman who travels least, and is content with farm and family all life long. Only a great unhappiness could have roused him out of this happy rut. And it befell him, when Cécile died, after less than a year of married life, in giving birth to little François André. As the child wailed, without a mother to take it up, the young peasant could not look forward and behold the years when this boy would solace his lonely travels, nor was he ever to know how François, after his own death, would carry on his life's work.

Without his mate, Michaux found the big, productive farm only meaninglessly fertile, and a great restlessness began to stir him. A neighbor, they say, interested him in horticulture, and presently, and very surprisingly, this rich young farmer of Satory turned from his ample fields. He declined, moreover, to increase his solid substance with further bargains in farmland, preferring to finance with it a private dream. He was able to see beyond barley and cabbages. He wanted to go and gather the useful and the beautiful and curious plants of this earth. He was not interested in collecting specimens for herbaria, save as they would constitute an identifiable record. His plants were to return living to France, and he saw his work as the service of the King and the state.

There are undoubtedly a few people who are born plantsmen or botanists, and it is an odd gift. They seem from the first to be intuitional, and their imaginations are lush with green underwoods, jungles and meadows. As the mathematical are apperceptive of truth before they have proved it, as the musical in a silent room compose pages of polyphony and remember it, so a man like Michaux, simple though the circumstances of his birth, has plant magic in his finger tips, that can make anything grow. And his mind grasps in advance what he has not yet seen; if he has no present opportunity to explore and touch and smell, his fancy clothes the mountains and makes the valleys blossom. The look and smell of fresh-sawn timber, the feel of a leaf between the fingers, harsh with hairs or glabrous, lacquered and evergreen, its individual pungence when thoughtfully crushed, these things are characteristic as the sensible properties of the elements to a chemist.

As for flowers — they are his business in life. They are not business as in the florist trade where, they tell me, one becomes as indifferent to the merchandise as if it were haddocks and flounders; they are realities, fundamental systems, faces, familiars, families, beauties, it is not too much to say, very much like women. Yet the plantsman and botanist does not speak an esthetic language. He veers away from the artist's use of flowers as a color blur; for him the esthetics of flowers lie in clarity, precision, a certain numerology, great purposiveness. And he carries his odd, green-blooded passion right on to the pod and the seed.

There is no fascination in the world like that of seeds; rattling in the pod they are like tiny jungle drums, scattered from the hand they are the hard sperms of an irrevocable creation. They have all forms; from the orchid pod they fall fine as pollen dust; from the coconut palm they drop like cannon balls. They have all ways and means of encompassing futurity; they float around the world upon the cat-tail down; the coconut will drift for months in sea water, populating the isles; the seed of the lotus, dried in the lakes of Gobi two thousand years ago, may be viable today.

Wilderness Plantsmen

I cannot tell you how Michaux conceived his odd predilection; I only know that he was trained at the Trianon gardens under Bernard de Jussieu, and that presently we find him in the company of the great, herborizing on the volcanic moors of the Auvergne with Thouin and Lamarck.

When at the age of thirty-six he set off for the East, he entered upon a period of his life about which little is known, and that little hard to believe in. I mean that it is hard to realize that a man who was born in a France I know and explored my own America was ever robbed and turned naked into the desert by Arab brigands, or like the young prince in a fairy tale cured the Shah of Persia of a wasting malady that had baffled his learned physicians. When I consider that this fellow rode across Georgia's red clay and talked with the drawling farmers of our south, it is nearly incredible that he was once fluent in Persian and paced the strand of the Caspian.

Back in Paris again, he was making plans to visit Samarkand and Karakorum, when royal whim decreed that he must go to America and collect useful trees and such shrubbery and game birds as might enhance a court which already had the most preposterous trifles brought to its gates. The forest of Rambouillet was to be the acclimatization plot, and Michaux had but to fill it.

On October first, 1785, Michaux arrived in New York with the boy François, then fifteen years old, and the excellent Paul Saulnier, a simple fellow but a splendid gardener. Michaux bought a tract of land over on the Jersey shore for his exportation gardens, and plunged into active work. But these years are the very ones whose record was lost by shipwreck.

In 1787, Michaux went south for the first time, and he was so enchanted by the climate and situation of Charleston that he purchased a tract of land at what is now Ten Mile Station. It was from this port of embarkation that his green emigrants voyaged to France. In exchange he gave to this new land the camellia and the tea plant, the tallow-tree and, from the lands that he had visited in the East, that soft and fernlike tree, *Albizzia*, that in the south is called mimosa.

Michaux was never happier than in the Carolinas, which spell a poem, whether you read them east to west, or west to east, from the balsams of the mountains to the strange white atamasco lilies of the coastal savannahs. Into the pattern of lowland life, blended of the aristocratic and the tropic, Michaux with high adaptability merged and was warmly accepted. Perhaps in his optimistic enthusiasm he was as yet oblivious to another quality in the country, that we feel today — the taste of a tragic destiny that has never wholly freed itself of such eventualities as hurricane and fever and the possibility that a minority rule may not be able to cope with its helots. Michaux saw the savannahs with the eye of a naturalist, and to him the grand, formal, and rather somber yet sunsmitten scene was not the familiar complex of evergreen magnolia and Spanish moss, egret and mocking-bird, that it seems to us. A Frenchman, from gentle Satory, where there are no diamond-back rattlers, *parbleu*, or animals who carry their babies in pockets of their fur coats, he saw all things American as curious and fascinating — and are they not?

It is in this new land, with the garden already well established, that Michaux's extant diary begins, as he sets off for the mountains with his son and a train of horses. At their heels trailed the redoubtable John Fraser, who esteemed himself a colleague; Michaux considered him a nuisance. Fraser, it seems, had resolved to go everywhere Michaux went, perhaps because he supposed that Michaux would lead to treasure, just as the jaded habitués at Monte Carlo place their bets with the lucky newcomer. Or perhaps he intended that Louis XVI should have no fowl or flowers of which George III (God bless him) was deprived. John was one of these traveling companions who ask questions all the time, and want to linger over quite different sights than you; he had a taste in fungi, galls, freaks and monstrosities. He was moreover one of those friends we take along under the impression that they have a head for the practical details, or can speak with the natives, only to discover that they do not fuss over the same trifles as ourselves and are hence impractical. Furthermore it is likely that, accented as Michaux's speech might be (he writes the name of the coach-whip snake as " veep-coach," which gives us some idea of how he spoke), the Scotchman Fraser's English was scarcely more acceptable in the red-hill country of Georgia. Finally, Michaux's horses having strayed, he proposed to his fellow botanist that it might be too tedious for him to remain, and so at last, with a sigh of relief the Frenchman saw the Scot's back, nor did they in their separate careers of renown ever again cross trails.

At last out of the still blazing monotony of the Piedmont pine woods in the heavy southern June, rose the first trembling mirage of the mountains — the Blue Ridge upthrusting a thousand mile wall of granite, and beyond it written in a grey dreamy scrawl upon the sky the Great Smokies, the Craggies, and the Balsams. The travelers were arrived now at the frontier village of Seneca, on the borders of the Cherokee Nation — one of those vile hamlets where two different races meet for the exchange of their characteristic cheaper wares, their national forms of deceit and immemorial vices. But above this rubbish heap rose the mountains. The sound of the Tugaloo and the Keowee, plunging into each other in a yellow, perpetual collision, rose above the harsh raven voices of the Indians bargaining blankets and rum, and petticoats for their wenches, in exchange for their services as guides in the peaks where no naturalist but mad William Bartram had ever before adventured. And when the Frenchman and the boy staggered up wearily from the feasting upon bear's grease and the strange wild sweet-potato of the Carolinas, they could step right out into the night and smell the wind from the mountains blowing fresh and damp, smelling of balsam and resin. The man thought of the morrow — and what strange treasures, never touched before, never suspected, might be in those mountain forests — a resin as precious as camphor, a flower of future fashion more fair than the rose, or a bark to rival quinine of Peru.

And in the morning the saddle rose under the travelers,

[208]

with the first uplifting swells of ground; the great rho-
dodendrons closed about them — and the mountain journey was begun. To those who have seen the Alps or the
Rockies, no Appalachians are likely, as mountains, to stir
the heart. They are, rather, a forest upon a high-rolling
floor, and on all the continent, in all the world, I believe,
there is no such hardwood or deciduous forest as this. All
the beauty of the Appalachians is forest beauty; one feels
it marching over the hills, filling the valleys, leaving
nothing bleak, nothing eroded, nothing arid. Everywhere
the murmur of leaves, the trickling or the rushing of
water; and, overhead, above this father and son, the roar
of wild bees in the June blossoms of the sourgum tree and
the chestnut.

Nor is the forest all kindly. Even today in the country
post-offices signs are placarded: Hunter lost. Seen last six
months ago, south of Bryson City. Woman lost crossing
the Balsam range on foot. Children lost, back of Sam
Knob, in rhododendron tangles where the forest floor has
never seen the sun, in jungles of thorny smilax. Even the
birds, wrote Michaux, will not sojourn or sing there.

" June 14. We continued still having the river first on our right,
then on our left; we had to pass over great boulders, straddle
monstrous trees fallen across the jungle of shrubbery, where one
could scarcely see where to go on account of the density of the
thickets. Lofty peaks towered over us, and the obscurity that a
rain-dark sky produced seemed to envelop us in a sombre night.
This trouble and confusion was increased by the noise of the
waterfalls and the crashing on the rocks of the river that we had
to ford up to our knees. The savages tore ahead through these
streams afoot, or ran along the logs, while the young man and I
had horses to guide, so that at last we were forced to dismount,

and one of us had always to run ahead to see what had become of them, for there are no trails in those places except those made by bears and occasionally by Indians. I was constantly afraid of treading on snakes, but terrified when I had to ride my horse across the stream on a rotting log covered with crumbling bark and slippery vegetation that had grown up on it."

After hours of this they arrived forespent in a little valley, one of those tender, tranquil meadow pockets amid gloomy peaks, where in the midst of so much wilderness, gay, shivering flowers lean on the lip of torrents suddenly quiet, running smooth over the white quartz rocks and the fragments of mica and garnet and gold in the dark sand. In such spots grow bluets darker blue than the sea, and yellow stemless violets and the fabled lost *Shortia*, flowers all that Michaux first found and named. And here the weary travelers rested, dining upon wild strawberries and the coldest pure water that ever Michaux had drunk. A shower swept out of the hills, passed by, and in the twilight, I think, the thrush, solitary priest, praised beauty.

When at last Charleston saw Michaux again it was at the head of a pack train laden down with hundreds of plants — packets of seeds, frail flowers in moss, and shrubs and young trees balled in earth, swaying and joggling to the gate of the garden, looking bewildered and unnatural in this lowland heat and glare.

In all our land there is no stranger or richer vegetation than the Appalachian. The great glaciers that in the Pleistocene Age ploughed the continent, pushed the ancient Tertiary flora into the southern mountains, isolated it there, trapped it in the mountain " coves " from which much of it has never escaped. There is a far-northerly element upon the highest peaks; subtropical vegetation steals up into the coves of the lowlands. But caught between them is a relict flora from ancient times, whose nearest of kin are still preserved today only in the mountains of Japan and China.

I have no space to tell of Michaux's forays into Florida and across to the Bahamas, nor his farthest north, Lake Mistassini where the Indian guides, terrified of the tundras, would go no farther. Michaux went twice to southern Illinois and was, I think, the first naturalist ever to see the prairies. There were flying trips to New Jersey to look after the garden there, always reported as in flourishing condition under the faithful Paul Saulnier. There were visits to Bartram in his garden, and to George Washington among his box walks at Mt. Vernon.

But always Michaux came back to his mountains, venturing higher and farther, to Grandfather Mountain, to Roan Mountain, to Yellow Mountain as it was called before ever Dr. Mitchell saw it, where the breath of the balsam forest was aromatic and the purple rhododendron blazed, mile on mile, in the unseen, the rapturous abundance of the montane wilderness. " *Les* wilderness " he calls it in his diary, taking it for a plural, thinking of it as it was, many wildernesses, the Appalachian, the Florida wilderness, the Canadian, the prairie. His routes became famous. Trappers and chiefs, planters and small farmers got to know him, had birds waiting for him, plants ready for him, passed him on with letters.

All these many years Michaux had been spending his own substance, or actually borrowing, in the expectation that the King would repay him. Horses and meal and guides all called upon his pocket; shipments and garden maintenance cried for money. Perhaps he paid, too, the wages of Paul Saulnier, and of Louis Bosc who was sent out from France to take charge of the Charleston garden. But Michaux had no inkling of the deplorable surprise that awaited him. The first change in the wind came with a letter from young François, who had been sent back to France for his education. The forest of Rambouillet was not, after all, grown tall with tulip tree and dogwood, red-bud and honey-locust, coffee tree and rare yellow-wood. Nor did the voice of the bob-white or the drumming of the ruffed grouse resound from the hunting preserves of France. All Michaux's trees and flowers had been sent by Marie Antoinette to her father the Emperor of Austria, or they had been parceled out among the nobles. What little ever reached Rambouillet fell into neglect.

For this we must chiefly blame the age; it had been a mistake in the first place to hope that so many foreign plants and creatures could adapt themselves to the European climate or supplant the established products of old civilizations. Only a few New World organisms have been able to do that much — the potato and the turkey, for example. But beyond this (and I am considering only New World beauty now), there was always a certain contempt for fruits of a continent which had so disappointingly turned out to be not the fabled East but a great natural obstacle to Cathay and the Isles of Spice. Instead of a voluptuous and adaptable Nature, America proffered a hard, clean, and somehow intractable biota. By this I mean the total life-community, plant and animal. Here were few living things useful to man, few bent to his will by selection and breeding. This was a land that with Nature's own disdain cared nothing for filling the bellies of the poor or catching the fancy of a queen.

It is in reality America that, biologically, must be considered an old hemisphere; it is Europe that has evolved a modern, aggressive biota, a pushing, compromising fauna and flora so subservient to man or so much cleverer than he, that it makes its way around the earth. In a way it is the highest praise to say that these plants and animals are very like the white man whom they accompany. But they are like him in their intolerance of rivals, their contempt for the natives, their lack of ruth. European man has entered the other continents and mastered them by virtue of persuasion that everything he is, and has, is and will be the best to the end of time. So he hoes out what he finds growing to make way for that symbol of chivalry and eroticism, the rose, his queen of flowers. The wild cattle of other continents must give place to his own herds. There is no injustice in all this; it is biologically right enough because it is the triumph of a species.

But there was in Michaux's America an aristocracy of primordially ancient lineage that would make no compromise with the invader. Nature here was a closed society, to which you could not add anything without first clearing something else away. The American biota was great without prettiness, strong but not elastic, proud to die, but not able to bend the knee. The human animal in its fauna, the red man, perfectly exemplifies the whole story. So one can see why it is that after all France, England and the rest of Europe could not take home and cage what sang and bloomed along the foaming torrents of the Blue Ridge.

I have always felt that Michaux more than any other early traveler was possessed by the animus of our Nature. But I am not maintaining that I know it to be so; I would remind you and myself of the clean severity of those diaries, unembellished with sentiment or reflection. Yet if he felt, as I think he did, that he wanted to bring to the feet of France these wild-growing riches, his story is somehow a tragic one. Neither his King, nor the glorious Republic, one and indivisible, appreciated his efforts.

When he left America, he had no expectation that he would never see it again. But the ship *Ophir* bore him away under ill omens, and off the coast of Holland she went aground and lay on her beam-ends. Michaux, all his cargo lost, was washed ashore unconscious on the beach at Egmont. But back in Paris honors awaited him, and his diary ends abruptly in the full flood of dinners, and visits of state. The Republic hastened him off on a new venture, dispatching him in the Baudin expedition for ultimate Oceania. On the way Michaux demanded to be put ashore at Madagascar. He foresaw new worlds to conquer, fierce tropic splendors to make his own. Instead the great black island claimed him, and he was brought out of the mountains, dead of fever.

François Michaux enjoyed all the success and good fortune that never attended his father. I do not mean that he did not earn them, but rather that the story ends happily for both of them in the triumphs of the son. His great

RESIDENCE OF JOHN BARTRAM, built with his own hands, 1730.

(See page 192.)

FRANKLINIA,
the "lost tree" discovered by Bartram in Georgia
and never since found in the wild state.
(Courtesy of The Wild Flower Preservation Society)
(See page 195)

classic work was the *Sylva of North America,* and in its preparation he traveled even more widely than André.

In his old age, dwelling in Paris in that leisure that is affluence to a Frenchman, nothing pleased him more than to receive visits from Americans. Their hosannahs of their country's progress appeared to amuse and astonish him no end. Where he had kept his camp-fire once and heard the wolves howling, factories now blackened the sky. Thousands were crying for bread now, where the shagbark had flung down the hard-shelled manna with an abundance that there was not one Baptist then to enjoy. He would lend an ear to the upward rush of our census, the bursting out of our restless frontiers, and he would shake his head and smile. " *Mon Dieu, mon Dieu, est-il possible?* "

Perhaps it was not all admiration, that question, nor wholly rhetorical. Perhaps Michaux the younger, now grown old, remembered the tameless abundance, the proud, ungelded, antlered beauty in strength. And so, wondering, he asked of his God if this new order were indeed His will. Is it possible, and must it be, *mon Dieu?*

IO

WILDERNESS BIRDSMEN: WILSON AND AUDUBON

I WALKED in the woods this morning, because I wanted the sky and no roof overhead. I wanted to begin to write about the great amateurs of American ornithology by reading first a page from their own grand original source book, and not from my toppling pile of notes.

It is May, the high point in the year for birds, when every one of them, from the northward departing juncos with their little sizzling notes to the late arriving orioles tropic in plumage, takes up its bridal song. The call of the oriole comes to me repeatedly out of the tree-tops, and every spring when I first hear it again I am struck with its alien charm. I hear the tropics in it, the molten sunshine of the Orinoco. Our books and our schoolmasters all attune us to a primrose by the river's brim, but we have no primroses, no nightingales, no skylarks. We are taught to think of Nature in terms not native here. And that Wordsworthian Nature is delicate, subtle, subdued to live with men. A flapping eagle scrawled on a tepee of buffalo hide by a red finger dipped in sumach dye is closer to American Nature than Wordsworth could have come if he had ever carried out his plan of founding a perfect state for poets on the banks of the Susquehanna. One can-

not imagine an ode to the whippoorwill by Keats. I will
not blame any one who for his vespers prefers a nightingale to the whippoorwill. But there you are. That is the
language that is spoken by the North American forest in
the night, in the soft, heavy, hot darkness of our Junes.
Call it guttural, call it savage; that is our accent, that is
the hardness of the forest's naked limbs, the texture of the
continent's coarse, vital hair like the high-grass of primeval prairie.

So it is in the darkness, at the heart, in the heartwood.
That harshness is a vestige of the forgotten, unwritten
history of our land, before we came to it. Now there is
morning, May morning, and the sky is a new-born blue.
The little hawthorn wood, so long dead-seeming, shut
up and inky bare, is suddenly fuming with white flowers,
not sweet like English may but with a tartness that our
bees adore. And over them, behind the bronze of young
leaves no larger than a mouse's ear, flit the warblers,
little treble notes up and down the stave, that you can
scarcely catch. I am never so reminded of our land's in-
exhaustible vastness as by the number of these tiny birds
still new to me. As they cross Cuba they are called simply
mariposas, butterflies. The name is apt, for they are
ephemeral, always on the way to somewhere else, often
brilliant of color but tiny of design, and exhibiting what
is for birds an extreme of sexual dimorphism, the females so unlike their mates that they might pass for
separate species.

You put off learning the warblers for a long time, conscious of snags, alarmed by the minute script one must
decipher. But finally you succumb to the sheer challenge

of them, the allure of complexity such as chess or Chinese landscape painting offer. Then the year will consist of waiting for May to come back, the thirty days within whose confines most warblers both come and go. The task begins easily with the arrival of the first, the myrtle warbler, bright among the leafless trees, but by the close of the month, when thirty or forty species have passed through, some lingering but a day, and you are come to the last scheduled arrival of them all, your head is in a whirl; you are uncertain of what you saw or which song, lost now in the dense leafage of coming June, belonged to which flick of feathers.

Later you begin to look for the nests of the few who consent to breed with us, and there is a proud day when first you find an oven-bird's woven cradle. You will be boasting a knowledge of the song of the water-thrush, you will know the redstart even in its autumnal plumage. And then one day, among the willows, you will see your first prothonotary, a flash of tropic gold against the tender green of spring, and a sweet but piercing note rising above the creak-crack-cricking of the frogs.

Presently, as you thumb your bird books, you become aware that two names are preëminent amongst those who first discovered and described the warblers of North America. They are Wilson and Audubon. Night and Day, tragic and comic masks, age and youth, are not more opposite than these two who loved alike. With all of empty early America to roam in, these two had to cross paths, cross swords. It is a story that has been told before; at least we are familiar with Audubon's account of it. His is a golden saga, and any one would choose the fortunate hero. But I have always had a perverse longing to hear Lucifer's side of the Fall and to defend against Juno the rape of Helen and the luck of Troy.

All that Audubon was to ornithology, all the golden light his personality shed upon it from a long, triumphant life, all the originality and vitality of his work, have been told again and again. I myself once gave myself license to admire and love him boundlessly; others have appraised his work in measured tones, correcting his every slightest slip, setting down the final high score of his life's labors exactly. But now, since it would always seem that one must choose between Audubon and Wilson, I am come this time to give the older man, the less lucky pioneer of American ornithology, his due, and I hope that I shall not fail in this just task, nor be understood to rate Audubon too low because I grant him here but few words. Audubon is secure; he needs no advocate.

Alexander Wilson was born in 1766 in the Seedhills of Paisley, which is hard by Glasgow town. They say that the Seedhills, though a little inland, are swept over day and night by the coursing white wings of the gulls. There is always something supernatural about gulls out of sight of the sea; it seems to soil their maritime immaculateness that they should take up with anything as heavy as terra firma, so crass as men. Or, look at it another way; it is eery to have the ocean send upon us its spies, sailing on soundless wings over the roof-tops and sweeping us with an unblinking, hunting, searching stare hardened in the liquid of those eyes, and when the gulls wheedle and scream, cruel angels seem to quarrel over us. These were the first bird voices to smite the ear of the thin, plain child in the tenement cottage.

Later, when a shepherd boy, Alexander was set to mind the sheep in the bleak meadow up above the smoking chimney pots of the town, above the clatter of the looms; he must have lain on his back then to watch the gulls passing and repassing in the sky. And he let his sheep stray, while he composed his first childish pastorals. There was just then a whole school of Seedhill poets — very minor, to be sure, but Wilson was destined to rise the best of them.

As there was not money enough to make a minister of him, the thirteen-year-old lad was to be taught a trade, and only one was conceivable. In the town of eighty families there were sixty looms. Factory evils, or more precisely the factories themselves, had not yet come to Scotland. But the industrial revolution was probably worse at this moment than after the advent of the factory, for every home was a sweatshop; the looms invaded the bedrooms; they never ceased, night or day; every old barn and outbuilding was filled with their clatter, their lung-filling dust.

The child Alexander was fortunate in signing an indenture to William Duncan, for the man was his brother-in-law, and could be relied on to feed him and whip him well, and to let him go neither ragged nor ill-taught his trade. When at last the contract of indenture was handed back, the sixteen-year-old weaver poet wrote across it:

> Be't kent to a' the warld in rhime,
> That wi' right muckle wark and toil,

Wilderness Birdsmen

For three lang years I've ser't my time,
Whiles feasted wi' the hazel oil.

He was free now to earn his living, if he could, but he had to deal with the master weavers, those middle-men who judged the work, hunting only for flaws in it, that they might beat down the price. And the iron entered his soul at the injustices and insults that he had to endure. He took to peddling instead, selling linens and hollands, linseys and silks, to be met with slammed doors, with the rage of mastiffs. And the iron was tempered into steel.

Motherless, sensitive, he must now face the world. Young and passionate, he was pure amidst companions whose only relaxations were drinking and wenching. Slight and (by his more realistic, less prettified portraits) not at all good looking, what he yearned for in woman was refinement. And his only mistress was poverty, to whom he addressed what strikes me as the best of his poems, for he knew all about her. He called her haggard harlot, strumpet; but he lay in no other arms, and all his life long he felt keenly his intimacy with her.

. . . So disfigur'd with thy scoffing,
Need I wonder why so often
Friends go past, nae answer gi'e me,
Look their watch, and never see me.

Wilson at this time was already a poet, who spoke in the Scottish vernacular of the things he knew and saw and felt most deeply. In his own language, but not in English, he could rise at times to a penetrating pitch. He wrote of looms and cruel overseers, of the peddler's weary miles, and of country sights and sounds, the

[221]

Green Laurels

. . . bonny wee bit wren
Lone, on a fuggy stane.[1]

He wrote out of a full heart, unconscious that his pen-point was only a common fowl's quill, not tipped with gold like Robin Burns's. He believed at first that the thin sheaf of his verses would save him from the " ragged spectre, poverty." So he hid his poems amid his calicoes and flannels, as the peddler Ulysses once concealed amidst his Tyrian stuffs and beads and mirrors a sword to catch the boy Achilles.

In vain Wilson addressed a duchess with his *Advertisement Extraordinary*:

Here are fine jaconets, of numberless sets,
    With spotted and sprigged festoons;
And lovely tambours, with elegant flowers,
    For bonnets, cloaks, aprons, or gowns.

Now ye Fair, if ye choose any piece to peruse
    With pleasure I'll instantly shew it;
If the Pedlar should fail to be favour'd with sale,
    Then I hope you'll encourage the Poet.

In the hearing of all the market place, the duchess waved all away with the parrot-like scream of a high-born lady addressing a menial: " I don't want any of these things! "

It rang in his head for days; it mocked him down the night hours, with the insolent contempt of the safely reared, of the doll-brained and beautiful, for the humble and insecure, with all of woman's indifference to any one who, in her mind, she has instantly and unconsciously

---

[1] mossy stone.

eliminated as a *man* — in a meaning of the word known best to herself. Never had he any luck with women. At this time, they say, he adored one Matilda McClain, but found no favor with her.

Wilson's most famous poem, *Watty and Meg*, appearing anonymously in 1792, was taken to be the work of Burns. Nothing at first blush could have delighted him more. Wilson had written to Burns, objecting to the improper tendencies in his poetry. To this Bobbie replied that he received such letters every day, but would undertake to answer this one; that, in short, he wrote about life as he knew it and saw it. Wilson, evidently struck by the manliness of this candor, went down to Ayrshire and visited the poet on his farm.

But there is a persistent rumor of Wilson's intense jealousy. I doubt if he fed it; I believe he fought against it; but it was stronger than he, and I mention it here only because it is so significant in the latter part of my story. It was agony to him to have others succeed at his own ventures, to be praised where he was neglected. He bore through life the touchiness of the self-made man, the acute awareness of the humbly born that some are conceived beneath a lucky sign. When at last he claimed the poem, it fell off abruptly in value, so slavish is the public to a name.

But Wilson's poetry was leading him into deeper waters. A group of three poems against the weaver's overseers and the early barons of spinning brought about a libel suit, and the man who recognized his own ill features in Wilson's lampoon obtained judgment for a fine of more than twelve pounds. This Wilson could not pay, and the irate gentleman showed no pity. Wilson went to jail. When he emerged, pale and altered, he was compelled to burn his diatribes in verse before the public. To this he added a private apology, and, broken in spirit and hopes, he set his face toward America.

Up to this point the future father of American ornithology had never, so far as I can discover, had any training as a naturalist, nor even read a book on ornithology. There are only poetical views of nature in his previous writings, and only one really striking mention of birds, when he speaks of the gannets of the Bass Rock.

But he brought to the New World which he was entering the gift of the fresh eye, the poet's quickness of ear, the artist's sensitivity. These, if you like, are amateurish equipments for the science of ornithology, but ornithology is an amateur's science. And now, while museum men roll their eyes and groan, let me explain.

Linnaeus knew of some two hundred species of American birds, his followers Gmelin, Brünnich and Vieillot rather more. They had the bones, the skins from which to draw up descriptions of New World oddities. But they knew nothing of the glory of New World bird life. If they were aware that we had many families exclusively ours — the wood warblers, flycatchers, vireos, tanagers, hummingbirds, and the oriole family — they knew nothing of all that goes to make our birds what they are. They were necessarily deprived of the very spirit of the whole subject, and what we lacked before Wilson's day was some Gilbert White, some patient, adoring amateur who would think nothing too small to set down. Indeed, ornithology cannot for a moment dispense with a whole chain of Gilbert Whites, a confraternity of gentle spies. What technical diagnosis by a Swainson, dissecting and book-delving in his cabinet, could equal one good picture, one flashing phrase? Song and flight, life habits, migration, the least mannerisms, food habits, courtship, juvenal plumage, winter and summer songs — these are the substance of ornithology. In the end it has been largely the amateurs who tell us what we want to know — amateurs, of course, upon the grand scale, men who have been unable to resist the call of the birds, who steal time from their professions, dream out of their windows at the flash of a colored wing, and promise the whole feathered choir, in the old Jacobite formula: " Whistle, my lad, and I'll come to you."

Such there have been, the world over, lonely light-housekeepers with the sea eagles and curlews and puffins wheeling about their sea-girt rocks, monks who walked the jungles of the Amazon barefoot, with their faces lifted up to the tree-tops, curious, intelligent army men, stationed at eventless tropic posts. But there is no country where birds have been loved with more personal pride of possession than in America. The true American cannot be made to feel humble about his avifauna. I remember listening quite unmoved to a description of the chorus of bird voices in the jungles of the Congo. While the man — a wandering Belgian — was telling me that it sounded like the inside of a canary store, I was listening even then to the whistle of a bob-white on an old-fashioned American snake-rail fence. If it is birds of brilliant plumage that you want, I would, in strictest veracity, be obliged to recommend you to the strutting beauties of New Guinea — and be damned to them. Have we not the cardinal, the tanager, the bluejay?

The first creature that ever fell to Alexander Wilson's gun, as he tramped the woods from his landing place at Newcastle, up to Philadelphia, was the red-headed woodpecker, and he thought it then, and forever after, the most beautiful bird he had ever seen. Next he shot cardinals and rose-breasted grosbeaks, and I suppose we must call this the beginning of his career as a zoölogist. But there is no evidence that he studied, saved, or drew these specimens. He brought them down, I think, in a thoughtless way, shot them because they were strange and brilliant and easy, and I doubt if he remembered much about them as he tramped into the intellectual capital of America in the summer of 1794.

He was friendless now, but free; jobless (he could get no employment as a weaver) but happy in a country which would take on a man, at a venture in any trade. His enthusiasm for democracy was at first boundless, fading gradually as he became a citizen instead of an onlooker, but turning instead into patriotism that would make his heart beat faster when, late in life, he visited Bunker Hill. He tried printing and surveying and peddling, and finally school teaching, in Pennsylvania and Virginia, and later in New Jersey. There he fell in love with a married lady, but, discovering the true state of his heart, beat a virtuous retreat. He mistakenly predicted this passion as final. " The world is lost forever to me and I to the world. No time nor distance can ever banish her image from my mind. It is forever present with me, and my heart is broken with the most melancholy reflections."

One year later, in John Bartram's garden at Kingsess, near Philadelphia, Wilson's heart again skipped beats, this time for John's granddaughter, Anne Bartram.

Wilson was by now the master of a one-room schoolhouse at Gray's Ferry, where his healthy, boisterous *Plattdeutsch* pupils had got out of hand under a weak dominie. Wilson, no stranger to the hazel as we have seen, after a little experience of the evils of rule by children, instituted the wythe, and so nimbly did it whistle that the most perfect deportment and application soon reigned. But I misdoubt me that he was ever an ideal teacher. He was too bitter, too conscious of having suffered, too much a poet, bound up in self, to love children as a teacher should love them. Yet he had many of the mental traits of a dominie — a fondness for detecting errors in the writings of others, an intolerance of being himself corrected; and, as a versifier, he supposed that the way to write good poetry is to imitate the style of the great; his English, or rather his American, poetry shows only too well how much he admired Pope, Gray, and Thompson's *Seasons*.

His schoolwork was always drudgery to him; his relaxation was all in Bartram's garden. Old John, of course, was gone, now, but young John and William were there, and it was under those trees that he met the learned naturalist Benjamin Barton, the excellent zoölogist George Ord (his passionate and unwise adherent) and Alexander Lawson, his future engraver. They found Wilson melancholy, vegetating, weary of work and unable to play, and suggested to him that he drop the flute, which seemed to deepen his dispond, and take up the study of birds. This was in 1803.

In that very year, not forty miles away on the banks of the Perkioming Creek, a young Frenchman, Jean Jacques Audubon, was banding the first little fowl ever to be studied individually for evidences that migratory birds return to the selfsame abode. The next year, this dandified young man, this Frenchman who startled Pennsylvania's woods by going shooting in a ruffled shirt, elegant pumps and satin knee breeches, this spendthrift and handsome lucky lad, met Lucy Bakewell, a girl of fifteen summers, the love of his life and heroine of his chequered career.

In this year Wilson allowed his " Nancy's " hand to guide his own in his first lesson in drawing; for this Quaker maid had a gentle talent whose slightness proved lamentable to science. Soon Wilson wrote to her uncle William:

" I am sending for your amusement a few attempts at some of our indigenous birds. . . . They were chiefly colored by candle-light. I have now got my collection of native birds considerably enlarged, and shall endeavour, if possible, to obtain all the smaller ones this summer. Be pleased to mark on the drawings, with a pencil, the names of each bird, as, except three or four, I do not know them."

It was well for Wilson, this growing taste in ornithology, for a new sorrow was in store for him. His Nancy's hand was bestowed by her father elsewhere. This did not indicate any falling off in the tender feelings of the Bartram family toward Wilson. William Bartram took him to live with him. And Wilson was soon offered a situation as editor of an American edition of Rees's famous cyclopedia. If we may believe reports, its publisher, Samuel F. Bradford, was his evil genius. Not so did it seem to Wilson then. For Bradford enthusiastically undertook to publish Wilson's dream, his *American Ornithology*, to be illustrated with plates engraved by Lawson. Wilson with his own hand engraved the first three. The rest were worked from the naturalist's water-color drawings by Lawson himself, and these were hand-painted in water-color by a Swiss journeyman artist. Wilson and Bradford and Lawson were all agreed on the unsurpassed excellence of this work. Wrote Lawson's daughter years after: " Never again will such engraving be seen! The day of fine work of that kind is over; and except one or two English works on natural history, nothing has approached it."

None of them seems to have been aware that Wilson's drawing was frequently childish and wretched. The rose-breasted grosbeak on Plate XVIII is execrably bad. Compare the inept goldfinch on Plate I with Audubon's enchanting study of the same bird. The engraving is only passable throughout, and the water-coloring like something done by a child. This is not to say that there are no worthy drawings. The bluejay on Plate I, the two nuthatches on the next, are good; there are well done drawings all through; I like the kingfisher most of all.

But great ornithologist as Wilson was, he was no artist. When he was woefully out of drawing, he sensed it no more than a poor singer off key. His birds are flat, two-dimensional, and all too obviously dead.

I am over the worst of the confession that an honest

biographer must make for Wilson, and I need only praise him now. When we turn to the letter-press of the *Ornithology* we are simply astounded at all that he knew of the life habits and histories of his birds. As an observer his patience was infinite, his attention faultless; he had the gift of accuracy that lifts him right out of the rank of the dilettante into the highest realms of science. And he was a pioneer in his field. Mark Catesby, writing of our natural history, was a medieval next to Wilson, credulous, slipshod, bent on telling wonder-tales.

But here was a man without money, without formal training, who traveled from Maine to Florida, from Pittsburgh to New Orleans, studying, collecting, looking (as Buffon abjured all naturalists to do), not once but again and again, to make sure, to be right, to be faithful, to be religious toward Nature. And all his work Wilson did without a predecessor. If, today, you wish to write about the egret, or the wild turkey, your task would be simplified by all that has been done before you. The range, the anatomy, the courtship, the nidification, the migration, the minor racial variations — all are already worked out. But beyond a little barren classification Wilson had no assistance as he set forth to tell the complete life stories of three hundred and twenty species of American birds.

Even on the systematic score it is remarkable that he made so few errors; that being no anatomist, he mistook very few species, and left very few, in all of eastern North America, for any newcomer to discover. He described some fifty-six new species, but actually only about forty were new. Mistakenly he supposed some twenty-three

ALEXANDER WILSON
Artist Unknown, American School.
*(Courtesy of the American Philosophical Society
and the Frick Art Reference Library)*

John J. Audubon,
after the rare engraving by C. Turner, A. R. A.,
of the miniature painted by Frederick Cruickshank,
about 1831; published for the engraver
by Robert Havell, London, 1835.

sorts to be identical with European counterparts, but all the others he correctly identified, though deprived of any great museum for comparative analysis. It is startling to see what birds are Wilson's own, first distinguished and named by him — the whippoorwill, the song-sparrow, the field sparrow, the black-billed cuckoo and long-billed curlew, the canvas-back and ruddy duck, and the raven and the magpie, the pine siskin and goshawk, beside all those warblers.

Such are the fruits of Wilson's book, the book he took with him as he journeyed up and down the land, seeking subscribers for a work to cost the unheard-of sum of one hundred and twenty dollars. The reaction of lesser men may be judged by the comment of Governor Tompkins of New York. " I wouldn't give one hundred and twenty dollars for all the birds you propose to describe, if I had them alive." Another, some character out of *Martin Chuzzlewit*, protested that such a luxurious and costly book, beyond the range of the average man, was contrary to our democratic institutions. Wilson retorted that so must be the fellow's fine mansion.

Much has been made of Wilson's suffering, rebuffs, and disappointments in his canvassing tours. But he succeeded in obtaining four hundred and fifty-eight subscriptions in this raw new country of ours. In New Orleans, where Audubon and his family nearly starved to death, Wilson gathered sixty subscriptions in seventeen days. Every college and important library took one or more copies. Though he complains that he wandered friendless in the cultivated society of Charleston, his South Carolina list contains all the most famous names, including Michaux's old friend General Pinckney. Copies went to Josiah Quincy, General Wilkinson, Gouverneur Morris, Thomas Jefferson, Bartram and Barton, of course, and William Washington, Benjamin West, Stephen Elliot. Wilson even sold a copy to that close old Quaker dragon, Miers Fisher, who had once been young Audubon's mentor and censor. Probably Audubon, now vanished into Kentucky's wilderness with his bride, had tilled the thin soil and planted the seed.

Why then has Wilson such a tale of woe for his experiences? How can he say that he never received a penny from his book, killed himself with fatigues, and endured every incivility, to forward an impossible venture? That he had produced something too good for the country? There might be various answers — that he suffered the nervous depression of one who had already begun the long process of dying of dysentery; that he had a persecution complex; that he had that modesty that is ingrown vanity, and no sense of humor about himself. These are all doubtless true, but there is another explanation, for which I cannot vouch. Some say that his publisher, finding himself saddled with a costly work, drove Wilson on without respite, demanding that the author accomplish the work of an entire sales force. And when the unexpected expense was still not recouped, Bradford indemnified himself as far as possible by impounding all returns.

When Wilson, wandering in search of subscribers, walked into Audubon's country store in Louisville, Kentucky, that March day (probably the nineteenth) in 1810, with his little tamed paroquet on his shoulder, and

PLATE ONE OF ALEXANDER WILSON'S
American Ornithology,
engraved by his own hand.
The stiff poses and the constant use of profile only
should be contrasted with Audubon's style.
(See page 229)

PILEATED WOODPECKERS, FROM
The Birds of America, BY AUDUBON
One notes in contrast with Wilson's bird paintings
the natural, animated Audubon style, and the use of
the three-quarters view and of skilful foreshortening,
as well as the suggestion of habitat and food habits.
(See page 233)

his portfolios under his arm, the two had never heard of each other. Wilson opened his drawings, as he had opened them so many times before, and asked the storekeeper's patronage. But I shall let Audubon tell it:

"I felt surprised and gratified at the sight of the volumes, turned over a few of the plates, and had already taken a pen to write my name in his favour when my partner rather abruptly said to me in French, ' My dear Audubon, what induces you to subscribe to this work? Your drawings are certainly far better, and again you must know as much of the habits of American birds as this gentleman.' Whether Mr. Wilson understood French or not, or if the suddenness with which I paused, disappointed him, I cannot tell; but I clearly perceived that he was not pleased. Vanity and the encomiums of my friend prevented me from subscribing. Mr. Wilson asked me if I had many drawings of birds. I rose, took down a large portfolio, laid it on the table, and shewed him . . . the whole of the contents, with the same patience with which he had shewn me his own engravings."

Yes, there they were, the beginning of all modernity in ornithological illustration, all the color and motion, the life and splendor of the matchless painter of birds. They may have been his crude, early work, but without a doubt the Audubon touch was already upon them. In all the history of science there had never before been seen such illustration. Europe had gaped when Audebert illustrated Vieillot's book on birds with metallic plumage, for with lavish bad taste the artist had splashed on gilt with a reckless hand. Sheer color effects there had been before, even birds in fantastic action. But these drawings were wilderness-born, created out of life. To the first startled eyes to behold them, Audubon's birds must have seemed to fly or spring with a cry right off the page. It is a triumph that to this day many people cannot forgive him. They want their birds stuffed, on the same old museum perch, forever. Scientists, particularly the English, still sometimes resent him. They charge him with scientific untruth, but what they really cannot endure is his personality. When Audubon fails, it is a breakdown in the attempt to represent bird life, aloft, afloat, as human technique can perhaps never hope to do. His perspectives and equilibria sometimes fall down, but for the same reason that Beauvais cathedral fell, because the builders sent the walls and vault to towering into a beauty that the mechanics of stone will not support. Alas, beside these, Wilson's drawings, when they fail, are the failure of a sod hut that has simply slumped in.

Audubon continues the narrative:

" His surprise appeared great, as he told me he never had the most distant idea that any other individual than himself had been engaged in forming such a collection. He asked me if it were my intention to publish, and when I answered in the negative, his surprise seemed to increase. . . . Mr. Wilson now examined my drawings with care, asked if I should have any objections to lending him a few during his stay, to which I replied that I had none; he then bade me good morning, not, however, until I had made an arrangement to explore the woods in the vicinity along with him, and had promised to procure for him some birds, of which I had drawings in my collection, but which he had never seen.

" It happened that he lodged in the same house with us, but his retired habits, I thought, exhibited either a strong feeling of discontent, or a decided melancholy. The Scotch airs which he played sweetly on his flute made me melancholy too, and I felt for him. I presented him to my wife and friends, and seeing that he was all enthusiasm, exerted myself as much as was in my power, to procure for him the specimens which he wanted. We hunted together, and obtained birds which he had never before seen; but, reader, I did not subscribe to his work, for, even at that time, my collection was greater than his. . . .

" Before many days had elapsed he left Louisville, on his way to New Orleans, little knowing how much his talents were appreciated in our little town."

Was Audubon vain, jealous, mistaken not to subscribe to Wilson's work? He has freely confessed all this. He has hung up his faults for all to point at, and many of his biographers and all of Wilson's have not failed to cry shame.

But what has Wilson to say of this meeting? I am not sure that we shall ever know, for Wilson's original diary no longer exists. IIis insanely jealous friend, George Ord, seems to have destroyed it, and all we have today is what Ord has seen fit to tell us Wilson wrote. There is more than a little reason to suspect that Ord, when Wilson was no longer alive to restrain him, changed or expunged the journal. And in my opinion there is no doubt that Waterton, the English naturalist, whom Ord stirred up to the most vindictive and underhanded intrigue against Audubon, has added some shameless and very clumsy and transparent forgeries. Here; then, is Wilson's diary as Ord gave it to the world with no other intent than to damage Audubon. The italics are Ord's, and the passages in parentheses are what Waterton says he personally knew Wilson to have written.

" March 17. Take my baggage and grope my way to Louisville — put up at the Indian Queen tavern, and gladly sit down and rest myself.
March 18. Rise quite refreshed.

March 19. Rambling round the town with my gun. Examined Mr. ——'s drawings in crayons — very good. Saw two new birds he had, both Motacillae.[2]

March 20. Set out this afternoon with the gun — killed nothing new. (People in taverns here devour their meals. Many shopkeepers board in taverns — also boatmen, land-speculators, merchants &c.) *No naturalist to keep me company*.

March 21. Went out shooting this afternoon with Mr. A. Saw a number of Sandhill Cranes. Pigeons numerous.

March 22.

March 23. Packed up my things which I left in the care of a merchant here, to be sent on to Lexington; and having parted with great regret, with my paroquet, to the gentleman of the tavern, I bade adieu to Louisville, to which place I had four letters of recommendation, and was taught to expect much of everything there, but neither received one act of civility from those to whom I was recommended, one subscriber, *nor one new bird;* though I delivered my letters, ransacked the woods repeatedly, and visited all the characters likely to subscribe. *Science or literature has not one friend in this place.* (Everyone is so intent on making money, that they can talk of nothing else; and they absolutely devour their meals, that they may the sooner return to their business. Their manners correspond with their features.) "

Behind these two accounts, however altered (and Waterton's additions, in the style of Mrs. Trollope, are grotesque), there is substantial agreement on everything essential. And beyond them we discover a touching, a pitiable insight into human nature, a glimpse behind the scenes of two heroic men such as the public ought really not be allowed. For Audubon has confessed to vanity and jealousy and mistake, but not to the one weakness that

---

[2] Motacillae — what we should now call warblers.

really prevented him from subscribing to Wilson's book
— a weakness that Wilson would have understood better
than any one else in the world. Audubon was simply too
poor to buy it. He and his partner Rozier were on the edge
of business failure, and his partner was right at his elbow.
With the account books in the red, what right had Audubon to buy an ornithological work for one hundred and
twenty dollars? Or even suppose Wilson had been able
to speak privately to him; Audubon would still have had
to think of his Lucy and his children, on the verge of
destitution.

And poor Wilson! If he had not been humbled and
hardened by a thousand rebuffs from a thousand doors, in
the days when he trudged with a pack on his back, he
might have approached Audubon with that suavity, that
open friendliness, that grace and persuasion which came
so naturally to Audubon himself.

As it was, he seems to have come abruptly to the point,
like the old-fashioned Yankee trader who had nothing to
say to you if you were not willing to buy at his price. He
had met with so much scorn and miscomprehension, that
when he encountered the one man in the world capable of
completely appreciating him, he displayed his wares with
the chill politeness of one who does not suppose you can
estimate them at their true worth.

Wilson was undoubtedly jealous. But who will blame
him? " A man," says one of his extenuators, " who has
given his heart to the accomplishment of an object, be-
lieving that he has no rival, must be somewhat more than
human, if he be delighted to find that another is engaged
in the same purpose, with equal energy and advantages

far greater than his own." Wilson intended to be silent
on the bitterness of his disappointment. Even in his journal he repressed his feelings, put down weakness. At the
most one can only say that he failed to recognize, in the
long-haired, quizzical, puckish storekeeper of the backwoods, the future prince of American ornithology. Having no Latin, no Linnaeanism about him, Audubon did
not seem, conceivably, a naturalist, as respectable Philadelphia gentlemen with libraries and cabinets, like Barton, were obviously naturalists. Audubon was a storekeeper who drew " very good " crayon pictures of birds
without any idea where to place these species in the systems of Linnaeus and Buffon, a rustic hunter who inevitably knew a little curious lore about wild birds. But
surely not a naturalist, to keep Wilson company!

It is not worth while to follow out the great Audubon-
Wilson controversy, with all its charges and counter-
charges of thefts of drawing and of Nature-faking. It is
not very creditable to Audubon, and to Ord and Waterton
it is disgraceful.

Wilson's engraver Lawson, dreading the rising popularity of Audubon's book, joined in heartily, as a matter
of business rivalry; he may be forgiven, but the two naturalists never.

In all this muck-raking, Alexander Wilson took no
part. For he was dead in his forty-eighth year, of fatigue
and dysentery, and of a chill caught by swimming an icy
river after a bird. Audubon says he died under a bookseller's lash, and that too may well be so. At his grave, in
the burying ground of the Old Swede's Church in Phila-

delphia, there was, at the end, one woman to weep for him, Miss Sarah Miller, his fiancée.

Wilson's name is commemorated in a genus of warblers, *Wilsonia*, which includes the beautiful Canadian and hooded warblers, and the modest Wilson's warbler. There are a number of others: Wilson's snipe, Wilson's thrush, that we call the veery, quiet singer of the northwoods, and Wilson's phalarope. And there is another bird that Wilson first discovered and that he describes thus:

" This new species inhabits the watery solitudes of our highest mountains during the summer, from Kentucky to New York; but is nowhere numerous, seldom more than one or two being seen together. It takes short, low flights; runs nimbly about the mossy margins of the mountain springs, brooks and pools, occasionally stopping, looking at you, and perpetually nodding the head. It is so unsuspicious, or so little acquainted with man, as to permit one to approach within a few yards of it, without appearing to take any notice, or to be the least alarmed. At the approach of cold weather, it descends to the muddy shores of our large rivers, where it is occasionally met with, singly, on its way to the south. I have made many long and close searches for the nest of this bird, without success. They regularly breed on Pocano mountain . . . in Pennsylvania, arriving there early in May, and departing in September. It is usually silent, unless when suddenly flushed, when it utters a sharp whistle."

I saw it only today, out in the mysterious shining chains of sloughs in the spring woods, dun of plumage, curious, silent, retiring with a sort of painful shyness, an exile from the country of all its kin, an inland shore bird, always seen singly, living, it would appear, ever unmated, a bird like the man who named it — the solitary sandpiper.

So I am come at last to the end of Wilson's story, without having done more than begun that of Audubon, for in truth the star of Audubon was only rising when that of Wilson had already set. Child of passion, of wealth, of bodily beauty, dowered with genius, lucky in love and blessed with long life, Audubon possessed from the outset everything that Wilson lacked.

The story of his birth, the natural son of Captain Jean Audubon of Nantes, and of a Creole of Haiti, is a mystery no longer. Old records have been made to divulge their secrets, and that which Audubon himself so carefully concealed no longer needs a cloak. We feel indulgent to Captain Audubon's infidelities, and only grateful to the woman, of uncertain identity, who gave to the world its greatest painter of birds. Madame Audubon, the lad's foster mother, plays a heroine's role in the story, tenderly caring for the child, imparting to him, I think, much of his gentleness and refinement, and some of those qualities that we call woman's, though I like to believe men have simply fallen into the way of leaving them to women. I refer to a certain unconcern with the hard-eyed world, a morality based upon personal ardor, the courage to acknowledge beauty.

These, too, are the qualities of the artist, and it is as an artist that you must think of Audubon during more than half of his life. At the time that Wilson approached him in his store in Louisville, Audubon really had no intention of publishing his drawings. In the scientific sense he was very nearly unlettered, aside from a summer of bird rambles with the excellent naturalist d'Orbigny, when he was about twenty-three and revisiting Brittany. One might add a little taxidermic experience in New York, which scarcely amounted to more than his brief months of artistic training, at seventeen, in the *atelier* of David.

Audubon the painter was Audubon the observer. To draw accurately is to study. In order to draw birds — and that was the consuming ambition of Audubon's life from childhood — the artist must needs move and dwell among them. He must be a marksman; Audubon was not only an excellent shot, not ashamed to shoulder a rifle by Daniel Boone's side, but an ardent general sportsman.

A great many naturalists have reached their calling by way of the sportsman's avocation. There is no way on earth to learn so much about the beasts of the field and the fowl of the air, as to track them down with the gun, to become their foe who must learn their every way, their spoor, their dung, their marks upon tree and mud, their travels and matings and trickery. I speak here entirely as an alien; I have never shot a living creature nor can I imagine so doing except under the compulsion of one necessity or another. For the atavism of finding pleasure in killing, I have not a drop of sympathy, unless it may be justified as more harmless than a love of war — a catharsis for the Neanderthal lust to break skulls. But Audubon's gun was part of his great equipment as a field naturalist. And sportsmanship in the old Northwest Territory was a way of life; it was life itself; it meant an actual struggle for survival. A man as incapable as I suppose myself to be of sheer animal craft and endurance would have been the prey, not the master, of the beasts.

So it was the wilderness that made Audubon, as it nearly broke him. For when Wilson walked into the

Louisville store, Audubon had already begun the long and agonizing process of business failure. How right it was that he should fail, how wrong we were to force upon an artist the go-getting code of the frontier, is now one of the parables of American history. His life, a golden success story, has soared like Lincoln's into the realms of morality, where it is not inappropriate that some legend should cluster.

Every one has his own pictures, I suppose, of Audubon's life, of its memorable moments. One of mine is of Audubon the failure, cleaned out by the sheriff, his wife and babies near starvation, and he walking to the city, covering his eyes so as not to see the wild turkeys that flew across his path and seemed to him delusive enemies that had betrayed him. For, all his life, and despite his great love for Lucy, it had been the birds he followed. And he was lost in the great darkness of the wilderness, until he took up that trail again, forever and in earnest.

Now I see Audubon drifting down the Mississippi in a flatboat, through a world of water fowl, between sunlit banks where the hymnody of the land birds was drawn out in a golden indolence. I see him tramping the streets of cities, New Orleans, Philadelphia, Edinburgh, London, his portfolio under his arm, seeking subscriptions for a work ten times as costly as Wilson's. Who'll buy? Who'll buy? Who'll buy the tiny jeweled beauty of warblers, the fish lust of the osprey, these raucous ungainly woodpeckers, this flamingo large as life, this turkey spreading her wings to shelter her chicks at the shadow of the hawk?

And they bought — they bought because no one before had ever seen the Audubon perspective, the animation, the three-dimensional veracity, the habitat backgrounds, the wilderness caught in the hand. They bought because — there was no precedent for it — every bird was represented life size. Sportsmen wanted their game birds for dining-rooms and dens; women bought the songsters; museums bought because the work was monumental, complete; collectors, even then, were wise enough to pick up stocks when they were still selling low.

But popularity is not always worth. It is only his science that brings Audubon into the company between these covers. For the purposes of scientific description, illustration is not less vital than words. And Audubon transcended illustration; he wedded art to science as no man has done before or since. He made the birds of America his own, and they are his still, even those that are gone from the rest of us — the passenger pigeon, the heath hen, the Carolina paroquet. He caught life, and kept it alive. Above the sunny glory that was his floats the pale fame of Alexander Wilson, wistful, like a daytime moon.

II

FRONTIER UTOPIANS: SAY, RAFINESQUE, AND OTHERS

His excellency, Thomas Jefferson, third president of the United States, was incidentally a scientist. His attainments, that is, were incidental to his politics. But they were not incidental to the whole man. Jefferson was the first president, perhaps very nearly the first American, who did not think eastward, look backward, toward Europe and particularly toward England. Washington and Adams behaved like Englishmen; politically, morally, in every mental twist, they were English gentlemen.

Thomas Jefferson was different. He had a slouch; he had an American crick in his mind, a talent for minor inventions, gadgets, levers, pulleys, almanacs, calculations; he had " knack," and a way with men — not always as ruggedly honest as Adams'. In the goodness of the common man he had a sentimental faith which may have been Rousseau-ish but is closer to Lincoln or Bryan. I can just conceive the possibility that Washington might have gone back to England and bought back the old family place. But Jefferson bought forward; he bought west. He bought stock in the wilderness and bought the Mississippi free for American commerce. So he let the hordes

New Harmony, Indiana
the scene of two great experiments in early American communism
and a great era of scientific development.   *(From an old print)*
(See page 251)

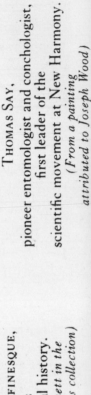

Constantine Samuel Rafinesque,
forgotten genius
of early American natural history.
(*From the painting by Jouett in the
Wisconsin Historical Society's collection*)

Thomas Say,
pioneer entomologist and conchologist,
first leader of the
scientific movement at New Harmony.
(*From a painting
attributed to Joseph Wood*)

loose into the Ohio valley, and began my story where I take it up.

I have spoken of his science; it was in itself nothing more than amateur, a smattering. But it was American, characteristic; Jefferson did not, like John Bartram, Dr. Garden, and John Clayton of Virginia, write to Linnaeus, or to anybody in Europe. He was Emersonian in his creed of self-reliance, proud of being self-taught. Infinitely curious, he had the quick eye of a woodsman; he believed, as we still do in America, in making surveys, taking inventories, taking stock. Like other Americans, he disbelieved in " professors." If he didn't actually laugh at them, he turned down, when he planned the Lewis and Clark expedition, such great men as Alexander Wilson and Rafinesque; he preferred the " practical man." He would perhaps have agreed with Thoreau, that a country boy who tempered his own rude knife would know more about steel than any one who spent four years on the theory of metallurgy. It is still the prevailing view.

He wrote to Alexander Wilson telling him that there was still one bird, absolutely unknown to science, which he had heard and some hunters knew, that sang divinely from the tops of the highest trees. But so adroitly did this chorister keep himself concealed aloft that though he, Jefferson, had outstanding a reward offered for a specimen, not the best shot had ever been able to bring down even one. Nor was it, Jefferson said, to be found in Buffon or Linnaeus.

I have never met a rustic westerner or southerner of today who has not some such wonder-tale to tell you,

" something the professors don't know." Most of them are snake wonders, some are botanical.

When at last Jefferson's ornithological mystery was winged and seen in the flesh it proved to be the ground robin, or towhee, whose modest " chewink " habitually issues from the underbrush. Quite incidentally, this bird *is* to be found in Linnaeus.

Perhaps there was a mistake in identification here. I don't mean that Jefferson was a liar, a Nature-faker; he may have meant the red-eyed vireo, which answers far better to his vague specifications. Or perhaps hunters had been playing a Nature joke on a credulous listener, as Audubon persuaded Rafinesque to believe in the red-headed swallow.

But more probably the bird was, quite unconsciously on Jefferson's part, imaginary. It was born out of a vague resentment against the precisions of science, the wish shared by Ruskin and Thoreau and Burroughs, G. K. Chesterton, Gene Stratton Porter and your state congressman, to discredit science, to be more truly, practically, and spiritually wise than the grubbing and rabbity men who are thought to profess it. And indeed I should add one other name — the average Fundamentalist American who, by wagon and skiff and flatboat and river-ark or on Shanks's mare, went west in Jefferson's day, his axe and his gun on his shoulder, and his woman and progeny and pots and kettles at his heels.

So they came, Daniel Boone, shooting Indians in the back, mighty deerslayer; Johnny Appleseed, more early-Christian than the Baptists and Methodists; George Rapp, leading German peasants to a celibate communism on the banks of the Wabash, there to await the end of the world, which was, God told him, at hand; Henry Clay, pacing the woods, practising Demosthenean eloquence to the beech boles.

Listen to the words, the voices, the letters and journals of the settlers themselves:

"Everywhere you hear, from the river, the ringing of axes."

"The sound of the axe, splitting fire-wood, salutes the ear every morning, instead of the birds' songs."

"The difficulty connected with the terrific labor involved in clearing the trees from the new country and opening farms was vigorously and cheerfully met by the settlers. Great personal kindness abounded; they assisted each other in every way . . . every private house was opened to the traveler."

"The flats of the Big Wabash are extremely fertile, and covered with immensely large trees, between which grows amazing luxuriance of that noble vegetable the Cane. . . . The Cane brakes are always full of herds of cattle, who are very fond of its leaves. . . . The trees growing on the banks, from their immense size, astonish everyone. The Plane, with its long white arms, and the Tulip-tree, attain to an enormous magnitude."

"Preached again two sermons in the old log court-house. . . . The text was Neh. ii, 20: 'The God of Heaven will prosper us, therefore, we his servants will arise and build.'"

"Floating down the Ohio, in a little stinking ark, full of unclean things, will prepare the mind and body for barbarizing in a little log-hole, where ten souls sleep in one room, and in three beds." [1]

---

[1] Lindley, Harlow (editor), *Indiana as Seen by Early Travelers* (Indiana Historical Commission, Indianapolis, 1916).

"The everlasting sound of falling trees, . . . night and day, produces a sound loud and jarring as the discharge of ordnance, and is a relief to the dreary silence of these wilds."

"*Indian Summer* haze . . . is caused by millions of acres . . . being in a wide-spreading fire, rising up through the woods and prairie, hill and dale . . . darkening the heavens and earth." [2]

So we made a nation; so we swept away the greatest hardwood timber reserve in the temperate world, simply to be free of it, while our cattle trampled down the wild bamboo, the cane; we exterminated the paroquet for its plumage, the passenger pigeon for its flesh. So we came on, brave and, as a race, incapable of fatigue, infinitely resourceful, and blessed with whiskey to buck us up over the worst of the bogs, and send us, roaring and insensitive to suffering, through hardship and accident. We had, too, an extraordinary run of luck, and a now extinct sense of primitive, brutal humor, no respect for the law, but a strong proclivity for making it and executing it personally. And we came with brave women who were consecrated to the intention of making ten tall sons grow where before only one savage had been. There were few old maids. As soon as a girl was old enough to blush she was married. The young man was rich if he had ten dollars and a shirt. But these were luxuries. What she asked was wild swans upon the bare table, and a blanket of beaver for her baby.

In this society there burgeoned most improbably a group of eminent naturalists, and the cause of the most theoretical science, to the wonderment and amaze of my

[2] Lindley, Harlow, (editor) *Indiana as Seen by Early Travelers.*

hardy ancestors, flowered exotically on the banks of the sluggish Wabash and in the Blue Grass. This thought still strikes the American mind as so absurd that simply to state it calls forth a patronizing smile. Yet in reality it was the most brilliant assemblage of original intellects in the field of natural history that the western hemisphere has ever witnessed, and in proportion to the poverty and physical disadvantages of the time and the places, it gave to birth and to print more pioneering published work than the great cities of today.

For, as far as natural history was concerned, the time had come for naturalists to go west. The flora and the fauna of the Atlantic States were known now; there was little likelihood that anything new might be discovered, and we were, it must be remembered, not yet in the stage of nice amenities in the way of parochial commentative science like *The Natural History of Selborne*. It is all very well for a Gilbert White to be enchanted because one new species of harvest mouse has been added to the animal fauna of Great Britain. Such raptures are possible only in a tamed environment, a world for gentle curates and learned maiden ladies. But in this young giant of a new country, what icthyologist would bother with Walden Pond, when the fishes of the Great Lakes were undescribed, unknown? In the Mississippi leaped the sturgeon; in the rivers of the Middle West were a thousand exquisite shells, fresh-water clams bearing perfect pearls. On the plains the bison charged, the coyotes howled, the prairie-dogs sat at their doors and gibbered. Between the Appalachians and the Rockies lay a promised land, spread out upon the fertile limestones, the black velvet loams, the wild meadows, of the Western Reserve, the Louisiana Purchase and the old Northwest Territory. God so loved this land that He put in it for naturalists' wonderment strange inland gulls, cliff swallows that dwelt in the clefts of our loess, pigmy owls that burrowed beneath the soil, and prairie chickens whose first booming notes proclaimed the coming of earliest spring, the western meadowlark of the voice sweeter by far than any skylark's, and the passenger pigeons in their millions.

Nothing so brings home to us the lavish abundance of the old biota as the stories of the pigeons. Naturalists and hunters, foreign travelers, all use the same phrases:

" Astonishing flights of pigeons. Such were their numbers, that they literally formed clouds, and floated through the air in a frequent succession of these as far as the eye could reach, sometimes causing a sensible gust of wind, and a considerable motion of the trees over which they flew."

" A pigeon roost is a singular sight, when the roost extends from four to six miles in circumference. The screaming noise they make when thus roosting is heard at a distance of six miles; and when the beechnuts are ripe, they fly 200 miles to dinner, in immense flocks, hiding the sun and darkening the air like a thick passing cloud. They thus travel 400 miles daily. They roost on the high forest trees, which they cover in the same manner as bees in swarms cover a bush, being piled one on the other, from the lowest to the top-most boughs, which so laden, are seen continually bending and falling with their crashing weight." [3]

This was the Ali Baba's cave of natural wonders in which Audubon struggled, and failed, and rose to greatness. Michaux had had just a look at it. The English naturalists, Nuttall and Bradbury, coursed through it in

---

[3] Lindley, Harlow, *Indiana as Seen by Early Travelers*.

the early days, and Wilson's little skiff had carried him swiftly into it and out.

But into this Eden, in the last of the year 1825, there ploughed an Ohio ark, *The Philanthropist*, known to posterity as " The Boatload of Knowledge," that was to bring " the wise men of the East," and a large number of elegant and blue-stocking ladies to New Harmony, the perfect communist state which Robert Owen had just founded in Indiana on the banks of the Wabash. Some thirty-five ladies and gentlemen, mostly from the cultivated purlieus of Philadelphia, comprised this precious cargo, and if brains had weighed materially as these intellects in worth, the frail ark must have sunk at the embarkation wharf in Pittsburgh. As it was, ice jams imprisoned the sapient voyagers for six weeks, and finally, becoming impatient of delay, Robert Owen, their leader, hastened ahead overland to New Harmony.

Robert Owen was not the sort of communist of whom Lenin would have approved. He was benevolent, kindly, tolerant. Class hatred, violence and bloodshed were not for Owen conceivable ways of accomplishing his revolution. Risen himself from the estate of the lowliest factory hand, he had seen children of ten maimed by machinery, and beaten for a moment's idleness, and had suffered every sort of hatred and suspicion from the mill owners without, himself, bearing any hatred. He had a fondness for establishing ideal communities, and in the appalling Scotch mill town of New Lanark, he had founded free schools on the lines of Fellenberg, built model tenements, raised everybody's wages and continued full salaries even when the factory had to be closed for months. For this the

Pharisees railed at him and spit upon him. But his triumphs as a social reformer were bound up with accusations of atheism and of what were then considered tenets of sexual license. To escape the prejudice and calumnies of his enemies he decided to remove to America, taking with him a daughter and his growing sons.

Once in America he rashly published an invitation for all aspiring spirits to join him in the kingdom-come, where would be carried into effect Franklin's dictum that if everybody in the world would only work hard two or three hours a day, nobody would be required to work more in order to sustain himself in modest and wholesome comfort, surrounded only by such lofty luxuries as the fruits of art and science.

Owen had no conception of the number of cranks, knaves, fools, ne'er-do-wells, lazy louts, religious maniacs, cracked-brained theorists, and fanatics for continence or incontinence, that America has always produced. When he had purchased and first visited Harmonie, a village built by the Rappite sect on the lines of a sixteenth century Swabian village, he found all these people waiting for him. And after eight months of wrestling with such riffraff, he was driven back to civilization for help.

In Philadelphia he enlisted the aid of the wealthy Scot, William Maclure, a seer and prophet of modern education, geologist, philanthropist, and donor of innumerable libraries. Maclure added his wealth to Owen's own, gathered up from Philadelphia an astounding number of excellent scientists and educators, and all set forth, as we have seen, covenanting in an ark for a vast program of human betterment.

Frontier Utopians

The sincerity of the people on the Boatload of Knowledge was undeniable, and it was indeed no ordinary menagerie of odd animals locked in this ark in the ice jam. Beside the eminent Mr. Maclure of whom we have spoken there were artists, teachers, and industrial artisans such as printers and engravers. On board was Mr. Speakman, a highly educated pharmacist, in whose Philadelphia shop it was so long the habit of scientists to meet that at last they formed themselves into a society, the Philadelphia Academy of Sciences. An excellent chemist and geologist was Dr. Gerard Troost, a Hollander, while the most famous of the cargo was Charles Alexander Lesueur, the sole survivor of the great La Perouse expedition. Left at Botany Bay to explore the marvels of the Australian fauna, Lesueur had escaped the fate of the brave admiral, whose ships went to pieces on the reefs of the New Hebrides archipelago, all hands lost. Maclure had picked up this ancient mariner in the West Indies, and now his impassive face was turned west, where he was to discover and describe most of the fishes of the Great Lakes and of the greatest river system of North America. As a painter he wielded a brush as dainty as a miniaturist's, but he devoted all his art to the illustration of Nature's smaller miracles. " He looked on," wrote a contemporary, " with a countenance weatherbeaten and worn, for the muscles of his ironbound visage seemed as incapable of motion, as those on medals." Beyond question he was the most brilliant and active zoölogist in his age upon our soil, save only Thomas Say. And at this very moment he was conversing easily with Say upon the deck of the ark.

Philadelphia Academician Say, one of John Bartram's

descendants, was already the scientific hero of Major Long's expedition to the Colorado Rockies, which had failed so signally to locate the sources of the Red River, to endear white Americans to red ones, or accomplish anything lasting save for Say's scientific soundings. He had penetrated north to Pembina, too, and at that moment was the foremost authority upon the insects and molluscs of North America. It is said of him that he described and discovered more species of shells than any one else in the history of conchology, save only two very hasty and slipshod workers in the British Museum. As for our insects, there is no guessing at the number that go to Say's credit. I can only judge from the manual I use for identifying beetles — that largest natural group in all creation — and here, it seems, Say is the author of one in four. But it is much the same story in almost every order of our insects, save only the butterflies, that fairyland for flittery amateurs from which good entomologists pray they be delivered.

From his western exploits Say had returned with hundreds of new insects and shells, mule deer, kit foxes, brown shrews, the coyote (new to science then) and eight of the finest western birds. Indeed, in the course of a shortish life he managed, upon a large share of the commonest animals out in my woods, to set like Solomon the seal of his great name.

Say was, withal, most personable — winning, cultivated, and in those the days of his youth, comely enough to catch a lady's fancy. He had a lively, curious face, and a quick, astonished eye. He wore his hair in a tuft high on his head, rather like a crested flycatcher. In dress he had Philadelphian traditions — the conventional white stock, a starched white waistcoat and a dashingly cut coat, and the same grey beaver high hat with which he had awed and delighted the Dakotas and the Winnebagos. Now as he talked zoölogical shop with the Frenchman, he kept one eye upon the bevy of enchanting schoolgirls that clung and whispered about the person of Madame Marie Louise Fretageot. This learned, positive and precise French lady, with side curls bobbing around her erect little head, was transferring a portion of her polite seminary for well-bred young ladies from Philadelphia to the wilderness, under the aegis of Maclure, and among the tender virgins whom she both loved and perpetually clucked over, was Miss Lucy Sistaire, fairest and brightest of her sisters. Lesueur claimed to be the " uncle " of the beautiful and vivacious Miss Virginia Dupalais, but this I take as the sentiment of a middle-aged man for a lass so young that he may laughingly proclaim his admiration for her. Not so with Say and the genteel Miss Lucy. The affair was serious, and hence unspoken, so long at least as that experienced shepherdess Madame Fretageot wielded the crook over her little ewe lambs.

The wise men from the East were hailed with joy by the dissenting Harmonists. A deputation of children conducted them from the Wabash into the settlement, and they were at once incorporated into the great scheme for sharing all work, disseminating wisdom and bringing about the millennium.

I leave it to a foreigner, Count Bernhard of Saxe-Weimar-Eisenach, to describe the condition of the naturalists under this regime:

" There is a particular costume adopted for the society. That
for the man consists of white pantaloons, buttoned over a boy's
jacket, made of light material, without a collar; that of a woman
of a coat reaching to the knee, and pantaloons such as little girls
wear among us. . . . I renewed acquaintance here with Mr.
Say, a distinguished naturalist from Philadelphia, . . . but unfortunately he had found himself embarrassed in his fortune, and
was obliged to come here as a friend of Mr. Maclure. The gentleman appeared quite comical in the costume of the society, with
his hands covered with hard lumps and blisters, occasioned by
the unusual labor he was obliged to undertake in the garden.
. . . In the evening I paid visits to some ladies, and saw the
philosophy of equality put to a severe test with one of them. She
is named Virginia, from Philadelphia; is very young and pretty,
was delicately brought up and appears to have taken refuge here
on account of an unhappy attachment. While she was singing,
and playing very well on the piano, she was told that the milking
of the cows was her duty, and that they were waiting. Almost in
tears she betook herself to this servile employment, . . . The
cows were milked, in doing which the young girl was trod on by
one and kicked by another. . . . In the evening I visited Madame Fretageot. . . . She is called ' Mother ' by all the young
girls here. The handsomest and most polished of the female
world here, Miss Lucy Sistaire and Miss Virginia, were under
her care. The cows were milked this evening when I came in, and
therefore we could hear [the young ladies'] performance on the
pianoforte, and their charming voices, in peace and quiet." [4]

It will surprise no one to hear that the great communis-
tic experiment lasted but two years. Charter after charter
was drawn up, every compromise tried, there were seces-
sions, expulsions, and finally a towering, scarlet quarrel
between Maclure and Owen. In this Say sided with his

[4] Lockwood, George, *The New Harmony Movement* (D. Appleton
and Co., New York, 1905).

old patron. At last the entire dream collapsed and every one who had come expecting a haven for his innate laziness left reviling Owen. No one except the really sincere remained. Yet New Harmony can boast that it established, in the illiterate backwoods, the first kindergarten in the United States, the first free co-educational board school and industrial school, and indeed the first modern education.

In the person of the brilliant but unstable Frances Wright, New Harmony became the center of early sentiment against negro slavery and for woman's rights. Much that was then ridiculed as impractical and reviled as contrary to morality and God's will, we have now come to accept as moral and natural — the right of a woman to own property in her own name, to receive higher education, to have equal rights in marriage and divorce. At New Harmony, Josiah Warren invented the continuous roller press without which newspapers of today could not appear, and this in an age, and a setting, when many of our pioneer ancestors were unable to read at all. The first regular weather bureau and weather reports in the country emanated from this unfinished capital of human happiness.

But the golden age at New Harmony did not begin until all political and philanthropic agitations had ebbed away and grass grew again in the streets. Learned men continued to flock westward to this goal; the meetings of the Philadelphia Academy of Sciences became so enfeebled by the exodus of naturalists as to be scarcely worth attending. In the period of 1827 to 1875 New Harmony was a spot to which many of the greatest scientists of

Europe made curious or respectful pilgrimages, and the name of New Harmony meant more than New York to the great conchologists, entomologists, geologists and paleobotanists of Paris, Nürnberg, Bremen, Kiel, Krefeld, and Cambridge. For some time the New Harmony post office ranked second in Indiana.

Say's great *American Conchology* began to take shape at New Harmony even in the days of communism; it was quite the sort of costly and learned work of which Messers Owen and Maclure both approved, and quite the type of undertaking that was calculated to annoy and disgust the sons of leisure who had gathered there. The exquisite hand of Lesueur engraved the plates, and Miss Lucy Sistaire found the utmost happiness in hand-painting them, aided by Caroline Tiebout, a little girl of the Fretageot school. This, the first book of its sort ever published in America, was set up, with infinite difficulties as to importing fonts of type and suitable paper stock, and keeping the printers sober. It was issued to an astonished Indiana and an amazed Europe in seven parts. There were interruptions of all sorts, including the elopement of the author and the water-colorist, who ran across the border into Illinois, appeared (apparently still in Harmonist costume) before an astounded preacher, set off home at such a merry pace that the carriage upset, scratching the features of the bride and bridesmaid (the fair Virginia), and returned to face Madame Fretageot and Maclure.

Lucy Say had endured many of the difficulties with Thomas that Lucy Audubon was then having with her John. Say had no care for money. He was content to let

Maclure support and paternalize him as long as he was allowed to go on with his insects and shells. As for mothering, Madame Fretageot continued to run things for the young couple along capable but decided lines. " Say hates business as much as I love it," she wrote, and felt — and enjoyed — the burdens of the whole print shop on her shoulders. She continued to instruct her former pupil, nursed Say through his sicknesses, thwarted the girl in her desire to take Thomas back east, made them both stick to their jobs, dragged the *Conchology* and the *American Entomology* (also the first book of its sort in America) through the press, and generally managed everything with great gusto and entirely to the advantage of science on the frontier, and of the feckless pair. Under her charge François André Michaux's beautiful work on forestry, the *North American Sylva*, was reprinted (after the Paris edition), colored by the girls under her charge, and given to the world.

When the zoölogist Maximilian, Prince of Wied-Neuwied, came to America with a staff of collectors and engravers and artists, he tarried two months at New Harmony.

" Here," he records, " I derived much instruction and entertainment from my intercourse with two highly-informed men, Thomas Say and Mr. Lesueur, . . . My walks and hunting excursions with the two naturalists were very instructive. Mr. Say's house was in a garden, where he cultivated many plants of the interior of Western America. I there saw a large *Maclura aurantiaca* (Nuttall), the bow or yellow wood, or Osage orange, from the river Arkansas, of the wood of which many Indians make their bows. It is a prickly tree, with very tough wood. . . .

" Mr. Say's zoölogical collection was confined to insects and shells. He was less anxious to possess a complete collection than to have a good library, which, thanks to Mr. Maclure, he really possessed, and new insects and shells were sent to him from all parts of the United States, which he immediately describes. He had a very extensive correspondence, even with Europe, and received many conchylia which he used and compared for his work on American conchology. Mr. Say's entomological collection was continually damaged by the rapacious insects, which are much more dangerous and destructive here than in Europe."

Lucy Say remains always a child in Madame Fretageot's letters, a child without judgment or natural inclination to do her duty. But this is unconsciously unfair. Lucy Say grew to the noblest stature of womanhood, a faithful helper, learned in her husband's own subject, herself an excellent conchologist and collector. After Say's death, Lucy remained at New Harmony for many years, receiving an annuity from Maclure. But she did not live to see the beautiful shaft raised to her husband's memory in the town where he had labored and loved. The redoubtable Madame Fretageot, following Maclure to Mexico, died of cholera.

But the light did not go out of New Harmony with all these deaths and departures. Robert Owen's splendid sons grew tall and great where he himself had failed. In 1835 Dr. David Dale Owen began a great geological survey in Indiana. The results were so splendid that the United States Geological Survey moved its staff of map makers and engravers to New Harmony, and more great names than I can mention cluster here about these years. Leidy and distinguished foreigners like Lyell were drawn thither as if by a magnetic pole. In the course of all this investigation, the ancient limestones of New Harmony yielded a wealth of fossils, and here the distinguished paleobotanist and specialist on mosses, Leo Lesquereux, did his classic work.

The full light of glory has passed from New Harmony, but there lingers a soft afterglow. American naturalists as well as students of early communism treat it as a Mecca. Still one may see there the old *Maclura* trees, the osage oranges, planted by Say, the osiers and locusts set out by the Rappites, the beautiful " golden-rain " trees (*Koelreuteria*) that Maclure brought from afar. Virginia Dupalais' spinet-like pianoforte, Madame Fretageot's little clock under a glass dome, precisely telling off the hours to rise and to bed, are treasured still, and over Say's grave his own bird, *Sayornis phoebe*, twirls a sweet monotonous note.

A visitor to New Harmony there was for whom one must reserve a special place — for though one of the most prodigious and prophetic scientists of the century 1750 to 1850, he has been the victim of a secret burial. Even today, when his bones have been lifted from potter's field to a place of honor, the Encyclopaedia Britannica gives not one line to Constantine Samuel Rafinesque. Why the silence? Only because to credit this pioneer with all he did, to show his credentials and claims to a vast amount of priority, would undermine half a dozen exalted scientific reputations. So he has been heaped with ridicule, and burned in the crackling flames of laughter that still feeds upon the man's own follies.

Rafinesque came to Harmonie when it was a Rappite

settlement, to visit the learned Dr. Muller. But he took the liveliest interest in Owen's New Harmony. In the bitterness of his constricted, wounded heart, he exulted, I make no doubt, in Robert Owen's stinging indictment of society. I fancy that he liked the spirit of economic experimentation prevailing in the capital of human betterment, for he devised a few variants of his own and drew up magniloquent plans and projects for his Harmonist friends.

But Rafinesque's career is only tangential to the glory that was New Harmony. It rose to the height of its pyrotechnic parabola in the Kentucky years, in Kentucky, bloody ground, strewn now with the bodies of passenger pigeons, populated by Tom Lincolns and razor-backed hogs. (The trappings of romanticism, the Civil War culture and derring-do were still far off.)

At Lexington there rose in 1789 the walls of a backwoods Oxford, Transylvania University. Its golden age (for its oak wreath withered early) coincided almost precisely with Rafinesque's professorship which endured from 1819 to 1826. That was the tenure of office of the learned President Holley. This classicist, the naturalist-physician, Dr. Short, and Rafinesque gave to Transylvania much of its glister, and though it may have been iron pyrite, it certainly had a golden reputation.

That light is now so thoroughly gone out (though another institution bears the name) that it is difficult to give it just credit. For a parallel to its anomalous, exotic growth in the forest primeval, one would have, I suppose, to go back to some medieval German university set in the forest, ruled by the clergy, supported upon a superstitious peasantry and somewhat scornfully attended by the petty nobility. A Dr. Faustus, dangerously experimenting, tempting the rack or devil-ridden madness, would correspond in a crude way to Rafinesque.

Every few years some one, within the realms of natural history or without them, re-discovers Rafinesque. He has been the most widely celebrated unknown man in science, equaling in brilliant obscurity Roger Bacon or Paracelsus, surpassing those Provençal wise-men, Nicolas Peiresc and Master Arnauld de Villanova. As a universal genius of every branch of science, Rafinesque ranks with Humboldt; he dabbled in more fields than even Réaumur, and it is plainly impossible for any one scientist to estimate the worth of this incredible fellow. For he distinguished himself in archaeology, botany, conchology, icthyology and the study of reptiles, mammals and meteorology. He dabbled, at least, in Indian languages, history, ornithology and insects.

Amongst all the naturalists who have ever worked on the American continent, Rafinesque is the only one who might clearly be called a titan. He had a voracious appetite for discovery, an energy that would have carried him triumphantly through the career of a Humboldt, a Darwin, a Linnaeus, all in one. But he had no mental discipline, no capacity to see any subject through to a conclusion, no respect for the work of others, no care for how he wounded feelings or made enemies, and absolutely no sense of humor. He carried Linnaeanism in its Flamboyant Period to the most strained and gargoylish insecurity, made himself absurd, failed at everything in life — and somehow remains greater far than the men who jeered at him, like peevish Dr. Baldwin the botanist, sarcastic Featherstonhaugh the geologist. When Rafinesque took the chair of natural history at Transylvania, he was already the author of some two hundred and fifty unread books and articles, an absentee member of a score of most learned societies of Europe and America, and an unrecognized authority on Mediterranean marine zoology. Cuvier had blasted his reputation because in the pickled specimens of Sicilian fishes he dissected he could not see the iridescent beauty Rafinesque described. Of his foreign fame the students knew nothing — hillbilly boys in coonskins who paid their tuition in tobacco leaf, young blades of emigrated Virginia families, eager to mock, to swagger, to duel, and to marry young and rich. To them he was only a comical, whimsical foreigner, a queer-spoken little mossback —

". . . in personal stature about the size and appearance of my deceased friend, the late John Quincy Adams, but I think he had a full suit of hair and black eyes. Professor Rafinesque had a room in the college proper and was a man of peculiar habits and was very eccentric, but was to me one of the most interesting men I have ever known.

" He often lectured to the students in College and in a most entertaining manner to the great delight of his audience. His lecture on the ants was peculiarly instructive and interesting, causing many of the students to laugh heartily when he gave us the history of ants, especially when he described them as having lawyers, doctors, generals and privates, and of their having great battles and of the care by physicians and nurses of the wounded." [5]

---

[5] From Call, Richard Ellsworth, *Life and Writings of Rafinesque* (The Filson Club, Louisville, Ky., 1895).

Frontier Utopians

A girl remembers:

" His classroom was the scene of the most free and easy behavior. . . . A most eccentric person, his extreme absent mindedness contributing to his foreign ways to make him peculiar. . . . He went into Society while in Lexington, and was a good dancer but had no conversation save on his favorite topics. . . . Mrs. Holley, the wife of the President, took a motherly supervision over this lone friendless little creature, while at Transylvania University, and saw that he ate his dinner, that the mud from his various expeditions was removed from his garments, and his hair was combed and his face washed." [6]

To this Rafinesque adds the crowning touch in the picture of the traditional professor of natural history — that he never went out collecting without carrying an umbrella. I could not say if it was a green one.

Audubon can be relied upon to limn a man with the puckish finger of caricature. In his *Episodes of Western Life*, he relates a visit from a Mr. de T——, but no one will question for a moment who it is that walks into his pages in " a long loose coat of yellow nankeen, much the worse for the many rubs it has got in its time and stained all over with the juice of plants."

Rafinesque, according to the storekeeper-ornithologist of Henderson, Kentucky, bore a letter of introduction from a friend who said he was sending Audubon an odd fish. Without cracking a smile the wicked Frenchman asked his visitor to show him the odd fish, and since no actual finny specimen was forthcoming, proceeded to fill him up with a Paul Bunyan yarn about the diamond-

[6] From Fitzpatrick, T. J., *Rafinesque, a Sketch of his Life* (Historical Department of Iowa, Des Moines, 1911).

scale stonefish, which he well knew Rafinesque would hasten to publish as a new species. " All is new, new! " mocked his friend Torrey, and Rafinesque admits the charge. When he visited the Falls of the Ohio, to collect the marvelous fresh-water molluscs, practically every one was new, he claimed. And they were! The astonishing thing about this fellow is that you no sooner set him down for a poltroon than he becomes a wizard. If the rules of priority were strictly and justly applied, Rafinesque would be found to have antedated a large part of the work of Say amongst shells, of his enemy Harlan amongst mammals, in botany of Gray and De Candolle. For well nigh a century there has prevailed a tendency to ignore him and all his works, that was broken up at last by David Starr Jordan and Edward Lee Greene, himself an eccentric, a Rafinesque of the western states.

But Audubon does not let Rafinesque off with jibes at his personal appearance. In the night, Audubon assures us, he was awakened by a roar from the guest-room, and entering he beheld the indefatigable naturalist stark naked and cavorting about the room as he essayed to knock down with the wreck of Audubon's Cremona violin a cloud of bats which, he gasped, were all new species. He was short, and out of breath, and begged his host to wing some specimens down for him. This, with the neck of his Cremona, the complaisant Audubon did.

The whole tale may well be a flight of Audubon's fancy, but it has fixed in the public mind the idea of bats and Rafinesque in an indelible and ludicrous cartoon. Yet try as I may, I cannot erase this connection. Like the fantastic mammals amongst whom he left a name, he was erratic, fond of caves, unjustly loathed and feared, creating many a repulsive impression, given to showing his entirely harmless teeth and grimacing, and withal a wonderful little creature, all ears and eyes, a fellow who unlike his brother mammals has the power to get off the ground of the literal, take flight above our heads in regions half-twilit but starry.

Rafinesque returned from one of his wandering journeys to find that President Holley, a headstrong man without interest in natural history, had thrown out all his specimens and turned his classroom and museum to other uses. The poor fellow departed without, so far as one knows, sympathy from any one, leaving his curses on Transylvania and Holley. And not in vain, for the very next year the Fundamentalist students drove the Unitarian Holley from his chair, and he was drowned at sea. And not long after, the college burned to the ground. So passed learning in the wilderness.

Rafinesque died alone, in agony and the most abject poverty, on Race Street in Philadelphia, surrounded by the hopeless confusion of his precious specimens, and copies of his nine hundred and thirty books and pamphlets. His effects were sold as old junk, his body flung into potter's field. Only after his death was it discovered, from his will, that long ago, in a golden clime, in an hour of human warmth and trust, he had loved a woman, a Sicilian girl. But when, far from Palermo, he lost his fortune, the jade ran off with a comedian. His little boy, Charles Linnaeus, had died in infancy; his daughter became a stage singer, and was never heard of more. So ended the bright stream in sands of oblivion.

But he too had seen the great pigeon flights, the rainbow-tinted shells, the flashing finny tribe, the lisping cane brakes, and the deep dark cypress swamps. He had known in his hour the purest delights of Nature's votaries.

"Every step," he wrote, "taken into the fields, groves and hills, appears to afford new enjoyments, Landscapes and Plants. . . . Here is an old acquaintance seen again; there a novelty or a rare plant, perhaps a new one! greets your view; you hasten to pluck it, examine it, admire and put in your book. Then you walk on thinking what it might be, or may be made by you hereafter. You felt an exultation, you are a conqueror, you have made a conquest over Nature, you are going to add a new object, or a page to science. This peaceful conquest has cost no tears, but fills your mind with a proud sensation of not being useless on earth, of having detected another link in the creative power of God."

12

ROSE SPECTACLES: GOETHE AND THE ROMANTICISTS

THE small Saxon capital of Weimar was asleep in its memories of Bach and Luther, when there arrived at the impoverished court of Prince Karl August a young god, Johann Wolfgang von Goethe. He was the archetype of that indefinable human sub-species, the Nordic, by which we never mean anything that can be anthropometrically described or discovered. But rather, those who fancy they belong to it would imply that it is everything upstanding, gifted, pure, great and superior.

Karl August was already supporting two poets, a middling one and the admirable but somewhat puritanical Schiller. Into their midst came Goethe like a swan descending among ducks, and Karl August, whose favorite and only companions had been soldiers and dogs, suddenly went *echt romantisch*, indulged in madcap hunts, caroused with Goethe in a bark-coated hunting lodge, reduced his girth by taking up the art of skating on the *Schwannsee*, and capped all by making this poet fellow his secretary of state.

Goethe was not one of those geniuses who demand to shine in solitary splendor. He persuaded the irritable poet Herder, the rash, precocious philosopher Schelling, and the peasant visionary and half-trained anatomist Oken to come and scintillate at Weimar. Add to this a group of brilliant women, poetesses and (something more difficult to be) wives of poets, and you have the famous coterie in which the German Romantic movement in poetry and science was born.

Everything at Weimar was " *genial*," that is to say, tinctured with genius; every one read his works and the others all applauded. Love affairs, too, were upon the plane of genius, so that when Schelling fell in love with the intellectual Karoline Michaelis, wife of the Romantic critic Schlegel, a gambit was played which astonished nobody in Weimar. *Herr und Frau* Schlegel offered as compromise their young daughter, but while Schelling was waiting for the maiden to grow up, she fell ill, and owing largely to the philosopher's confidence in his medical powers, she died. So, by mutual consent, Schlegel divorced his wife, and Schelling and Karoline were married. It was all acceptable because so *genial*. This is not the proper place to tell all one might about Goethe's life, and indeed with all this company of luminaries it were best that we keep our minds severely upon their cerebral attainments.

Romanticism was in the air; Rousseau was the first symptom of it, with his belief in the good peasant, the natural goodness of the primitive. He made naturalness fashionable, persuaded court ladies to suckle their babies, and put his own little daughter in an orphan asylum. Or, turn to music; they say that Romantic opera was born with the opening bars of the *Freischütz* overture. You will remember the lisp of the forest leaves, the murmuring of brooks, and then those shivering strings that suggest some mystery at the heart of Nature. In poetry it is not possible in English to find the beginning of Romanticism, because ours is a naturally romantic poetry, and classicism is exceptional; we may admire classicism but never love it. But in France they first felt the coming of Romanticism as the century opened. Nature invaded the consciousness of the world. No longer the property of naturalists only, it went suddenly into a vulgate edition. It became a Bible in the vernacular, in which every one could read at least a little, and from which he might preach in plenty.

The temper of science today, and normally, is so far from the Romantic that even to repeat the formulae of Romanticism, which was called " natural philosophy," is to rouse the scorn of the scientific mind. Not so with poets and the public. Romanticism believed, as we have all at one time or another longed to believe, in the oneness of Nature — the greater Nature, embracing God and man, stars out in space, rocks and crystals here on earth, pollen and sap, seed and womb. Kant put it for himself when he wrote his gravestone legend, " The starry heavens above me, the sense of duty within me." A poet — perhaps you can tell me who it was — proclaimed that every star is needed for a rose.

In short, Romanticism set out avowedly to establish a universal science, and I am far from ridiculing this aim. Our aims today are cautious, niggardly, unattached to fundamentals. One science is out of touch with another, and they are all shockingly out of touch with philosophy, art and religion. There *is* a one-ness about Nature, but scientists are lazy about looking for it.

Take a single example, the sexuality of plants. If ever there was a case of one-ness, this is it. There is not a point of difference between the fundamentals of animal and vegetable sexuality. If the two kingdoms had, back in that protean stage and age when organisms were as much plant as animal, derived sexuality from a common source, there would be nothing surprising in it. But their connecting links and primitive forms are asexual. Yet in spite of this they moved toward male-ness and female-ness and conjunction, on parallel tracks, just as if one and the same cause evoked the troublous mystery of sex from all living things. What mechanical or vital force this was, no one knows, but could we discover it, we would have made a great step toward the establishment of a universal science. I think that even the mind most skeptical of Romantic natural philosophy will appreciate the value of such a science, and indeed what good are the sciences if they are not expressions of universality? I do not see how there can be more than one science. It is really what both the mechanists and vitalists are striving for.

The Weimar school started off so badly that you have to look hastily in the back of the book to reassure yourself that things are going to end well. No matter how you try to defend Goethe and the Goethesque, you must admit at the start that in spite of its high aims, natural philosophy opens the door to the most rose-water teleology — the belief that everything is for the best in a sweetly Transcendental world, everything serving a useful and appointed purpose. This is the soft food on which many people prefer to feed, and they are angry or tearful if you take it away from them. The only trouble with it is that its professors will not allow you to cite any exceptions against them. Anything that does not fit into their picture is a puzzle piece which you are still too stupid to find a place for, but a divine intelligence knows where it belongs, even if you do not. Under these conditions, inquiry into the nature of Nature goes forward very fast at first, while its devotees are working to the glory of God, every circumstance offering evidence of divine ingenuity. But as soon as the work grows difficult, its leaders throw up the job, saying that it is the business of tiresome specialists to work out the details. So in the end, research languishes; the magnificent bridge to the stars remains an uncompleted arc reaching into the stream of ether. But then, it might not have borne traffic, anyway.

It was from Plato that the Romantics derived the idea of archetypes, and like some concepts Platonic it both is and is not. If the Republic did not exist, it ought to. So Goethe, writing to Herder from Naples, could say that he was about to penetrate —

" at last the mystery of the origin and organization of plants. The aboriginal plant will be the oddest thing in the world, and Nature herself shall envy me. With this model and this key, one will invent an infinity of new plants which, if they do not exist, might exist, and which, far from being the reflection of an artistic and poetic imagination, will have an imminent, real and necessary existence, and this creative law may be applied to everything that has any sort of life."

Goethe means that when you walk in the cool of the evening amidst your garden beds, where the sphinx moths are hovering and sipping in the long tubular corollas of the phlox, you will, if your mind be tranquil and attuned, begin to perceive how every flower face has its fundamental plan. There is not only symmetry but an underlying numerology, and upon a very few number schemes Nature has, as it were, improvised the most enchanting variations. Three, four and five, or their multiples, rarely two, more rarely still one or seven, these are the primitive motifs of floral arrangement. The most fanciful orchid in the world is but a play upon the fundamental symmetry of three. The botanist can make a conventionalized schematic diagram of any floral plan, such as will instantly convey to a colleague who may never happen to have seen such a flower in his life, the relationships of the various parts — that is, their position and number. The botanist can even construct for a whole family of plants a schematic picture so generalized that it will fit any member of the family without, however, being actual representations of an individual, real species. Such is an archetype, and Plato and Goethe both knew that archetypes do not exist. They thought of them as those perfect fundamentals entertained in Eternal Intelligence as beautiful ideas. Of these ideas, basically mathematical, as so many thinkers agree God's ideas ought to be, a living being is but an imperfect copy.

Goethe wrote Herder about this notion, but the fact seems to be that he derived it from Herder. Goethe had seven great scientific theories and could seldom remember from whom he had borrowed any of them, but he frequently returned them with a fine flourish, as if they were original with him and generous gifts. If there is anything we hate, it is to be reminded of our debts.

Archetypes became the rage. What a fascinating problem, with pencil and paper, by numerology or by right elevations, to construct the archetype of man and his ape cousins! Or to extend it till it was the skeleton key that would fit any anatomical lock amongst the mammals. Back of this archetype there must flit one even archer, a creature that abstracted both the mammal, the bird, and the reptile, contained all within itself, both was and was not any one of these. As Oken so succinctly put it, " All is in the All," and " the ground principle of all mathematics is this, that zero equals zero."

The great anatomist for the Romantic school, Richard Owen, was faced with the dilemma of finding an archetype for all vertebrates, but in order not to include anything in it that was not found in the simplest vertebrate, namely the lampreys, his fabulous animal became reduced simply to a backbone, and as there is no way to separate the vertebrates sharply from *Amphioxus*, a sandburrowing, inter-tidal dweller as much a worm as not, even the vertical rod will have to be abandoned and in its place we can put nothing but a flaccid notochord of cartilage.

Goethe took a passionate partisan interest in the argument between Cuvier and Geoffroy St. Hilaire on unity of plan; he was, of course, dead against Cuvier. And the German poet himself contributed the most remarkable theory of all in support of a single structural schema throughout all animal anatomy. He tells this story: He was walking in the old Jewish cemetery in Venice when his servant picked up a ram's skull, jokingly proffering it as the cranium of some Shylock; he let the skull drop, and the cranial bones broke open along their sutures. It suddenly flashed upon Goethe that the skull, after all, might be a sort of compacted, foreshortened, anastomosed vertebral column, grown together into a helmet-like whole over the brain.

This fallacious short cut to universal truth was fruitful of the worst results in the Romantic movement. Oken found unity of plan in every part of the body; the head he considers a sort of small torso, the mouth corresponds to the stomach, the nares to the trachea, the gray matter to the spinal marrow, and the head even has its articulated appendaged limbs, man's much overworked jaws. Such hallucinations speak for themselves.

There is no space to tell of Goethe's theories of light, that flew in the face of Newtonian optics, of his physics of music and his long anatomical investigations that proved the existence of the curious intermaxillary bone in the walrus but not, as he supposed, in man. He is most famous for his metamorphosis theory, and as coincidence would have it, he hit upon it while musing upon palm flowers at Monaco, whose vegetation had proved so thought-provoking to Lamarck (of whom Goethe never, unfortunately, heard).

In case you have no palm handy, the easiest way to see what Goethe meant by the metamorphosis of plants is to pluck yourself a water-lily or a peony; you will observe that the outer parts of the flower, the green sepals, are scarcely distinguishable from leaves, and there appears to be no definite zone where you can tell the sepals from the petals. Petals pass almost imperceptibly into the male circle of the stamens, and it is not too hard to imagine that the pistils at the center are themselves merely modified leaves expressed in female-ness. As a fruit is but a ripened ovary, so every fruit, whether a berry or a pod or what have you, is but a variant of the archetype of vegetation, the green leaf. As it were, the exalted poet saw the vegetable world one great, light-sensitive, creative, protean and nutrifying Leaf. Given vegetative conditions, this Leaf is photo-synthetic and respiratory in function. But starve it a bit, and in fear of death it hastens to save its life by reproduction; it is metamorphosed into those sexual leaves we call the flower.

This bold hypothesis, by no means original with Goethe, pre-Linnaean indeed, is right in principle (however romantically exaggerated in detail), if any Platonism is admissible to science. Such metamorphosis is Ideal; if you are a Platonist, this makes it realer than real, but you must be careful not to make Goethe's mistake and confuse it with the cases of actual metamorphosis when by freakery one organ turns into another.

His *Spiraltendenz* was another effusion of genius. Here he sought to show that the upward growth of stems is due to a natural, inscrutable life-force, and is male, but the spiral tendency of climbing plants is female. It would be frivolous of us to suspect that Goethe's conception of himself as an oak and Romantic woman as the twining ivy in any way influenced his views. It is more important to remember that this charming theory twisted and spiraled up until it was metamorphosed into quite something other — the phyllotaxis of plants.

Take any commonest weed in your fingers and turn it slowly about, counting how many complete revolutions of the stem you must make ere you encounter a leaf that springs directly above the one from which you began to calculate. For the disposition of foliage is not random; it is so devised that leaves shall overshadow each other as little as possible, and the orderly rhythm which plants thus keep may be expressed as a fraction, the number of turns divided by the number of leaves.

Here is a simple, solid, interesting fact, but to what ethereal delights it led the Romantics! It has been taken to prove that grand and loose assertion that numbers are at the bottom of everything. Pythagorean numerologists soon saw God in these vegetable fractions; they found rhythms and vibrations in the twirling of a mint stem; (they ignored the fact that mints with their leaves opposite in pairs are a direct argument against the spiral theory of leaf arrangement). They discovered that if you arranged the well-known phyllotactic fractions in a linear series, you can have all sorts of fun juggling numerators and denominators, forecasting the next logical fraction, even though Nature never practises it. A long time ago Aristotle tweaked the long nose of the Pythagoreans. They seem to think, he said, that numbers are themselves the essence of things, whereas they have no existence at all.

Numerology soared superbly, in the quinary system. Here the number five is taken to be God's own, and not only can we see that many flowers are arranged upon a

JOHANN WOLFGANG VON GOETHE,
founder of the Romantic School of natural history and philosophy.
(Portrait by J. K. Stieler, 1828)

plan of five, but the British ornithologists Swainson and Vigors were able to perceive that God had arranged all species, genera and families in quincunxes or five-systems. It was a case of the Emperor's new clothes — if you could not see quincunxes you were a dolt and a knave. If you professed to see them, it was wiser not to try to describe what you saw, and in consequence the elect would never define or explain. You had to worship a mystery. But presently no one was deceived by it except the two weavers themselves. If you want quincunxes at their best, I suggest you do not go to science for them, but to the fragrant pages of *The Garden of Cyrus* by Sir Thomas Browne, who seems to have worked out the fractions of phyllotaxy long before any one else, and indeed to have been the first and still unhonored discoverer of the sexuality of plants.

So, of course, Natural Philosophy after all discovered no universal science. That science is still needed, and any one who has a desire to carve his name even higher than Aristotle's has but to conceive and prove it.

But I promised that the Romantic chapter would end well, as romances should. Practically nothing was wasted of all this high-flown thinking. Archetypes were metamorphosed into Darwinian prototypes, that is to say, those simplified, generalized animals and plants that actually once existed, ancestral forms, " missing links," as they are popularly called. A great deal came to be learned about the spiral ducts of plants as a result of trying to find the *ewige Weiblichkeit* in clinging ivy. The Romantic Carus's " spheres within spheres " end happily in von Baer's discovery of the most interesting sphere in the ani-

[279]

mal world, the mammalian egg cell. There is, after all, a kind of unity of plan, connected with the metamorphosis of organs; the search for it cleared up the confusion between resemblances and relationships, got us free of analogy and established homology.

Metamorphosis itself implied that the stuff of life is plastic, that one thing may become something else. Change was shown to be possible. Where men had thought that Creation Once and For All was self-evident, and the fixity of species something to cling to in a naughty world, a new hope dawned upon them. Instead of fixity there might be plasticity, fluidity, an upward surge. The flaw that had prevented Buffon from doing anything with his furtive *transformisme* was that he saw it in reverse; it looked to him as though man had deteriorated into other forms of life; he saw things as " degraded." Change was a sinking. But the Romanticists did this for the philosophy of science: they put a poet's upward gaze into our vision, they put a hope in men's hearts to make them ready for the great fact about to be proved, the fact of evolution.

13

ULTIMATE ISLES: DARWIN AND WALLACE

IMAGINE some planet, before man came upon it, called it home, and pretended to himself that the sun and the moon and the stars wheel around it, as some celestial storm upon its epicenter. Imagine, say, the third planet from the sun (not yet called Earth), in some bygone age, when Time was not marked off, save by the rhythm of night and day. Imagine the ocean, spawning up nameless things neither beautiful nor hideous since there is no intellect to pass a childish judgment upon them, and the earth still raw, belching forth from volcanic vents rivers and sheets of lava descending to the sea, pouring out plains, primordial fertility. Think of a world of primitive colors, unweathered metallic greens and blues, of flame and ash, of blackness and pure whiteness — nothing anywhere softened; never a drifting, dream-castle cloud in the astronomically abstract and featureless blue sky, save a single inky condensation that may not escape its mooring to a few of the highest peaks. Conceive of a nearly windless world, save for one empty-hearted meaningless wind that sets perpetually from the same quarter, a mere eternal stellar draft ever upon the same cheek of the mountains, and, on the other, a constant stagnant doldrum. Imagine lunar scenery, harsh and cruel, rocks unweathered, new, just barely scaled with the first sprawling sage crust of lichens; no trees, only scrub; no sweet sandy beach for lisping waters and long sleep, only rock against sea, bordered by a fringe of sea-wrack, kelp, sargasso-weed, all the strange leathery Algae of the ocean, red and brown, sage green and emerald, rising and falling with the breathing of the tide.

How would the modern mind people such a setting? People it, that is, with animals, with creatures of the by-gone past. If you pretend (and who has not?) that of all humans only you had power to step back into Time and walk the rocks and breathe the airs of bygone ages upon earth, you would bring back to life the monsters among whose reconstructed, upheld skeletons you have wandered in a museum. Their creaky joints would move again; skin and scale and hide and hair and feather would come back to clothe them; here and there a voice, a hiss, the cracked beginnings of bird song, would break through an awesome silence. And from the pasty red earth, first emollient of the naked lava, would thrust up the stems of primitive plants that seemed to struggle, but half fail, to flower.

This world of yours, conceived as a group of undiscovered, enchanted islands far out at sea, as a bubble world that no wind came to break, conceived (let us say) in a fever dream, or under the influence of ether, might contain lava-colored lizards crawling up out of the sargasso slime of the tidal rocks, to stare inland at the erupting volcanoes. Ashore, there swarms another lizard species, whip-quick and vicious-fanged, the color of ash and flame; you see one knock at the base of a great cactus like a stone pillar, until the spiny scarlet fruit plops down. Then the lizard gobbles it, spines and all, down her leather throat. Presently a male rears himself as in a dance before the female, nods this way and that for her; but instead of granting her reptilian favors, she starts up, taller than he, her scarlet throat swelling, and suddenly spits upon him and darts off. As she goes she scuttles amid the enormous plastrons and carapaces, the empty top and bottom shells, of a giant land tortoise that became extinct only last year. In the half-marshes (copper-blue, brackish sheets of water lying upon quicksand) the gutted shards lie about like fragments of Ali Baba oil jars. Short time ago these creaky giants, traveling three or four miles a day in their search for rare sweet water, made tracks through the impenetrable cactus and thorn-tree jungle, a thicket so nearly leafless that though the wind blows stiffly through it, it makes no sound, whispers nothing, has nothing to say, since it, age-long, experiences nothing.

But perhaps it will be more entertaining not to have all the giant tortoises extinct. Postulate for your amusement other imaginary islands in your enchanted archipelago, with other species on it. Say that it is spring now, when the tortoises mate — a spring not distinguished from summer or winter by any special sweetness or renewal of life, but only by a ripening of sluggish reptilian glands, the awakening of a thoughtless hunger. All over the island now the males are roaring and bellowing with it, fighting, clawing, and falling from the lava cliffs.

But you may sweeten this world with birds. Primitive,

most of them must be — yawping pelicans, and gracile albatrosses wandered in from the sea to brush you with the fixed glassy focus of an alien intelligence. You may have strange gulls the color of lava, and members of all the primitive, now decimated and retreating families. There will be flycatchers (that order that just begins to have a singing voice), mockingbirds who do not keep the trees but run upon the beaches, bobbing and teetering like sandpipers, ground-doves with black and white wings, little scarlet feet, and cerulean blue faces, grosbeak finches the color of the newest black lava, cormorants that have forgotten how to fly, penguins washed hither upon some ice-flow from the Antarctic, frigate birds with blazing scarlet throat pouches swelled out in the pride, the waste beauty of procreation, stilted incredible flamingoes, egrets in snowy bridal plumage — you may listen in fancy to all their harsh, primitive cries. You may even add a northern bird or two, something familiar to you, something sweet of voice and graceful of form; fancy, if you like, that the rather honeyed lisping twitter of our yellow warbler rises from the sun-baked thorn scrub distilling its alchemical stench. A flight of Hudsonian curlews, migrating and crying thinly, sweeps across your island. A bobolink in his winter moult is there, and a yellow-crowned night-heron that, even in Illinois, looks like something left over from the Tertiary.

One may paint these sea crabs scarlet or cobalt, that twiddle their eyes on long stalks, and gesticulate with their appendages. It is too early for all land mammals, but you may have female sea lions rolling on their backs on the rocks, to have their teats sucked, hypnotized with the sensuous delights of furry maternity. Through your empty airs black bees will dart, and black butterflies, grasshoppers more gorgeous than fritillaries, and giant dragonflies.

Your modern mind, anachronistically peeping thus, perceives the gaps, the lacks, the lacunae, the eloquent absences from this scene, of so much that makes up modern richness and beauty. The tops of every branch of evolutionary development seem to be missing, or merely sketched with a suggestive line here and there. Where are the mammals, where all the singing and perching birds, where the snakes, the frogs?

And above all, the one wanderer in this harsh Eden is astounded at the tameness of the animals. They look at him with curiosity, follow him about. Ground-doves settle on his shoulders; a hawk allows itself to be knocked down with a stick; a sea lion when stroked becomes almost cataleptic with the pleasure of the manipulation. This same truce the beasts have between each other. There is eating and being eaten, but there exists, too, a tremendous, nerveless insensibility. Creatures of unlike species roll over each other with the indifference of sand grains in a hurrying stream. It is a world so old and so new that change has not come to it, a charmed circle within which no intrusive organism with new means of aggression seems ever to have stepped. It is a dream that does not fade. It is *Las Encantadas*, the Enchanted Isles — Galápagos.

On the sixteenth of August, 1835, H.M.S. *Beagle* dropped anchor among the Enchanted Isles. A delicate-looking young man of twenty-six, named Charles Darwin, came ashore, stepping gingerly upon the razor-edged lava that cut his shoes at once to their uppers. Darwin's first impression was one of repulsion:

". . . the whole black Lava, *completely* covered by small leafless brushwood & low trees. The fragments of Lava where most porous, are reddish like cinders; the stunted trees show little signs of life. The black rocks heated by the rays of the Vertical sun, like a stove, give to the air a close & sultry feeling. The plants also smell unpleasantly. The country was compared to what we might imagine the cultivated parts of the Infernal regions to be." [1]

But perhaps any land looked better to Darwin than the open water, for it is a prime handicap with a naturalist upon a world voyage on a sailing ship, to be as subject to seasickness as he. It was a painful surprise to him, this malady, but his very presence on the *Beagle* was astonishing. There were half a hundred young men better trained than he for his berth. The education befitting a young Victorian gentleman, as taught at Dr. Butler's school in Shrewsbury, consisted in Greek, Latin and the principles of religion, and fitted him for Christ's College, Cambridge. From those Gothic halls and green lawns one might emerge a gentleman or a doctor, but scarcely a naturalist. The actual scientific training of Charles Darwin was so scanty that the modern mind would dismiss it as a smattering which would probably best be unlearned, so that the young man might start all over again at fundamentals. The Victorian method of emphasizing dead languages made the Englishman incapable of handling modern ones flexibly, and Darwin knew practically

[1] Darwin, Charles, *The "Beagle" Diary* (edited by Nora Barlow) (University Press, Cambridge, 1933).

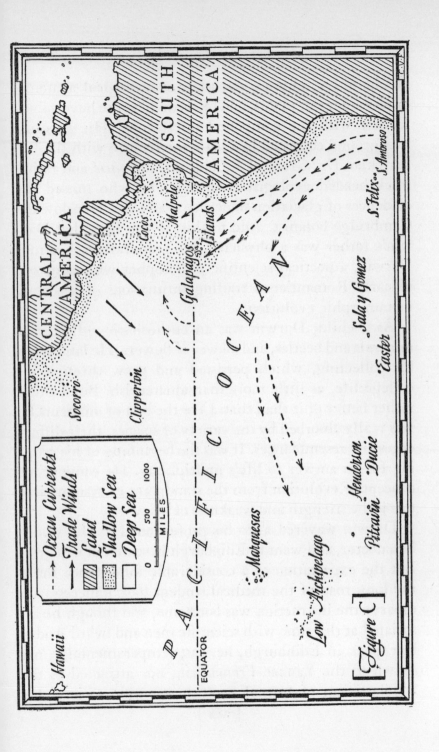

[Figure C]

no chemistry, physics, essentials of zoölogical anatomy, or physiology of plants, and he seems never to have gained facility with the compound microscope. His scientific background consisted in a little intercourse with the Lamarckian Dr. Grant of Edinburgh, the *passé* and rather thick-headed geologist Sedgwick (he who missed the evidences of glaciation under his nose) and Henslow the Cambridge botanist. Add to this, if you like, that Darwin's father was a physician, his grandfather, Erasmus Darwin, a poetical scientific philosopher who came out of early Romanticism trailing intimations of a sort of metamorphic evolution.

As a child, Darwin was an enthusiastic collector of minerals and beetles, and a lover of flowers. He later rated his collecting, which persisted and grew through his college life, as little more than amateurish. But I think rather better of it than that. Like the best of amateurs he was really absorbed by the variety of species, their differences and resemblances. It was the beginning of his groping for an answer to life's multiplicity. He came at his concept of evolution from the standpoint of systematics; this is the strength and weakness of his case.

Darwin wavered as to his profession. First he would be a doctor, and went to Edinburgh in search of a degree. But the expectation of a considerable inheritance made the long road of the medical student look unnecessarily dreary; the instruction was boresome, and though he associated at this time with scientific men and heard Audubon speak in Edinburgh, he was, temperamentally, not drawn to the Yankee-Frenchman, nor attracted to the Scholasticism of formal Scottish scientific society. He finally fled the medical theater altogether, for reasons with which I am personally sympathetic — his heart had failed him at the shrieks of a child bound to the operating table in the days before anesthetics.

Next he pondered the ministry, read Pearson on the creeds, took it all for revealed truth, and (this gives us great hope for him as a future genius of science) finding there was nothing further to argue or discover, lost interest in theology. Still, he took a Greek Testament on the *Beagle*, resolved to read a few verses every day. But there is no evidence that one crackle was ever heard out of its leaves.

The greatest scientific influence of his young days was undoubtedly Lyell's book on the principles of geology. Philosophically it prepared him for the theory that bears his name, by expounding the chronology of geological time, and practically it served him as a manual on all his travels. Indeed, geology was the one subject in which Darwin was thoroughly founded. Reading Humboldt's *Travels* had fired him with a desire to add a great page to science.

One autumn day he returned from pheasant-shooting in Wales to find a letter from Professor Henslow which stated that Captain Fitz-Roy of the *Beagle*, about to start upon a hydrographic and geodetic survey of the world, had offered to share his cabin with any young naturalist who would consent to come without pay. I suppose that the fates in their infinite prevision and wisdom had arranged for the elimination of every other conceivable candidate. Swainson, Waterton, Owen and Lyell should certainly more properly have gone, but doubtless they were too old or too occupied, too burdened with family or too canny to work without salary. And so, wiser than he knew, Henslow picked young Charles Darwin.

Darwin went to London to meet Fitz-Roy, one of these infallible judges of human nature who make up their minds about you from an occult ability to read physiognomies. Fitz-Roy misdoubted Darwin's nose, but finally consented to let the young fellow share a cabin with a descendant of Charles II (whose own nose was not too modest). It is but fair to add that Fitz-Roy, though a short-tempered unreasonable martinet and Tartar on the quarterdeck, was an excellent marine surveyor and expert meteorologist, and that the very idea of including a naturalist on the voyage was his own. He poured his personal money into the expedition, and was never reimbursed by the government.

Even in the harbor (where they lay for weeks) Darwin was seasick. And when at last, in black December weather, they put out to sea, the poor fellow began his five years of constant suffering, for the *Beagle*, at best no more than a bobbing cork by modern standards, was probably a wretched ship even for its day. Nobody, Darwin wrote home, who has been seasick for twenty-four hours knows anything about it; the disease is scarcely felt until at the end of a month or so it sets in with full vigor on top of total prostration, starvation and despair. There is little doubt that five continuous years of nausea and a disarranged system wrecked Darwin's health, and made him the rest of his life a nervous and physical invalid. The food was wretched, the cabin cramped. He had not as much space for his specimens, books and instruments as a lady would need for her clothes on a luxury liner. And the life of a ship was undoubtedly distasteful to him. The voyage began with the swinging of the cat and men in irons, and probably never rose high above the eighteenth century level of sea life made famous in the voyage of the *Bounty*. In this harsh life Darwin, of course, passed as a privileged character, but he was sensitive, beauty-loving, scholarly. Aboard, his nickname was " Philosopher."

And deep were the thoughts he pondered, as the *Beagle* sailed her leisurely five years around the world. More than the Galápagos did Darwin see — coral atolls, volcanic isles of the South Seas, last, lost bird-rocks of the antarctic waters, and South America, afloat and afoot. Better scientific expeditions there have certainly been, better equipped, more thorough, richer in collections. One thinks of Bates's years and years in the Amazonian jungles, where he worked out his theory of mimicry and protective coloration, of the poet-naturalist Chamisso among the coral islands, of Savigny collecting all of three continents' wildfowl in their common meeting ground of upper Egypt, of Pallas everywhere in the Tsar's Asiatic dominions. There is a great saga in the world travels of Humboldt and his even more adventurous colleague, Bonpland, he who fell into the hands of Dr. Francia, the mad dictator of Paraguay, and was kept an honored prisoner for years, while Francia defied all Europe, and Bonpland, hiding from his spouse, kept Francia between himself and her. The story of the exploration of China and Tibet by naturalists is packed with adventure, and I have not even touched upon the history of our own West, where David Douglas carved his name so high, or of arctic America, where Sir John Richardson penetrated so long ago, and left so little for his followers to discover.

Great days, great adventures, mountain-high results. But the *Beagle* voyage outweighs any ten of them. Yet the *Times* sent no reporters down to interview Darwin when he sailed away. Destiny is seldom recognized until it has changed its name to history.

By the time that Darwin had returned to England, after five years of voyaging, his specimens and letters had already made him famous. He had the *entrée* now to all of scientific Britain. The great anatomist Richard Owen was his friend at once, and glad to serve him with identifications of his collections. Young Joseph Dalton Hooker, the botanist, was his intimate; Lyell the geologist was eager to cultivate him. Robert Brown, the gentle, soft-spoken Linnaeus of Australia, allowed him to peer through a microscope at a cell; when Darwin asked what was this curious circulating current he saw, Brown smiled and characteristically murmured, " That's my little secret." It was the " Brownian movement," the spontaneous streaming of protoplasm, as disturbing for human eyes to see as the procession of the suns of space across a telescopic field, and fraught, as much, with human destiny.

There were dinner parties and important meetings to dazzle the young man; he met the great historians of the age, Buckle and Macaulay, Carlyle, Grote, and Motley. Humboldt, visiting, asked especially to meet the naturalist of the *Beagle*. But Darwin was a shade disappointed in the titan; after all, he was only a paunchy little German.

Darwin and Wallace

But all this time, at the back of Darwin's mind, was the perplexing problem of the Galápagos species. His scientific friends, identifying his shells, his insects, his bird skins, had discovered the same strange endemicity. Every Galápagos species seemed similar to some of the American mainland, but not identical, and all the islands had faunae and flora of their own. Long ago Lamarck had pointed out that it is hardly conceivable that God created a special set of species for various islands. Now the animals and the plants on the Galápagos, Darwin saw, could only have come from America, and that by wind and current, or, as seems more likely now, along a land bridge that is now sunk below the surface of the waves. But in any event, they had changed, once they reached the islands. And, enisled, marooned there through a stagnant eon of time, their several differences had all been exaggerated; each race on each island, under enforced inbreeding, had intensified its eccentricities. Cut off from all but the rarest of conceivable fresh incursions of the great mainland life-forms, these island forms were never swamped by the norm as any passing variations would have been on the continent. They were insulated, protected in a group of glass cases, as it were, alive in a museum world that never before had echoed to the footsteps of a naturalist.

For islands do queer things to life, and the more isolated they are the queerer. True oceanic islands have certain peculiarities in their biotas. The resident sea birds are apt to be heavy, to live in dense colonies, to be very tame and often nearly flightless, as if from disuse (in the Lamarckian style) of their wings. Resident land birds are usually confined to a very few families, or even only one, but that family will be remarkably developed, with scores or hundreds of species playing every conceivable variation on a fundamental structural plan, and specialized for adaptation to every local condition. Of native land mammals there are usually none at all, or at best a few bats, often no snakes, frequently no toads, frogs or salamanders, and of insects sometimes the lower groups will be largely absent, as in Hawaii, or the higher groups will be poorly developed, as on the Galápagos. Among the plants the lacks are quite as startling, and of those present a few peculiar families are extraordinarily developed; on St. Helena, for instance, the great Composite family, that runs with us to weeds like daisy and dandelion, develops into trees.

It is in the *Journal of the H. M. S. " Beagle "* that the world first read of Darwin's doubts of the timeless fixity of species. Did it hear the footfalls of his approach to a great new truth?

" The natural history of these islands is eminently curious, and well deserves attention. Most of the organic productions are aboriginal creations, found nowhere else. . . .

" By far the most remarkable feature in the natural history of this archipelago . . . is that the different islands to a considerable extent are inhabited by a different set of beings. . . . I never dreamed that islands, about fifty or sixty miles apart, and most of them in sight of each other, formed of precisely the same rocks, placed under a similar climate, rising to a nearly equal height, would have been differently tenanted. . . .

" Seeing this gradation and diversity of structure in one small, intimately related group of birds, one might really fancy that

H. M. S. *Beagle*,
in which Darwin voyaged around the world,
laid ashore on the South American coast.
(See page 289)

CHARLES DARWIN AS A YOUNG MAN

from an original paucity of birds in this archipelago, one species had been taken and modified for different ends. . . .

". . . one is astonished at the amount of creative force, if such an expression may be used, displayed on these small, barren, and rocky islands. . . .

" Hence, both in space and time we seem to be brought somewhat near to that great fact — that mystery of mysteries — the first appearance of new beings on earth."

Yes, he has almost seized it; it is almost within his hand. But still he pondered, pottered, read, and remembered things he had read. He recalled Thomas Malthus's essay on population, the struggle for existence and survival of the fittest that Malthus saw in the striving of crowded mankind upon this finite mud-ball of a planet. He recalled his grandfather Erasmus's Natural Philosophy, his poetical but prophetic hints of evolution.

And he bought a small, cheap notebook (his habits were all very economical) and began to record in it his first groping thoughts, and to take notes on every evidence he could find for his mushrooming ideas. In this style he continued quietly in leisure hours (for he was at work on several forms of the report on the *Beagle* voyage, as well as on a theory of coral atolls, and a tediously long monograph on barnacles) and page by page the little yellow notebook was filled.

All this time he made a confidant of no one but young Hooker and Lyell. He was in no hurry, certainly, to risk his theory to the sharp-fanged criticism of his veteran elder brothers in science. And he had no itch for print, and certainly no wish for publicity. For twenty years he kept his plans all strictly underneath his hat — a record for the cerebral continence of an intellectual passion that is, I fancy, unsurpassed. Time seemed not to matter to him; the years moved as sluggishly and silently as the gentle Cam, winding among the green closes of Cambridge. Darwin considered that he had not enough data at hand; he always wanted more evidence, more and more. He might have died with his secret, leaving only an unintelligible notebook behind him. But destiny was preparing at last to force his patient hand.

And the story predestines me once more, and gladly, to talk of islands. In all of natural history there is nothing to compare with the fascination of island life. The exhilaration of mountains, the icy ringing call of the arctic, the receding horizons of steppes, the treasure cave of the sea bottom, and the chiaroscuro of the jungle floor — each and all of these have called men up and away from comfort to die in far places. But I think that for almost every homekeeper the far-away dream is an island. A thousand miles inland, at the heart of a rich continental biota, he longs with a long ache for an atoll, a volcanic peak afloat upon blue ocean, a self-contented kingdom that shall be his.

But isles as fabulous as any man can fancy lie around the corners of the continents, and of these one of the most secret is Ternate, for this small pebble of a land is hidden where one most successfully hides a pebble — amidst a thousand others on the beach. Native land of the nutmeg tree, it was one of the Isles of Spice that, discovered by medieval Arab merchant mariners, was kept a monopolistic secret by the wily heathen. Turmeric and cardamom, ginger and camphor, sandalwood and pepper, clove and nutmeg, these were the precious cargoes of the Arab's lanteen-rigged cockle-shells that etched the Persian Gulf, the Indian Ocean, the China Seas and the East India waters with the thin crystal lines of its wake. Europeans call them spices of Araby. Yet in truth Arabia has not a spice of its own. Beyond, far, far beyond, in coral seas and amid the stagnant leeward isles southeast of Asia, these costly trifles grew.

It took centuries, and incredible adventures, for the Portuguese, the Dutch and the English to smell out each of the spice lands. A thousand feverish, unbearable, unprofitable islands had to be attempted, explored at human cost, to find the one right dot upon the map where the sought-for product could be had. With time, pepper was traced to Penang, sandalwood to the isle of Timor, camphor to Formosa, cloves to Amboyna and nutmeg to Ternate. Native prices were overthrown, Portuguese, English and Dutch massacred each other, attempted preposterous monopolies, destroying every spice tree on one island to foster it on another, destroying it even there to keep up the falling prices, as spices sank from an economic position literally equal to many times their weight in gold, to their trivial importance of today.

But of all the Isles of Spice, none is so mysterious even now as the enchanted circle of little Ternate. You will hunt long for it ere you find it on any ordinary map. Among the Dutch Indies find first the broken swastika of Celebes, and the ugly reptilian head of New Guinea which seems to be hissing at the west. Between the northeast arm of Celebes and the northwest tip of New Guinea

there is the Molucca archipelago, and in particular a
sprawling mass called Jilolo, like a miniature Celebes.
Just off the west coast of Jilolo lies Ternate, whose fantastic human history epitomizes human follies as its natural history epitomizes the fascination and paradox of island life.

For here are not the harshness and aridity, the antedi-
luvian reptilian angularity of the Galápagos, but modern
life forms in their multiplex splendor. By some sort of
pedantic blindness we imagine that life was richer in the
Carboniferous, but there never was before in the world
such beauty as we have on earth today. We live, I think,
in life's golden age. What in our post-Darwinian wisdom
we know as the most modern and " highly evolved " of
families elaborate themselves to a point where it would
seem that the innate power of an organism to be fantastically fair must break down. I cite you hummingbirds and
butterflies of Brazil, quetzals and orchids of Guatemala,
and all that grew and flew and was plucked or caught for
the specimen cases of Alfred Russel Wallace, collecting
in 1857 on the island of Ternate.

For the East Indies are the isles of five times ten thousand beetles, the country of the gorilla, the archipelago
of birds of paradise, each species with an island to itself.
Take the avifauna alone, the parrots, paroquets and lories,
dressed each more gaudily than a gypsy queen, white and
black cockatoos, fruit-pigeons delicately and variously
colored as sea shells, kingfishers big and proud as falcons
or pigmy-sized, ground-thrushes blue, green and black,
bee-eaters, rollers, flycatchers, Papuan grackles, sun-
birds like a school of bright tropical fish and paradise-

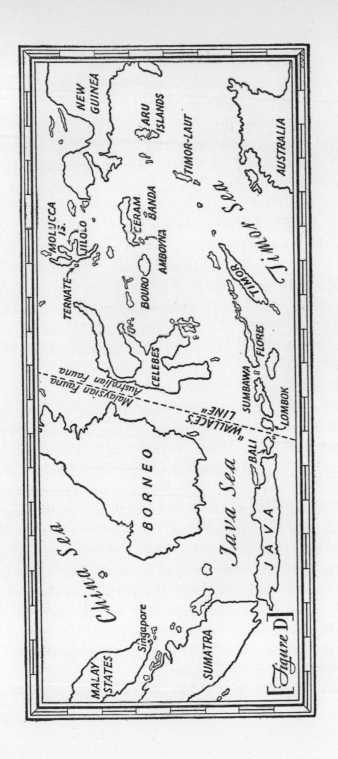

[Figure D]

crows — for such diversity and endemicity reasons must be found that overwhelm reason.

Of all the long list of professional collectors, Wallace appeals most to me because he thought as he collected. It had come about in the history of natural history that the athletic grind of professional tropical collectors had fallen necessarily to a class of men specially fitted but not especially gifted. The thinking, when any at all was done, was left for those at home, and it consisted mostly in a will-o'-the-wisp light dancing over a morass of specimens, a light that illumined nothing and had no warmth.

Wallace was indeed a professional collector; he had no expectation of his dinner unless he could sell his specimens. This obliged him to go after the rare, to get off the beaten track, to stay months or years in a fruitful region, however savage. With Bates he had explored the Amazon valley, and if there is one faunal province in the world richer than the Indo-Malasian, it is the Brazilian. He was already a veteran, then, of the deadliest climate, most hostile jungle, and a wild life of then inexplicable variety. By the time he reached Ternate his mind, I think, was the best stocked in all the field of natural history. He had observed, and he remembered, thousands of details about the animals he had seen, the rhythm of their lives through seasons, through metamorphosis, rut and birth. He knew more than Humboldt about distribution, ecology, interrelations, symbioses, animal socialisms, multiple parasitisms, the pyramid of swarming tropical life. He discovered " Wallace's line " — the great cleavage through the East Indies, of two life zones.

All of this about Wallace was of course unknown, or

not more than half known, in Europe. Not many of his customers and the museum and university men knew him personally. Some could remember him when he got back to England, ten years' collecting work just lost in a fire at sea, but as soon as he recovered the insurance, he had gone out again, this time to the East, leaving the recollection of an almost incredibly idealistic and romantic young fellow. I see from his youthful photograph that he was near-sighted, shy, careless of his appearance, sensitive and passionate about the mouth, the sort to make a tender lover and father but not to attract a young girl, a man slow-maturing, intense, visionary.

While alone in Ternate, fever seized him, and there was only his faithful Malay boy, Ali, there beside him in the hot, confused night. It must have seemed to the sick man that all the curious creatures with which his brain was crowded advanced converging upon him with a rustling of pinions, a gesticulating of antennae, a fateful, feral, quadruped step. He tossed and burned, in the burning night, his marvelously stored brain alive with the activity of fever.

For years he had been aware of a mounting sense of problem, and now the great wave of it had broken upon him. Lying on his tropical bed in the hot night he was drawn upon a strong current of facts, hints, premonitions, certainties, toward some immense ultimate solution of the vast multiplicity of Nature.

His mind ran on all he had read on the great subject — a shelf almost identical with Darwin's: Humboldt, Darwin's own "*Beagle*" *Journal*, Chamber's *Vestiges of Creation*, Lyell's principles of geology. There was that paper he had published, a mere groping that culminated in nothing satisfactory, but there had come a letter from Charles Darwin, praising it, hinting that he too was searching, feeling out some darkling path. Wallace remembered Bates's theory of the development of protective coloration, he pondered Malthus's studies in population — the struggle between classes of men, between individuals, the sense of crowding, of gradual emergence of some dominant force —

And then he had it! The light of revelation poured into his head, overwhelmed him with its beauty. Natural selection proclaimed itself, the great organic law by which life, always at heart the same thing, always plastic, is moulded, warped, modeled, set, made multiplex, broken, discarded, refashioned, perpetually changed, inconceivably varied.

With the first abatement of the fever he arose from his cot and sat himself down to write in measured words the sense of the great vision that had come to him.

". . . There is no limit of variability to a species, as formerly supposed. . . .

" The life of wild animals is a struggle for existence. . . .

" The abundance or rarity of a species is dependent upon its more or less perfect adaptation to the conditions of existence. . . .

" Useful variations will tend to increase; useless or hurtful variations to diminish. . . .

" Superior varieties will ultimately extirpate the original species. . . .

" There is a tendency in nature to . . . progression, by minute steps, in various directions, but always checked and balanced by the necessary conditions, . . . which . . . may, it is believed, be followed out so as to agree with all the phenomena presented by organized beings, their extinction and succession in past ages, and all the extraordinary modifications of form, instincts and habits which they exhibit."

When he was done, he enclosed his many pages of writing in a letter. Presently, in the fullness of lost equatorial time, a Dutch boat called at Ternate and took the letter away on its journey of many months, toward England, to Charles Darwin at Downe House in Kent.

14

DARWINISM AND THE MAN BEHIND IT

WHEN Miss Emma Wedgwood, of the ceramically renowned family, was " spoken to " by young Charles Darwin, her cousin, she declared that it was all very sudden and surprising, but she required no time to make up her mind. Both families were as delighted as if they had arranged it for their own benefit. The high contracting parties were not too young nor yet past the age of romance; combining their resources they made sure of such an income that Charles, in delicate health, need never bear fardels, and as he later put it to his children, who took it with literal gravity, " they would always have bread and cheese when they grew up."

Emma's portrait, painted just before she married, shows many Victorian traits, the sloping shoulders and idle hands of a genteel frailty and the child-like side curls of a *Dora*. But her face sets all this at naught. Her eyes are candid and level, her round face and strong chin are forceful and unimaginative, and mouth and expression bespeak pleasantness and decision. One might suspect that she might be a natural husband-manager, if we did not know how she outdid her sex in self-sacrifice for her mate.

For Charles was certainly in need of care. He was never well again after the *Beagle* voyage; even the most agreeable excitement might cost him a week of bodily and nervous suffering; a half-hour visit from a friend or fifteen minutes' work beyond his strength would result in the loss of days from his tasks. There were many periods in his life when he could work only an hour a day, others when he could not work at all but only think and that not more than for a quarter of an hour in all the day. Emma Darwin fought unremittingly the battle of her husband's bodily life, lifting from his shoulders every least care, staving off the hosts of friends and enemies and curiosity seekers that plagued him, guarding his sleep, his working hours, his every step, taking in the tedia of the home the place of the master as well as mistress. She gave up completely the social life she loved, for the utmost retirement in deep country. Beyond all question, she preserved the length of his life, and hourly made possible every stroke of work that came from his brain and pen.

What entertaining she did was oftenest of scientific grandees, and sometimes that was heavy sledding. Emma writes her sister:

" I must tell you how our learned party went off yesterday. Mr. and Mrs. Henslow came at four o'clock and she, like a discreet woman, went up to her room till dinner. . . . We had some time to wait before dinner for Dr. Fitton, which is always awful, and, in my opinion, Mr. Lyell is enough to flatten a party, as he never speaks above his breath. . . . Mr. [Robert] Brown, whom Humboldt called 'the glory of Great Britain,' looks so shy, as if he longed to shrink into himself and disappear entirely; however, notwithstanding those dead weights, viz., the greatest botanist and the greatest geologist in Europe, we did very well and had no pauses. Mrs. Henslow has a good, loud, sharp voice which was a great comfort, and Mrs. Lyell has a very constant supply of talk. . . . Charles was dreadfully exhausted when it was over, and is only as well as can be expected today."

At last Emma, who was passionately fond of the play and concerts, gave up the house in Gower Street near the British Museum, and the Darwins with their children moved out to Downe House in Kent. This was a fifteen-acre estate near the sleepy little village of Downe. There were fine old trees, herbaceous borders complete with sundial, shaven lawn, wagtails and fieldfares, and the somewhat rambling house was wreathed in roses and ivy as a good English country house should be. Here was no formality, and though life was maintained in tranquility deliberately, the garden was bright with children. They became their father's collectors, proudly laying grasses on his breakfast plate and beetles on his blotting pad. They recall with gratitude how they were always allowed to push all the chairs to the side of the room to make way for games; they remember that though Father's working hours were sacred because he was doing a *very* important book about limpets and another on corals, they were more attracted by his closed door than by anything in the house. And as his work desk held all the scissors, paste, knives, stickummy and measuring things and string, there were endless tiptoe visits to him, and they supposed that since they whispered to him they did not interrupt him. Games indeed were scarcely any fun without him, and a future astronomer, *aetat circa* ten, offered his father sixpence to come and play with him.

So Darwin, with a sense of infinite leisure, went along perfecting his careful labors, nursing his delicate stomach, enjoying his family, and coming to the final page of his little yellow notebook with the colossal idea in it. Here are a few lines of the last letter from his quiet privacy:

"The weather is quite delicious. Yesterday . . . I strolled a little beyond the glade for an hour and a half, and enjoyed myself — the fresh yet dark-green of the grand Scotch firs, the brown of the catkins of the old birches, with their white stems, and a fringe of distant green from the larches made an excessively pretty view. At last I fell fast asleep on the grass, and awoke with a chorus of birds singing around me, and squirrels running up the trees, and some woodpeckers laughing, and it was as pleasant and rural a scene as ever I saw, and I did not care one penny how any of the beasts or birds had been formed."

The next letter is to Lyell:

"Wallace . . . has today sent me the enclosed. . . . Your words have come true with a vengeance — that I should be forestalled. . . . I never saw a more striking coincidence; if Wallace had my MS sketch written out in 1842, he could not have made a better short abstract!"

With no more flourish than a butcher's bill, the letter from Ternate had arrived at Downe House. Darwin wrestled with his angel:

"I should be extremely glad now to publish a sketch of my general views in about a dozen pages or so; but I cannot persuade myself that I could do so honorably. . . . I would far rather burn my whole book, than that he or any other man should think that I had behaved in a paltry spirit."

This was penned in the midst of agonizing fear — all the children, and their nurse, were down with scarlet fever, the boy Charles desperately sick. The day after, the little life went out. The lives of the other three hung in the balance. When at last he knew they were safe, Darwin's relief softened his sorrow. And he found that Hooker and Lyell had taken his perplexities into their competent hands. On their own authority they undertook to present before the Linnaean Society, and to publish, the joint papers of Wallace and Darwin.

Science has no finer page than Darwin's stand, willing to seal his lips forever or to place his work at the disposal of Wallace, unless it be that opposite page, where Wallace for his part waived every claim and placed himself as a simple soldier under Darwin's banner. No efforts of detractors, to make it appear that Darwin took credit for something only partially his, have any foundation, nor has science for one moment forgotten to honor the independent originality of Wallace, and his splendid spirit. So many disgraceful wrangles the scientific world has seen! But never between these two.

On July 1, 1858, the joint papers were presented. The effect upon the Linnaean Society was electric. When the formal discussion broke up and the spontaneous knots of talkers gathered about, men spoke with bated breath. For the moment the old fogies among them were too taken by surprise for retaliation.

But in the year and a half that intervened between that

meeting and the publication of the *Origin of Species*, the armies gathered. There was a sound as of the grinding of axes and the sharpening of swords, and that sound was heard, but only dimly understood, by the public. Still, the agencies of publicity were astir, so that though the publisher Murray thought that " the theory is as absurd as though one should contemplate a fruitful union between a poker and a rabbit," the *Origin* sold out its first edition of twelve hundred and fifty copies on the day of sale.

Darwin had sent advance copies to a few friends and friendly enemies. His state at this time was one of exquisite apprehension — the " wibber-gibbers," he called it — coupled with something like physical prostration. What would the scientific world say of his theory? Where would Lyell stand? In his day Lyell himself had drawn scientific and clerical fire for his revolutionary views on geologic time; but now if he accepted the *Origin* he would have to discard half his tenets. In America towered Louis Agassiz, a Cuvierian anatomist and dogmatist, a guardian of the cataclysmic theory and the divine fixation of species. Right at hand, the mighty Owen, with his sacred fetich of archetypes, though he was old now, could still wield a sword.

In Germany Von Baer might take any unpredictable attitude; in France Cuvier's own students were still alive and in the saddle. At home, what would Herbert Spencer say, young Huxley, stupid old Sedgwick who had met his Waterloo by opposing the theory of glaciation? So Darwin nervously told them over and over, counting on some like Lyell who always wobbled and wavered, forgetting opponents who suddenly cropped up, like the Jesuit biologist Wasmann, and that dogged old Fabre over in Provence, and underestimating the venom and villainy of Owen.

Huxley came forward with all the fire of championship. He startled the world with a review like a trumpet blast, calling on all men to say where they would stand, daring the most powerful to take him on. In America the botanist Gray, invincible in his suavity and piety, undermined his colleague Agassiz (they were both Harvard professors) before Agassiz's batteries ever really swung into action. Spencer and Henslow and Hooker marched up loyally. The reverend Charles Kingsley, speaking as a minister and as a littérateur, proclaimed that evolution did not diminish the glory of God or the beauty of Creation, but enhanced them. Sir John Lubbock, a power in the financial strongholds of the City, a philanthropist and courtier and scientist, went over to Darwin's camp with all his shining arms.

By this time the embattled prelates were thoroughly alarmed. They relied upon what they took to be the preponderance of British sentiment against any attempts upon traditional thought, and were enchanted by the snarling articles in the *Quarterly* and the *Edinburgh* reviews. These excellent old mouthpieces, with their infallible instinct for placing themselves on the wrong side of every question, the same that hounded Keats and Emily Brontë, were full of all the old and now familiar forebodings of calamity. Testy old gentlemen, curates and maiden ladies wrote hotly to the *Times* against Darwinism — pantheism, atheism, they called it. Sedgwick wrote to Darwin that the book had pained him deeply. The natu-

WALLACE IN HIS OLD AGE.

ALFRED RUSSEL WALLACE AS A YOUNG MAN

EMMA WEDGWOOD,
shortly before her marriage to Charles Darwin.
(Portrait by George Richmond, R. A.)
(See page 304)

ralist Duke of Argyll, always a personally friendly and generous gentleman, was full of objections difficult even for Huxley to answer. And Owen, peevish in his dotage, penned a series of venomous attacks to which he did not sign his own name, though he constantly cited " Professor Owen " as an authority.

The time seemed ripe for the church to strike, and so it drew the battle line at Oxford, in a debate between Bishop Wilberforce (" Soapy Sam " to his enemies) and Thomas Henry Huxley. The president of the meeting was Henslow, Darwin's old teacher; on his right the Bishop of Oxford sat smiling, confident of his pulpit style, coached in sarcasm and shaky Romanticism by Owen; on the left Huxley waited. Hooker and Lubbock were on the platform, as well as several other friends of the new cause, but down in the center the clerics were massed like a hired claque. Far at the back sat a few undergraduate sympathizers with Darwinism, while ladies were perched in the window embrasures, ready to cheer the sweet, handsome Wilberforce, Sam of Oxon.

President Henslow arose and announced that only valid scientific arguments would be tolerated. But the clerics had no intention of observing such a rule. One after another they arose and, in the best style of the lobbying forces of American prohibition and the broadcloth apologists for negro slavery, informed the world of the will of God as made known exclusively to them. The President stopped them, and a Reverend Mr. Dingle got up and attempted some mawkish science till his own supporters booed him down. Then up stood Admiral Fitz-Roy, he of the *Beagle*, and talking down his long Stuart nose, testified that his former friend Mr. Darwin was " a damned scientific Whig " and gave him most acute pain by entertaining views so subversive of morality. Fitz-Roy thoroughly condemned himself for having once bunked with so perverted a fellow.

Now, when excitement was well whipped up, arose Soapy Sam, equipped with all the loud and soft pedal effects known to the pulpit, skilled in dialectic evasion, exegesis, threats of hell fire, and appeals to innate prejudices. Turning to his opponent, he spoke with condescending gentleness: Was Professor Huxley descended from an ape on his grandfather's or on his grandmother's side?

While the audience cheered and stamped and rocked, and the ladies waved their handkerchiefs, Huxley leaned over to his neighbor. " The Lord hath delivered him into mine hands," he whispered.

If there were an ancestor — he began, rising suddenly tall and calm in an infectious certainty of power — an ancestor whom he should feel shame in recalling, it would be a man — and here he paused, they say, with telling effect — a man who plunged into scientific questions with which he had no real acquaintance and, by skilled appeals to religious prejudice, used his brilliant intellect to obscure the truth.

He went on, but for several moments no one heard what he said. For the cheering had burst out more wildly than before, and this time upon the other side. The clerics themselves wavered, glanced at Soapy Sam, saw that he had disgraced the church, and burst forth into applause for Huxley. By the time that Huxley had done with them and Hooker arose, the opposition was pulp. Hooker could scarcely get on, for the cannonading of applause, and " the blackest coats and the whitest stocks of Oxford " were the first to congratulate the evolutionists.

All ahead promised further triumph. In lectures and articles Huxley slew foes right and left. Owen went to the grave, disgraced and defeated. Gray carried America, Haeckel unexpectedly rode up in Germany and put the foes of evolution to rout. Weismann brought seemingly invincible alliance when his experimental biological evidence dealt Lamarckism a resounding blow. Clergymen discovered that evolution could be considered God's will and part of the Divine Plan for turning men ultimately into angels. British imperialism liked " the struggle for existence," since it was winning the struggle; capitalistic imperialism could approve of " the survival of the fittest." Darwin's auxiliary explanations of evolution, such as sexual selection, the predominance of beauty, the suggestion that every organ and function in a living being serves, or has once served, some useful purpose to a designed end, were highly acceptable to nineteenth century sentiment.

And all the while Darwin conducted his life along lines sure to win over British opinion. He himself remained aloof from the battle, his life unimpeachably modest, virtuous and serious. He utterly confounded the moralists by upholding an unsmirched standard of Christian behavior; where his enemies looked for a snarling seducer and blasphemer, here was a kindly English gentleman known by his good works. No day went by that he did not receive floods of abusive letters; instead of ignoring them, he replied in tones such as he would have used to intelligent beings. In time the cumulative effect of this patience triumphed. He remained personally invincible, and in the scientific world it could only be said of him that he neither exulted in publicity nor did he rest on his laurels; unruffled, steadily, he worked at other books, flank attacks, he called them, upon the opposition.

Abroad there has always remained a certain opposition to Darwinism. The French object that it is not a logically deducted explanation, but merely a mass of special cases tediously gathered, like the testimony of witnesses in a legal brief. This they call English naturalism, by which they mean a certain myopic literal-mindedness, a willingness to accept unquestioningly mere evidence of the senses, an assumption that such evidence over-rides pure reason.

The quarrel here is based upon incompatible fundamentals. The Franco-Platonists assume that that which is logical and appeals to reason is a sound hypothesis. But it strikes me that life is not to be called reasonable at all. No one who proceeded by logic would be able to conceive a butterfly's wing, or the Brownian movement, or a pterodactyl. When you think upon it, that which we call commonplace Nature, all about us, is fantastic and astonishing. What is so queer as an oak? a silent living thing that does not move or speak, and yet is sensitive to light even more intensely than ourselves — seventy feet of woody vegetable shooting up from the earth, intricately and unpredictably branched, having racial and personal individuality as great as any human's.

The foreign mind has also challenged what is called Darwin's teleology. They find that Darwin's explanation of the survival of organs and forms of living creatures by

reason of their utility was conditioned by the English
moral law (suitable to a commercial race) that that which
serves is right, that utility is the first virtue. Just as Linnaeus has been called the culmination of Scholasticism, so
Darwin has been viewed as the flower of Romantic Natural Philosophy. This pays a very high compliment to the
Romantic movement, but there may be some truth in it.
That the struggles of the church against evolution ended
swiftly and gracefully is doubtless due to the fact that
the Darwinian explanation seems to allow for a Divine
Plan. And so important is this consideration for many
temperaments that if you will but grant the existence of
that plan, and promise never to bring in any evidence
against it, the church will welcome all your findings. For
it would like to regard biological facts as handsome blocks
out of which to build a cathedral.

For myself, I cannot see the teleological element in
Darwinism that his critics jeer at and his pietist adherents
admire. Upon a close reading of his book on such a likely
subject for teleology as the nice mutual adaptations between insects and the orchids which they intimately visit
and pollinate, I find not at all the spirit of teleology,
though the letter might so be interpreted.

Aside from scientific criticism of Darwinism, there
have been many attempts to psycho-analyze the man behind the theory, and so to find in his early training, in the
conditions and limitations of his life, the explanation of
his thought. In this way a nimble journalistic mind may
cheapen the motives and make trivial the achievements
of Buddha or Lincoln. If, in Darwin's case, there is a grain
of truth in such attempts to be smarter than a wise man

without trying to understand him, it is lost amid a great deal of chaff.

It is interesting to query, what would be the difference if Alfred Russel Wallace, instead of Charles Darwin, stood for natural selection? The answer lies in the personality of Wallace. I do not deny his idealism, warmth, unselfishness and purity. But his final standing in science is deeply modified by his unscientific inclinations. He was a humanitarian before he was a scientist; his heart ruled his head — a virtue only in a Romantic. For instance, he was completely satisfied by Robert Owen's Utopian brand of Socialism. He tried his best to revive phrenology, accepted the possibility of long-range weather forecasting by means of grossly superstitious almanacs, thought that human ills would end when George's Single Tax went into effect, and rated spiritualistic séances as unquestionable science.

Though there is not in the world today a reputable scientist who denies the fact of evolution, Darwin's natural selection has undergone from its beginning to the present moment the most searching fire of criticism by the peers of the founder of that faith. Men who personally esteem and love Darwin have not been able to exempt his theory from the tribunal of their own reason and experience. In the laboratories of Germany, in the quiet studies of France, in America where the science of genetics has reached its culmination, natural selection has been challenged. It is doubted that it accounts at all for the origin of anything new. Rather, in that marvelous profusion and individuality that we call life, natural selection acts only as an agent of destruction. It can discard; it may explain

[316]

why forms have become extinct. But it seems impotent, charge its critics, to create anything at all. Others have doubted that natural selection actually operates, have denied that it can be proved by observation or experiment.

Darwin was obliged to avail himself constantly of the theory of use and disuse. Though he did not always recognize it, he continually assumed that the altered circumstances of environment could cause an animal or a plant to vary. Though he was never a declared Lamarckian, he was one at heart, and it is regrettable that Lamarck was the only scientist about whom Darwin was not wholly generous and candid. Admiring Lamarck as one who failed signally to prove what he guessed so surely, I cannot see that the Lamarckian element in Darwinism weakens Darwin's case. It lends it more strength than some of Darwin's own allies and their ideas.

One of the weaker sides of Darwin's theory was natural selection's handmaid, sexual selection. He supposed that the beauty of male birds, the rapture of their songs, were intended to attract the female, so that, the handsomest male always being chosen and the less engaging beaux remaining unmated, beauty, like strength, swiftness and intelligence, was ever increasing in the world. Darwin never discovered a case of such selection; he trusted, unfortunately, to the persuasiveness of the idea. He assumed that animals had a sense of beauty, and that it was similar to his own. And, unlike Thoreau, Darwin did not see beauty in subtle shadings, soft or somber tones; he never considered the possibility that a female beast might be attracted by that which he called ashen, dun, unlovely. I sometimes wonder if Darwin did not also assume too much in supposing that female animals make any choice at all of their mates. In Victorian times one " spoke to " a young lady, and she bestowed her hand or refused it. The possibility that outside the human species most mating is an acceptable sort of rape did not occur to his gentle mind.

And Darwin had but the shakiest notions of heredity. His case desperately needed aid from his contemporary, Gregor Mendel. But Father Gregor, superior of an Austrian monastery, was working in his marvelous sweet-pea plot all unknown to the world of science. He died still unhonored, and his researches were not discovered until 1900.

Finally, the fundamental quarrel between Darwinism and its critics has been put by Rádl, the historian of science: Darwin's aim was simply to describe evolution; his opponents complained he had not helped them to understand it. Darwin sought its mechanisms, they its motives. To him it appeared that evolution supplied a chronicle made up of countless small incidents, as is daily living, but they abhorred incidents; they charged him with failing to discover behind development any great plan.

Only a very young scientist would pull down Darwin's statue for no cause save that the cut of his mental coat was Victorian and out of style. Because we do not believe completely in him now does not mean that he misled us, or was somehow a false prophet. It is quite amateurish and unscientific to ask more of a theory than that it should excite the search, in its own generation, for deeper truth.

And whatever you think of natural selection, the fact remains with us that Darwin was the effective founder of evolution. He had many forerunners, but, whether due to the times or due to his power and personality, he was the first to establish it in the human consciousness. In the entire history of biology it is the most exciting and fruitful idea that has ever dawned upon the mind of man. It has infected the world with hope, with belief in the worth of effort; it has given us such a sense of history as we never enjoyed before.

For the concept of evolution has spread out far beyond biology. It has proved to be the magic key to history and government and education. Before its advent we literally did not know that we grow, that we change, that there has been progress. Perhaps the reason why Gibbon's works head the list of eminent books that nobody reads any more, is that, lacking any idea of evolution, Gibbon is today simply unreadable. Though in his pages facts, events, float thick as motes in a dusty old library, he seems to us never to get anywhere. In Gibbon's own breast were Ciceronian pompousness, Augustan imperialism, Constantinian religiosity, Merovingian ideas of feudal class, Visigothic brute impulses veneered with English restraint. He did not know it; he did not know that man himself evolves, is gradually becoming a different animal, his brow growing heavier, his jaw more slender, his appendix already a vestigial nuisance, his small toes perhaps on the way to obsolescence.

All our notions of man's destiny upon earth have been altered since we confessed evolution. The taste and the feel of life are different. It seems briefer, more fleeting, intensely sweeter and more vivid. How carelessly men once turned away from the sight of the earth, how they could spit upon life, and look forward to the end of the world! Now we think of ourselves as descendants, heirs, children of Time and characters in a great and noble planetary drama.

And this change in the very color of human thought was wrought in a generation and — explain it away if you can — it was initiated by one man. If, one of these days, the remaining details of his theory go into the discard (and if necessary science will junk them without sentiment), the reverberations of his essential abstract concept will echo from age to age. More primal, lasting mental spade-work was done at Downe House than in any other spot since Plato pulled his beard in the shadow of the Par-thenon.

I seem to draw near a close without ever having men-tioned why, aside from Darwin's preëminence as a theo-rist, I consider him a great naturalist. Now there is scarcely room left to speak of the major importance of his minor works. The charm of these writings is not in their style, for Darwin was not an entertaining author; it rests in the reverence of the man for what lies all about us.

To gather material for his little treatise on the fertili-zation of orchids, Darwin used to climb slowly up into a sloping pasture beyond Downe House, and stand there, quietly, patiently, quite happily, in the soft English sun-light, waiting for a bee to come to a flower and perform its progenitive rites. He called it the orchis meadow, thick strewn with the delicate spires of the genus *Orchis* itself, with the quaint devices and escutcheons of *Ophrys* whose hanging lip so puckishly simulates the very bee that alights upon it that you are almost afraid to pluck the flower for fear of a sting. In autumn, ladies' tresses starred the grass. Small, common orchids, these, the little terrestrial species of north Europe, nothing at which a florist, an orchid hunter would look twice. But for Darwin there was nothing commonplace. If life has any meaning, any beauty, any wonderment at the heart of it, then it must run as red and thrum on the same high golden pitch, just above audibility, and root and thrust as deep at Downe as on Las Encantadas.

There in the orchis meadow Darwin pushed natural history to the very limits of its unaided powers, unaided, that is, by the microscope, the test tube, the spectroscope, the centrifuge. He saw all that it is possible to see with the naked eye, probed as deep as the bare hands will go. I cite but a single case: with the tip of his pencil he touched the stigmatic surface of an orchid ovary. Though never fertilized by pollen the ovary set seed. So, after all, he discovered, all these intricate mechanisms for insect fertilization, all these elaborate mutual adaptations of bee and flower, all the miracle of the penetration of the ovary by the pollen tube, the descent of the tube by the ultimate, microscopic male cells, could be cut short. The ovary did not need the pollen or the bee. It needed only a tap from an old man's pencil. A blow to teleology, a cruel caricature of Divine Plan? No matter. Darwin records it.

Or he would ramble afield in search of sundews, those dainty little bog and ditch plants whose sensitive leaves, covered with a gleaming enzymic fluid, entrap and digest insects. In preparation for *Insectivorous Plants* he sent to America for our pitcher-plants and for the famed *Dionaea* which closes up its spiky leaves when an insect alights on them, crushing it like a sort of vegetable Iron Maiden.

The fantastic *Nepenthes* of Madagascar, that hangs, a death trap for insects, from the boughs of rain-forest trees, little insectivorous butterworts from the Siberian tundras — he fancied them all; he preached a classic biological sermon from a subject limited as strictly as a sonnet.

When he was feeling too rocky and ill to walk so far, when it seemed to him that the decks of the *Beagle* heaved again beneath the raving seas off the Horn, he would call for the old " trap " — not ordering it, but asking the servant if he might have it — and then drive over into Surrey for a fresh supply of *Drosera*, the sundews.

There were three more botanical studies, based, as always, on the simple flora of the English countryside, and on what Wallace, and Dr. Gray in America, and Hooker could tell him of the far places of the earth that he was destined never again to see. He investigated the cross- and self-fertilization of plants, the different forms of flowers on plants of the same species, and the power of movement in plants. There is nothing in any of these works that you and I could not have discovered upon the most casual weeds about us — had either been a Darwin.

The last work of his life, the child of his old loins, is one whose subject cannot be contemplated without a smile; it concerns the importance of earthworms. But the smile is one of affection for the old fellow, digging down ten feet and more through banks and turfs, to see what the blind worm is up to. And what he discovered is that every inch of the earth's surface has passed, and will pass again, through the bodies of worms. He learned that worms bring up fresh soil from a depth of many feet and, perpetually at work, perpetually stir and turn over and aërate and renew the loam on which our lives depend. He even investigated the intelligence of worms, endlessly taking notes on the particular way in which they plug up their burrows with leaves.

Amid these placid and profound works, sorrows came to Darwin. Three children died. There were disappointments, and long spells of ill health. Fewer and fewer people saw him. When he actually attended a public gathering, a great hall full of scientists at his appearance rose like a sea before a mighty wind, and applauded with the sound of thunder.

One wonders how Emma liked the fame of her husband. Concerning the impending production of *The Descent of Man* she wrote: " I think it will be very interesting, but that I shall dislike it very much as again putting God further off." But in after years, a widow, she noted some oxslips in the woods, that differed remarkably among themselves; she wrote then: " How [Charles] would have been pleased to see so much variation going on! "

That day of her loneliness was approaching; with his shawl about his shoulders and his feet in old fur-lined house boots, the gentle titan would pace up and down, dictating. From time to time he would step into the hall to get a pinch of snuff from the box where he kept it, temptation once removed. His strong voice, still dictating, would float through the open doors.

Or, at his desk they found him seated on a chair with extra long legs to match the extra high table; as he had neutralized the effect of the one elevation by the other, he would often put a footstool on the chair and sit on that. In this position he would work at his old simple-lens dissecting microscope, or measure with a plain yardstick, or pour liquids from one beaker to another. The hundreds of experimental seedlings sprouting on his windowsills, bookcases, tables and desks, were grown in a motley of household jars, and covered over only by sheets of broken glass collected from the cold frames in the kitchen garden.

On his walks he had an extraordinary talent for finding bird nests. He would sit so still in the woods that presently all of life came and played about him as if he were a mossy rock; baby squirrels ran on his arms and shoulders while the mother, in the trees, had the wibber-gibbers. Presently the butler would hear him coming back along the old gravel walk beside the house; he knew the elderly shuffle of those feet and would hasten to the door. In the house a metal-tipped cane, ringing on the floors, would proclaim how Darwin that day felt worse. His color was always high, child-like, rosy, denying his suffering; his eyes sparkled and were bright as a bird's. When friends came, he would swing his hand into theirs in a great arc, like a big hound giving its paw joyfully. His laugh had a peal in it, a chime of bells like an old-fashioned door-pull. In the evening he lay down and listened to novels, of which he asked only that the heroine be pretty and the ending happy. He liked to hear Emma at the piano, but had no ear at all. Hans Richter, the great conductor and pianist, came down from the Albert Hall and played to him, set his spine to tingling with excitement, but he could never with certainty identify anything he had heard before.

Darwinism

Before he died, on April 18th, 1882, he had asked to be buried at Downe. But England claimed him. He was borne to a vault in Westminster Abbey by Hooker, Huxley, Wallace, Lubbock, Canon Farrar, Spottiswoode the president of the Linnaean Society, James Russell Lowell, the Earl of Derby, the Dukes of Devonshire and Argyll. No one within those walls so revolutionized human thought; no one strove more purely and honestly for his ends. He was the archetype of the naturalist, the best type of *Homo sapiens* in his ascent from the simians.

15

FABRE AND THE EPIC COMMONPLACE

I BEGAN this book in winter, the lashing tail end of winter, amid a wilderness of books, and it seems to me that I intended then to trace a great many threads and describe a number of ancient worthies of science that have never got into these pages at all. I still think it might have been a very good idea to write quite a different book whose subject should be Nature in the mind of man. In this, instead of dealing in personalities, we could treat the scientists as all one mind that slowly came of age.

There you would follow out, for instance, the history of what man has made of the hive; and so, besides Réaumur's, I should have told the story of the blind naturalist Huber and have brought the illuminating narrative of our dawning comprehension right down to the present when, though the hive and the honey-bee are the most intensively studied phase of the insect world, discoveries are still coming to light. In this story I would have had a chance to express my affection for Sir John Lubbock and to praise the bee epic of Maeterlinck, the finest since Virgil wrote of honey-getting in the Apennines.

And there would have been a chapter on the discovery

JEAN HENRI FABRE
(Courtesy of G. W. Herrick, Ithaca, New York)

of the sexuality of plants, the gradually perfecting, refining knowledge of the flower. This story goes back to the half-forgotten Nehemiah Grew, Sir Thomas Browne, and the last and the best of the herbalists. I would have found place for the scholarly John Ray of England and for the melancholy Swiss Haller, poet, anatomist and mountain lover. I have always wanted to tell about the tragic and neglected Kurt Sprengel who knew more about the flower than ever Linnaeus himself. And I imagine there is a tale in Müller, who wrote that delightful, leisurely book on the fertilization of flowers which, already dog-eared, was given to me by an old Nature savant when at twenty I was just setting out plant-hunting in the Blue Ridge.

One might unfold the plot of that book that wasn't written, through theories of bird migration, through the struggles of vitalism against spontaneous generation, through increasingly subtle studies in the sensitivity of plants. And there is marine Nature on which I have not touched — a great book in that, for some one, with heroes from Aristotle to the Prince of Monaco.

Now it is summer; I am done with books, as I come now to write of one who cared little for them. I can sit on the ground, on a knoll between two ponds, my back wedged into the bole of a burr oak and my heels in the layered leaf mold that is rather like the very finest pastry, with my inviting composition book on my knee. I have that haunting feeling that spring this year again performed all her old tricks and showed me just how life is made and what it is made of, but her hand has such sleight and she so distracts the attention with waving green scarves and birds let loose from the loft that just when you think it is time now to watch carefully, the thing is done.

The spring is done, and summer is here, and it is too late to go back now and try a fresh attack. The leaves are out in full and, late from the tropics, the yellow-billed cuckoo has arrived and is already complaining that there is no rain. But the tree frogs prophesy that it is coming. Rain and warmth and growth, singing and eating, flight and flower — they flood the days bewilderingly. They are Nature; they are what the men I have been thinking about were thinking about always.

As I come now to the chapter that should bring us in a last step down to modernity, I have no illusions that this book has made something perfectly clear, or follows a consistent thread to its logical end, an end to which is attached a satisfactory plum — the comfortable feeling that the accumulative wisdom of the ages was only a groping to discover what we so wisely know. I have no feeling that matters nowadays are grown simplified or have arrived at any sort of finality. As this summer world is more splendid, more developed, more intricate and confusing than that raw March one, so when I face the modern and almost modern naturalists, I encounter so many counsels, knowledge so ultra-specialized, personalities so carefully tailored, intellects so long and highly educated, that I am bewildered where to begin.

Even by rigidly excluding the living great ones, like Forel, the Thucydides of the ants, among them men whom I am honored to know slightly, like William Morton Wheeler and Dr. Leland Howard, and barring those others about whom all of us know something, and who can tell their own stories better than anybody else can tell them — Andrews of the Gobi, our modern Polo, and Beebe of the deeps and jungles — I am still at a loss to choose. The last generation saw the birth of naturalists in Japan, Australia, South Africa, but I should have no capacity for appreciating what they have done. I felt, as I walked out here among the shagbarks and May-apples, that I would choose some American, perhaps Baird who knew more than any one else has ever known about the North American mammals, or David Starr Jordan who made the blood run warm in the subject of fishes, or that somewhat flamboyant, astonishingly gifted Charles Valentine Riley, a Gulliver in the Lilliput of the insect world.

For insects, warns the brownie-bug hopping on my notebook page, insects have yet to be reckoned with. Insects, thrum the bees, are nine-tenths of the animal kingdom. Beetles, the passing lady-bug reminds me, are more numerous than all the other insects put together, and weevils, nods the maggot in the acorn, are the highest and newest, most successful and abundant of all beetles. So the world, from a weevily point of view, seems to exist for weevils; half the shagbarks in my wood are dead of them, and maggots, it seems, are destined to triumph in the last act.

It is not clear for whom this world was made, but certainly it suits the convenience of the insects wondrous well, and to perfection they are adapted to live in it. They can fly without the bird's drastic sacrifice of the fore limbs; they breathe not through one tube but through every pore in the body; when men march out to slay them, they turn into some other form, and what is harmful to the adult stage may be powerless against a caterpillar. If we delay a day in the assault upon the larva, it has become a winged thing, off and away and catch it if you can.

The fear or loathing that some of us feel for insects inevitably vanishes upon acquaintance. Some dread goes out of them, merely at hearing them called by their names; a *Thing* is more frightening than an ichneumon fly. And though, trailing her ovipositor like a sting much longer than her body, the ichneumon inspires respect, a moment's reference to nothing more than the dictionary will alter your mind about her, for she is the enemy of our enemies, the terrible predator and parasite of grubs against men.

The insects are bizarre, fantastic, thoughtless but knowing, differently motivated than we. Their language has not one root in common with our own, unless it be sex, but theirs is sex so expanded, contracted, fractionated and refracted as to be nothing sympathetic with our own. In fact, theirs is a way of life so unlike ours that it is astonishing to find them on the same planet; perhaps on a globe in some other island universe there may be things as strange.

In my woods at least there are very few insects that I hesitate to catch in my hand or pick up with my fingers. Forgive me if I play the pedant and remind you of what you know — that scorpions, centipedes and spiders are none of them insects, so that of the true *Insecta*, the six-legged, I actually go warily only with wasps, bees and hornets, and that sub-family of ants that sting at one end and bite at the other.

Fabre and the Epic Commonplace

Yet in my zeal for ants I have handled even these, and wrung my fingers afterward. For the fascination of ants surpasses for me every other charm of the insect world, where there is but one important social bee, and the wasps are scarcely inviting. Every ant species has its own form of civilization; there are ants always underfoot, and of all creatures visible to the naked eye, they swarm individually the most numerous. Their great cities, their marches, their castes, their armies and battles and their treasuries delight something in the human mind that loves near-human fables.

So I lay once in the dust in a sub-tropical summer garden just reached by the Mediterranean breeze, and learned about ants. That dusty garden had the perfume of the *maquis* in it, salt from that classic sea, and, where I lay with my face close to the inhabited ground, a faint tart taste of formic acid. For an invisible pall of that breath of the ants hangs over their nest, and in this I seemed to pass much of my days while I watched the ways of the handsome harvesting ants, witnessed a three-day battle between two species, investigated the peaceful industries of the Golden Miners, and explored the mud domes of the shiny big carpenter who had built himself an emmet Samarkand in my property.

From ants I went on to the other insects in this neglected Provençal garden, where weeds strange to my American eyes, with harsh stems and fiercely brilliant flowers, were tangled underneath the old lemon and mandarine trees. The insects too were many of them new to me. I had never before seen blue bees, or tiny golden spiders that lived colonially all in one nest. I surprised the

[331]

sacred scarab beetle at his oddly scatological profession (for which, I suppose, he was canonized by the curious-minded Egyptians) and I fell in with the processionary caterpillars of the pine moth, and regretted sharply having handled their poisonous hairs.

Here were ant lions, long-horned beetles, parasitic wasps that precisely mimic ants, fireflies dancing above the heavy fragrance of the caper vines by night, and cicadas that shrilled with ecstasy in the arid golden glory of August, when the acanthus flower sprawled along the walks. And monstrous among the other chitinous folk was the mantis, fore limbs folded in a hypocritical attitude of devotion but with a predatory swaying in its watchful stance.

This savage, glittering sub-kingdom was all mine, and mine because it had been another's. What my own vision was too blunt to see was shown me here by a gentle old man, native not only to that Provence, but naturalized into the very insect world itself.

To re-work classic ground is a joy antithetical to that of the discoverer. It is like visiting the Parthenon with Pausanias in your hand. The material that some great scientist has exploited has far more meaning than the throne some prince once sat on, or the violin of Paganini or the brush of Fragonard, for those are lifeless things, and the hunting wasps that Fabre studied still hover in his garden and in mine, fanning the hot dust with their wings. And as insects vary not from age to age, these are in effect Fabre's very creatures. Again perforce they follow through their various rituals, for me as once for him — the wasp paralyzing the caterpillar with one acute thrust, the fecundated mantis devouring her mate, the hornets, despairing at the coming of autumn, dragging their children out of the cells and slaying them.

All this was nothing horrible or incomprehensible to Jean Henri Fabre, but only infinitely curious and attractive. From the time he was " a monkey of six " in his first braces and the black smock of the poor French child, in his native village of St. Léons, he began to observe the child's living world of grasshoppers and sparrows, snails and lizards, weeds with curious properties like milky juice or popping fruit. He saw them with the eyes of the born poet. And the child who listens with all his ears, who crouches to watch, whose curiosity surpasses his fears, who collects and compares, remembers where he saw things and looks for them again in season — he is a born little naturalist. This is small Henri Fabre, as he remembers himself for us. He was, more than any one I have yet mentioned in this book, born close to Nature, as the saying has it.

For the childhood of Fabre was passed in that Provençal intimacy with beasts and roots and weather that would be inconceivable to an American farm boy. When the icy mistral went sailing through the chinks of the house, the family would retire to the barn and abide there a week or so, warmed by the heat of the beasts and the fermenting dung and hay. In summer the child Henri, having as his first duty to drive the ducks to a pond each day, employed his time there in collecting beetles and water-weeds and those fossils that are strewn about every bared bit of limestone in the Midi.

This fancy of his was greeted at home with jeers and

complaints, and presently the boy was sent to a one-room, one-window school, where the pigs and chickens wandered in, and the teacher counted five or six years none too long to allow the intricate art of reading to trickle through thick little peasant skulls. The boy Henri taught himself to read and write and do sums far in advance of his class. So he was admitted finally to the one study that French education offered a country boy so far a freak and outlaw of his caste as to cultivate an effete taste for it. This was Latin, and of all living tongues Provençal is the nearest to that dead language. Thus it was not so very dead to Fabre, and when he reached Virgil he recognized (as we all do after getting through Caesar's telegraphic style and all that tedium that Senator Cicero had read into the records) that here, at least, was a poet. Aeneas is a stick, and Virgil touches us not at all with Dido or any other woman, but he is a Nature poet, the greatest of antiquity. And the Provençal peasant lad, when he reads of the honey-bee, the vine, the fig, the olive, in the *Eclogues*, reads of his homeland in a tongue that seems only a little grander and more rigid than his own. Virgil speaks of the turtle-dove, the goat, the golden broom, the cicada — it was Fabre's own, the same that momently was shrilling in his ears. To meet the smells, the sounds, the sights of home in the classic page gave young Fabre the feeling that what he loved, the great and good loved; at once the poet and the observer were aroused in him.

But his family, failing at farming, drifted to the cities — the great, windy, stone-built Graeco-Roman-medieval cities of the Rhône. They ran cafés of the poorest sort, and repeatedly failing, repeatedly fled from the attentions of the *huissier*, that ogre of every French community, the licensed prosecuting bill-collector who makes his money out of the sorrows of creditor and debtor. Of these days Fabre speaks as " an inferno."

But that which is purely loved never deserts us, and in time of need our secret passions, however airy, however impractical, are our only succor, our life line. Audubon's love of drawing saved him to let him become an ornithologist; Latin saved Fabre. In their great Chinese system of education and civil service that prevailed before Duruy reformed it, the French put the classics before all, and at twenty Fabre was teaching a class of fifty overgrown, stupid boys. This was his portion, at Carpentras, this and about a hundred and fifty dollars a year — enough, as Fabre put it, to keep him in cheap red wine and chick-peas.

Such is the fare of the Provençal whose sun-burned, physically impoverished culture is a matter not of palaces and cathedrals but of song in the fields, a philosophy finely tuned to natural forces — mistral and midsummer glare — and ripened out of doors, like the grape. This part of Provence, at the foot of the mountains, the edge of the plain, is classic ground, land of Laura's birthplace, of Petrarch's passion, of Mistral's *Mireille*, and deeds, real and legendary, of good King Réné, Queen Jeanne, and the astrologer Nostradamus. But, for science, it is classic now because Jean Henri Fabre's first great work was done upon the slopes of Mont Ventoux, that last rampart of the Alps that rises up, just beyond Carpentras, some six thousand feet out of the great, burning plain of the Rhône. On the same trail that Petrarch took in the fourteenth century, Fabre, on his precious Sundays and Thursdays (the Saturday of the French schoolroom) with nothing but a piece of bread in his pocket, would climb to the summit, whence one may see the Alps, the Cévennes, the sea, and, once in many months, the Pyrenees.

I was going to tell, somewhere in these pages — but now I shall never get to it — of the strange magnetism of mountains for the naturalist. The sense of mounting, of quitting complexity for the sparse, of obtaining a clearer and clearer and longer view of things, breathing sharper air — it is very like attaining maturity and gaining wisdom, strangely like the soul's experience in science. Actually the naturalist passes from one zone of vegetation to another. Fabre so climbed from the blazing red pomegranate of the plains to the alpine forget-me-not of the summit. And those other ranges, tossed against the sky — what treasures are in them, too? Like islands in the sea of the rolling levels, mountains have their endemicity, yet, reaching to the snows, they touch the alpine zone. Those southern heights smell of the tropics and the tundra in one, bear on their flanks the primeval forests that long since were swept from the lowlands.

And there, on Mont Ventoux, mounting up through Spanish broom and chestnut zone to the summit, Fabre's first great collecting was done. It was characteristic of him that he made no research after the rare, but began with the mason bee, the commonest creature in all the *maquis*, frequenter of rock-rose and wild lavender and narcissus. He began indeed, at this time, many lines of inquiry, perhaps most of his multifarious observations, so that, long as he lived, he never had need to travel; Mont Ventoux was, he found, what every place is, a world in itself, biologically reckoned. He never came to the end of it, and when he could no longer go to the mountain, the mountain must come to him, its vegetation and insects transplanted to his garden.

So was laid the foundation of much work that was forty years a-growing, and there is no time (mark this) in a naturalist's life like the adventure of first findings. Years may bring a wealth of knowledge, a sounder judgment, all the reading, all the associations, all the comparative specimens a man needs for a rounded, definitive work. But it is not ambition to fill heavy volumes that makes the naturalist's heart beat quicker, that sets the young man to climbing cliffs like a cony under a broiling sun, that flings him upon his belly to lie hour after hour patiently awaiting some eclosion, some stirring in the chrysalis or unfurling of a nocturnal flower. Every old dog knows in his heart that it is beginnings that matter to him personally, fresh surfaces, morning experiences. The shelf of his works, usually not too readable even to his fellow workers, belongs to his public existence. But who with salt in his blood prefers a public existence? He would trade it on the instant to have back Lapland again, the singing wall of Kentucky's woods, or Mont Ventoux fifty years ago, sixty . . .

In this same twentieth year, the first youth and turning point in his career, Fabre married Marie Villard, a young girl of Carpentras. A child was speedily born, and at the same time his parents, always in trouble, were obliged to come and live with him. To support this family by his teacher's pay, even on chick-peas and *rosé*, was no longer possible. He gave private lessons and crammer's reviews, grubbed at every sort of hackwork that stole away his precious Thursdays, in addition to all this teaching himself physics, chemistry and mathematics, in order to compete for higher degrees. The city of Carpentras was constantly two and three months behindhand in payment, and in the midst of all these distractions and sordid strains, the child of his first passions died. The empty degrees were awarded, but no promotions came, no better circumstances offered. Serene, above the plain, Ventoux turned a stony face to the clouds and sun.

The years went by and went by, in the fields, on Mont Ventoux; the hours of the bee in the broom spilled in a golden waste. And still the man who loved them best and best deserved them seldom came, to watch and understand. Whether at Carpentras, Avignon or Orange or, once, in Ajaccio, he was the slave of the most crushing drudgery, the pay of which must clothe seven bodies, feed seven mouths. The children came as the fruit to the flower; with small clutching fingers they clung to him, their lives fastened to his own, dependent upon his fidelity to duty, his sacrifice of the great conflicting claim.

Under such restraints great talents in a woman have almost no chance of survival. A man has some hope of ultimate escape. With patience he may just possibly battle his way through, and Fabre was patient with a self-discipline that it is painful to read of. He had a capacity, an actual appetite, for doing the hardest thing in the most thorough way. His attack on Latin and Greek, and still more the heroic efforts by which he taught himself and completely mastered algebra and geometry, are characteristic of him.

What, one wonders would have been the result had fortune but smiled on him? Suppose that he had been given wealth and education, leisure and freedom — what a scientist then we should have had! Instead of a short shelf of works, would there not have been ten shelves for us to revel in, instead of flawed works, perfection? So think we all, of our own selves. What we could accomplish, had we our hands free!

But poor Fabre, after months of waiting, would sometimes be called away from gazing on some crucial moment in an entomological drama, by the clang of the school bell, the cry of a child, the presentation of a bill. We pity him, and yet it is not certain that the stern school to which he sent himself was not the best. As a profession Nature, like the arts, requires the Greek spirit — the willingness to bleed or to die for one stony, sweet, but unprofitable acre. Persian mercenaries will not fight for that; voluptuous charity cannot build a royal road through geometry's briar, nor through the mire of entomology. Pay, leisure, equipment cannot replace passion and cerebration; they may well wither invention, substitute machinery for discovery.

So, one comes to believe, the stolen moments, the rocky path, the years of striving hard at harder tasks, of submission to duty, these are part of Fabre's greatness, and discipline was one secret of his success. Training so stern would have disheartened mediocrity, but mediocrity is a rock in the earth that the stoutest heart has never been able to lift.

One whom his neighbors appreciated so little, whom the world of science recognized (through his disguise as a writer) slowly and with misgivings and reserves, one who neglected his correspondence, fled from visitors, had no talent for utilizing publicity — such a man, cramped by poverty, cannot lead a life teeming with encounters. It is possible to enumerate the high spots in Fabre's public existence on the five fingers: the day when the liberal Minister of Education discovered him, and that other moment in Paris when this same Duruy gave him the red ribbon of the Legion of Honor. The meeting with John Stuart Mill, at Avignon, that led to Fabre's rescue when he and his little flock were dispossessed and thrust out on the street. The visit from Pasteur in 1865, when the great chemist, fresh from his victory over anthrax, came down to the Midi to combat the silkworm disease. Not a success, that meeting. Fabre was patronized, commanded, coldly treated, unappreciated; the noble Pasteur, in his preoccupation, failed to recognize in his host anything more than a school-keeping peasant with an untrained knowledge of insects, possessed of a stubborn peasant pride and secretiveness. And finally there was the jubilee in 1910 — just one day of honor, a simple luncheon in a café in Fabre's home village of Sérignan. Not a single delegate from the world of science, or of the French government, presented himself. The honors from the outside world came from Rostand, Mistral and Rolland.

In Fabre's private life there were many poignant sorrows — the loss of his growing son, his collaborator, the death of Mill, and that of his first wife, bitter financial disappointments and the cruelest treatment by those who advantaged themselves of his simplicity. But great joys came to him, too. The daughters of his old age became his helpers at his studies, his companions and the sight of his shrewd but failing eyes. Duruy obtained a microscope for him, Mistral a tiny pension.

And there came a day when with savings scraped together out of a lifetime's penury, at last he bought himself his *harmas* — a tract of stony wilderness that even the peasants had abandoned, at the foot of old Mont Ventoux climbing forever to a sunny sky. Here, he said, where no one would have thought it worth while to drop a turnip seed, in the weeds and tares that he had bought himself, he would keep open house with his beloved insects. Here he established his living, natural laboratory. Later he refurbished the deserted house, and brought his family thither, and from his old, insect-drilled desk flowed forth the exquisite biographies of his *Souvenirs Entomologiques*.

Never have there been in all the pages of entomology such life histories as these. The secret of the hunting wasp's paralyzing attack, the terrible tyranny of the mantis, the love swarm of the peacock moths, the epic of the cicada (the very voice of Provence), the glow-worm's luminous existence, the labors of the Sisyphus beetle, the geometry of the spider's web — these were Fabre's own discoveries. Even when others anticipated him they never equaled his descriptions and seldom discovered anything he failed to notice, for no one else had his patience, his approach that explored the *maquis* world for every lisping cricket sound. In the course of such intensive parochialism he discovered rare and many totally new insects,

[341]

missed by the ardent collectors, in a land so old one would have thought nothing remained unfound. Finally, no other one scientist ever learned so much about instinct — that sphinx of natural history.

And all this peeping on a cryptic underworld was reported in a style so light, so sure, so gay, that many scientists reproach him for it. This on the wobbly basis that it could not be science and at the same time poetry. True, there are no obscuring technicalities here. The brook-like clarity reveals any flaw of fact as plainly as a pebble. A thousand such may — and do — besprinkle the dry stream beds of pedantry. In my view of it, it is high time the world lost patience with the opacity of dullards, for it is no guaranty of profundity or accuracy. On the contrary, its presence in the style of a scientist should seriously alarm us about his vision.

What Fabre did was to tell what he saw, in a style that would have swept Thoreau off his feet — Thoreau the noticer of little miracles, who, alas, was New England bound, lax, even slipshod. Goethe could have given his right hand to have done in science what Fabre does, as it were with one hand behind him. Nothing in Darwin is so well expressed. Indeed, Fabre could not read the *Origin of Species* for the dullness of its style. He abhorred Buffon and Racine, loved Rabelais and Réaumur and Audubon.

There are faults in Fabre's science, and I shall confess them clearly but all in one breath. Fabre did not know enough about what the rest of the world was doing; he was inclined to rely too much on what his senses and good sense told him, and to scorn what was done in experimental laboratories. He resented the entrance of chemistry and physics into the field of natural history. He read too little, ignored criticism as though it were personal calumny, fancied that no one else observed as well as he, made experiments to test the psychology and physiology of his creatures, but neglected controls and left gaps in his methods and reasoning that even the casual may see. And finally his mind was simply incapable of conceiving a theory about anything, whence he supposed that theories are so much rubbish. (But it was with accuracy that he pricked the bubble of Bates's mimicry theory.) Although his writings constantly employ the fundamental idea of evolution, he obstinately refused to admit that it was not a solemn but ludicrous hoax. He could describe exquisitely, and discover the necessity, the motive for the most paradoxical insect behavior, the most fantastic of structure. But he had no feeling that the *how* of Nature, not the *why*, is what we must explain.

These flaws make Fabre seem pre-Darwinian. But in many ways he was more nearly one of us moderns. Above all he gave himself heart and soul to the intimate, patient, sympathetic study of that life which lies all about us; he saw that the same secret, the same beauty, the same tremendous significances are everywhere. Any life is all life, and the line of attack for the naturalist begins at the front door — or better still, the back gate.

Fabre emphasized not the discovery of the new but the comprehension of the familiar. With infinite care he traced out life histories; he meant to let nothing escape him, regarded everything, down to an ant's excrement, as a vital clue, studied plants as minutely as his insects, for he knew that, in the field, botany and zoölogy are one science. He despised nothing; his hands were not too fine to plunge into the very stuff of life, and in his old head perpetually revolved the immemorial, the sacred patterns of life as it takes shape on this third planet from the sun — eye and wing and sting, passive egg and lashing sperm, coupling, devouring, dying, disintegration. He was, for all his peasant-born, pre-Darwinian reluctances and obstinacies, the type and model of a modern field naturalist.

For the future course of natural history lies precisely along the latitudes that Fabre was traveling. Exploration, the discovery of new species, indubitably fascinating and necessary, indubitably superficial, will of necessity lose momentum till they approach, if they never quite attain, inertia. Such inertia exists, for instance, with regard to the flowering plants, mosses and ferns of Europe, and it is only a question of time before the same will be true of these organisms in North America. The birds, butterflies and molluscs and the mammals of Europe are also known to sterility. It is nearly forty years since any one discovered a new species of bird in the eastern United States. In the highly civilized portions of the earth only the insects and fungi and other minute or micro-organisms still offer opportunities for extensive discovery.

But Adam's task is now more than the giving of names. Man has learned to ask a multitude of new questions of Nature. Science today wants to discover the seasonal and diurnal rhythms of living creatures — not necessarily the creatures of New Guinea but equally, or even more so, those of New Jersey. Natural history seeks now not specimens, not qualitative analyses (to borrow chemical jargon) but the far more difficult and perhaps more significant quantitative analyses of the biota. The great cycles of rabbit abundance and rabbit scarcity, for instance, are recognized today not as mere curiosities but as first class phenomena, considerably more important than earthquakes, in the health and the life-and-death of the entire North American continent. The airplane is called in now, and expert photography, for the making of duck and other wild fowl censuses, for numbers are even more important than kind. Diseases and parasites of the upland game birds, signs of increasing or decreasing fecundity of species, viability of eggs and embryos, and food habits, above all food habits, especially when these show signs of shift, are now rated as first magnitude constellations in the great field of natural history. In short, what science calls for today are life histories, and ecological studies — the precise measurement of the environmental factors and the inter-relations of organisms.

There remain great theoretical and philosophical fields to be explored. Instinct is still the sphinx of Nature, and sex is still essentially mysterious. Educability of animals, irritability of plants, the new types of " species," (the so-called physiological race, which differs not in bodily but in behavioristic characters) — these are fields for philosophy plus experiment. There is not space even to mention many others — migration, pigmentation, problems without end.

The life of Fabre points the moral of all this to perfection. It was his pioneering along these lines that made him, as I have claimed, more modern than Darwin. I have mentioned his lacks and his faults; they were the flaws inherent in a highly amateur attack. But the amateur spirit is also precious; the amateur is coming to the fore; he is increasingly indispensable, for in the future it is likely that natural history, afield, is going to need fewer great leaders, but more and more servants. Any one who begins to acquaint himself with the field of present day natural history is impressed with the fact that there are not simply scores, but hundreds and hundreds of people all over our country, all over the world, working, recording, finding delight and doing great service — men who know all that Linnaeus and Réaumur ever knew and far, far more, men without name or fame or desire for it. In art a mediocre accomplishment is perhaps worse than none; in the free masonry of science every ant's grain of knowledge enriches the common fund.

And at last the distinction between biology and natural history is becoming both clear and reasoned. The biologist, the man of the laboratory, is not to be reproached for keeping to his rooms. He is the assayer, the tester, the one who takes apart the stuff of life, analyzes its composition, exercises its individual units to test their pure properties and behavior. To him theory, in the future, must be handed over for verification. He is not to be reproached for his mechanism. Within the limitations of his province, mechanism is his business, his instrument, and his signed search warrant served upon vital mystery.

The rôle of the naturalist is not antithetical to this. It is rather complementary, a mated profession. It has the more passive, or at least the more tender functions. Toward the findings of the laboratory it should make a certain amount of submission. But it dwells in its own house, and is mistress in it.

And that mansion is the earth, rolling upon its pre-destined course through space, its poles glittering with snows, its flanks with the oceans, its continents with the deep true green of the jungles and forests. This whole, this planetary life entity, breathes with the rhythm of tides, of day and night, enacts the drama of the colored seasons, and plays out the titanic epic of the geologic ages. On earth and only on earth are sunset glow, green leaf, and eyes to see them. Here is all we know of reality, all-sufficient to our destiny, our thoughts and passions. There will never be truer interpreters than the naturalists, of this beloved, dusty, struggling, fateful and illustrious ex-periment called life on earth. For those interpreters to come, the yet unborn, the growing, the bay tree even now thrusts deep its roots, and in the ancient sunlight of today it ripens and keeps green its leaves.

SOURCES AND REFERENCE
MATERIAL

SOURCES AND REFERENCE MATERIAL

GENERAL

Burckhardt, Rudolf, *Geschichte der Zoologie*. G. J. Göschen, Leipzig, 1907.

Hoefer, Ferdinand, *Histoire de la Zoologie* (Second edition). Hachette et Cie., Paris, 1890.

Locy, William A., *The Growth of Biology*. Henry Holt and Co., New York, 1925.

Nordenskiöld, Erik, *The History of Biology*. Alfred A. Knopf, New York, 1928.

Sachs, Julius von, *History of Botany*. Clarendon Press, Oxford, 1890.

CHAPTER ONE

Arber, Agnes, *Herbals*. University Press, Cambridge, 1912.

Bauhin, Caspar, *Prodromus Theatri Botanici*. Frankfurt, 1620.

Belon, Pierre, *L'histoire des Oyseaux*. Paris, 1555.

Gesner, Conrad, *Historia Animalium*. Zurich, 1551.

Greene, Edward Lee, *Landmarks of Botanical History*. Smithsonian Institution, Washington, D. C., 1909.

Leyel, Hilda, *The Magic of Herbs*. Harcourt, Brace and Co., New York, 1926.

Lones, Thomas East, *Aristotle's Researches in Natural Science*. West Newman and Co., London, 1912.

Miall, Louis Compton, *The Early Naturalists and their Work*. The Macmillan Co., London, 1912.

Sources and Reference Material

Pouchet, Félix Archimède, *Histoire des Sciences Naturelles au Moyen Age*. Paris, 1853.

Strunz, Franz, *Geschichte der Naturwissenschaften im Mittelalter*. F. Enke, Stuttgart, 1910.

CHAPTER TWO

Borelli, Alfonso, *De Motu Animalium* (Second edition). Leyden, 1685.

Leeuwenhoek, Antonj van, *Opera Omnia*. Leyden, 1722.

Locy, William A., "Malpighi, Swammerdam and Leeuwenhoek." *Popular Science Monthly*, April, 1901.

Malpighi, Marcello, *Opera Omnia*. Leyden, 1687.

Miall, Louis Compton, *The Early Naturalists and their Work*. The Macmillan Co., London, 1912.

Ornstein, Martha, *The Rôle of Scientific Societies in the Seventeenth Century*. University of Chicago Press, Chicago, 1928.

Swammerdam, Jan, *Bibel der Natur*. Leipzig, 1752.

CHAPTER THREE

Buffon, Georges Louis Leclerc de, *A Natural History*, 9 vols. Paris, 1791.

Flourens, M. J. O., *Histoires des Travaux et des Idées de Buffon* (Third edition). Paris, 1844.

Miall, Louis Compton, *The Early Naturalists and their Work*. The Macmillan Co., London, 1912.

Réaumur, René Antoine Ferchault de, *Mémoires pour servir à l'histoire des insectes*. Paris, 1734.

Réaumur, René Antoine Ferchault de, *The Natural History of Ants*, translated, with an introduction and notes, by William Morton Wheeler. Alfred A. Knopf, New York, 1926.

CHAPTERS FOUR, FIVE, AND SIX

Banks, Joseph, *Journal . . . during Captain Cook's first voyage in H. M. S.* Endeavor. The Macmillan Co., London, 1896.

Green Laurels

Bioletti, Frederick T., " Reminiscences of an Amateur Botanist." *Scientific Monthly,* October, 1929. This article humorously expresses the excesses of " Linnaeanism " in modern times.

British Museum (Natural History), " Memorials of Linnaeus." *Special Guides No. 3.* London, 1907.

Caddy, Mrs. Florence, *Through the Fields with Linnaeus.* Longmans, Green and Co., London, 1887.

Holm, T., " Linnaeus." *Botanical Gazette,* volume xliii, 1907.

Kalm, Per, " Travels into North America." *A General Collection . . . of Travels,* (edited by John Pinkerton). London, 1812.

Kerner, Anton von Marilaun, *Natural History of Plants.* Henry Holt and Co., New York, 1895. See the Introduction.

Linnaeus, Carl, *A System of Vegetables.* London, 1783.

Linnaeus, Carl, *General System of Nature.* London, 1806.

Linnaeus, Carl, *Lachesis Lapponica.* London, 1811.

Thunberg, Carl Peter, *Voyages.* Paris, 1796.

CHAPTERS SEVEN AND EIGHT

Cuvier, Georges, *Recherches sur les ossemens fossiles de quadrupèdes.* Paris, 1812.

Cuvier, Georges, " Éloge de M. de Lamarck." *Mémoires de l'Académie Royale des Sciences de l'Institute de France,* volume xiii, 1832.

Daudin, Henri, *Études d'histoire des Sciences Naturelles.* Félix Alcan, Paris, 1906.

Lamarck, Chevalier de, *Zoological Philosophy.* Macmillan & Co., New York, 1914.

Lee, Sarah, *Memoirs of Cuvier.* London, 1833.

Packard, Alpheus S., *Lamarck, the Founder of Evolution.* Longmans, Green and Co., New York, 1901.

CHAPTER NINE

Bartram, John, *Observations on . . . his Travels.* London, 1751.

Sources and Reference Material

Bartram, William, *Travels through North and South Carolina.* Philadelphia, 1791.

Coker, W. C., "The Garden of André Michaux." *Journal of the Elisha Mitchell Scientific Society*, volume xxvii.

Crèvecoeur, J. Hector St. John de, *Letters from an American Farmer.* London, 1782.

Darlington, William, *Memorials of John Bartram and Humphry Marshall.* Philadelphia, 1849.

Harshberger, John William, *The Botanists of Philadelphia.* Philadelphia, 1899.

Michaux, François André, "Travels." *Early Western Travels.* London, 1843.

Michaux, André, "Journal." *Proceedings of the American Philosophical Society*, volume xxvi.

CHAPTER TEN

Burns, Frank L., "Miss Lawson's Recollections of Ornithologists." *Auk*, volume 34.

Burns, Frank L., "Alexander Wilson." *The Wilson Bulletin*, volume iii.

Herrick, Francis Hobart, *Audubon the Naturalist.* D. Appleton and Co., New York, 1917.

Ord, George, *Sketch of the Life of Alexander Wilson.* Philadelphia, 1828.

Wilson, Alexander, *Poems and Literary Remains.* Paisley, 1876.

Wilson, Alexander, *American Ornithology.* Philadelphia, 1808–1814.

Wilson, Alexander, and Charles Lucien Bonaparte, *American Ornithology.* Edinburgh, 1831.

Wilson, James Southall, *Alexander Wilson, Poet-Naturalist.* Neale Publishing Co., New York, 1906.

CHAPTER ELEVEN

Call, Richard Ellsworth, *Life and Writings of Rafinesque.* The Filson Club, Louisville, 1895.

Fitzpatrick, T. J., *Rafinesque*. Historical Department of Iowa, Des Moines, 1911.

Fretageot, Nora C., *Historic New Harmony*. Library of the Workingmen's Institute, New Harmony, Indiana, 1934.

Goode, George Brown, " The Beginnings of American Science." *Report of the Smithsonian Institution for 1897*. Washington, D. C.

Jordan, David Starr and Amos Butler, " New Harmony." *Scientific Monthly*, volume 25.

Lindley, Harlow (editor), *Indiana as Seen by Early Travelers*. Indiana Historical Commission, Indianapolis, 1916.

Lockwood, George B., *The New Harmony Movement*. D. Appleton and Co., New York, 1905.

Maximilian, Prince of Wied, " Travels in the Interior of North America." *Early Western Travels*. London, 1843.

Ord, George, " Memoir of Charles Alexander Lesueur." *American Journal of Science*, series 2, volume viii.

Peter, Robert, " *Transylvania University, its Origin, Rise, Decline and Fall*. The Filson Club, Louisville, 1896.

Podmore, Frank, *Robert Owen*. Hutchinson and Co., London, 1906.

Say, Thomas, *American Conchology*. New Harmony, 1830.

Weiss, Harry B., and Grace M. Ziegler, *Thomas Say, Early American Naturalist*. Charles C. Thomas, Springfield, Illinois, 1931.

CHAPTER TWELVE

Browne, Thomas, " The Garden of Cyrus." *Works of Sir Thomas Browne*, (edited by Charles Sayle) volume iii, John Grant, Edinburgh, 1912.

Carus, C. G., *Natur und Idee*. Vienna, 1861.

Goethe, Johann Wolfgang, *Sämtliche Werke*. Stuttgart, 1851.

Hanson, Adolph, *Goethes Metamorphose der Pflanzen*. A. Töpelmann, Giessen, 1907.

Lewes, G. H., *Life and Works of Goethe*. Everyman edition, E. P. Dutton, New York, 1908.

Sources and Reference Material

MacLeay, W. S., Remarks on . . . General Laws which . . . regulate . . . Natural Distribution of Insects." *Transactions of the Linnaean Society of London,* volume xiv.

Nees von Esenbeck, C. G., *Handbuch der Botanik.* Nürnberg, 1820.

Newton, Alfred, *A Dictionary of Birds.* Adam and Charles Black, London, 1893–1896. *Vide* " Quinary system."

Oken, Lorenz, *Naturphilosophie.* Jena, 1809.

Owen, Richard, *On the Archetype and Homologies of the Vertebrate Skeleton.* London, 1848.

Perrier, Edmond, *La Philosophie Zoologique avant Darwin.* Félix Alcan, Paris, 1884.

Schelling, F. W. J., *Sämtliche Werke.* Stuttgart, 1856.

Swainson, William, " A Treatise on the Geography and Classification of Animals." *The Cabinet Cyclopedia,* London, 1835.

Vigors, Nicholas Aylward, " Observations on the Natural Affinities that Connect Orders and Families of Birds." *Transactions of the Linnaean Society of London,* volume xiv.

Virchow, Rudolf L. K., *Göthe als Naturforscher und in besonderer Beziehung auf Schiller.* Berlin, 1861.

CHAPTERS THIRTEEN AND FOURTEEN

Beebe, William, *Galápagos, World's End.* G. P. Putnam's Sons, New York, 1924.

Darwin, Charles, *Expression of the Emotions in Man and Animals.* D. Appleton and Co., New York, 1873.

Darwin, Charles, *Insectivorous Plants.* D. Appleton and Co., New York, 1875.

Darwin, Charles, *The Variation of Animals and Plants under Domestication.* D. Appleton and Co., New York, 1876.

Darwin, Charles, *Cross and Self Fertilization.* D. Appleton and Co., New York, 1877.

Darwin, Charles, *On the Various Contrivances by which Orchids are Fertilized by Insects.* D. Appleton and Co., 1887.

Darwin, Charles, *The Formation of Vegetable Mould through*

the Action of Earthworms. D. Appleton and Co., New York, 1892.

Darwin, Charles, *The Origin of Species.* D. Appleton and Co., New York, 1860.

Darwin, Charles, *The Descent of Man.* D. Appleton and Co., New York, 1871.

Darwin, Charles, *Journal . . . of the Voyage of H. M. S. "Beagle" round the World.* Everyman Library, E. P. Dutton and Co., New York, 1912.

Darwin, Charles, *The "Beagle" Diary* (edited by Nora Barlow). University Press, Cambridge, 1933.

Darwin, Erasmus, *Zoönomia.* Philadelphia, 1818.

Darwin, Francis, *The Life and Letters of Charles Darwin.* D. Appleton and Co., New York, 1887.

Darwin, Francis, and A. C. Seward, *More Letters.* J. Murray, London, 1903.

"Expedition of the California Academy of Sciences, 1905–1906." *Proceedings California Academy of Sciences,* volumes i and ii, 1907–1918.

Fifty Years of Darwinism (Centennial Addresses). Henry Holt and Co., 1909.

Huxley, Thomas H., *Darwiniana, Essays.* D. Appleton and Co., New York, 1912.

Litchfield, Henrietta, *Emma Darwin: A Century of Family Letters.* J. Murray, London, 1915.

Rádl, Emanuel, *The History of Biological Theories.* Oxford University Press, London, 1930.

Schmitt, Waldo, "The Galápagos Islands One Hundred Years after Darwin." *Nature Magazine,* volume xxvi.

Wallace, Alfred Russel, *Island Life.* Harper and Brothers, New York, 1881.

Wallace, Alfred Russel, *My Life.* Dodd, Mead and Co., New York, 1905.

Wallace, Alfred Russel, *Natural Selection.* Macmillan and Co., New York, 1871.

Sources and Reference Material

Ward, Henshaw, *Charles Darwin; the Man and his Warfare.* The Bobbs-Merrill Co., Indianapolis, 1927.

CHAPTER FIFTEEN

Fabre, J. Henri, *Social Life in the Insect World.* Century Co., 1912.

Fabre, J. Henri, *The Life of the Spider.* Dodd, Mead and Co., 1913.

Fabre, J. Henri, *The Life of the Fly.* Dodd, Mead and Co., 1913.

Fabre, J. Henri, *The Life of the Caterpillar.* Dodd, Mead and Co., 1916.

Fabre, J. Henri, *The Sacred Beetle and Others.* Dodd, Mead and Co., 1918.

Fabre, J. Henri, *The Glow-Worm and Other Beetles.* Dodd, Mead and Co., 1919.

Herrick, Glenn W., " A Visit to Fabre's Harmas." *Scientific Monthly,* volume xxvi.

Legros, C. V., *Fabre, Poet of Science.* The Century Co., 1913.

INDEX

INDEX

Index

Index

Index

Index

Index

Index

Index

A NOTE ABOUT THE AUTHOR

Donald Culross Peattie was born in 1898 in Chicago. In 1922 he was graduated *cum laude* from Harvard, and thereupon entered the Office of Foreign Seed and Plant Introduction in the Department of Agriculture at Washington, where he spent three years in botanical research. He then became a free-lance, publishing novels and non-fiction, as well as such technical works as the FLORA OF THE INDIANA DUNES. After six years abroad, he returned to America and the interpretation of its Nature. AN ALMANAC FOR MODERNS was published in 1935 and was awarded the first annual Gold Medal of the Limited Editions Club, as the book written by an American author during the previous three years most likely to become a classic. It was followed by SINGING IN THE WILDERNESS, *A Salute to John James Audubon.* GREEN LAURELS is the fruit of years of preparation; it tells the story of the discovery of the living world by the mind of man. Donald Peattie is married to Louise Redfield Peattie, novelist; they have three sons.